Science Annual

Fall | 1997

Published By Webster's Unified, Inc.
99 White Plains Road
Tarrytown, New York 10591

ISBN 0-7614-0750-2

Printed in the United States of America

Designed by Patricia Moritz, Moritz Design

Science Annual

Fall | 1997

Scientific knowledge advances at an ever increasing pace. News of a breakthrough six months ago can become obsolete by knowledge gained in the past month or week. Therefore, we at Websterís Unified want to more frequently offer readers interested in the sciences much to capture their interest. We are pleased to introduce the first Fall edition of the Science Annual. Beginning in 1997, we will bring you the best of current science news in two editions of the Annual a year.

Science Annual, Fall 1997, has been redesigned in a new attractive format, intended to make reading about complex topics a more pleasurable experience. The contents of this book has been compiled from popular scientific publications such as Discover, Science News, Smithsonian Magazine, and The New York Times. In addition, we have commissioned articles from qualified professionals, both from the worlds of academia and journalism, to bring you up to date on ongoing scientific stories, such as the latest findings from the Hubble Telescope.

Readers can learn how microtagging can identify the origin of such diverse products as perfume and explosives, allowing them to traced. Where development of a commercial electric car stand. What scientists have concluded about life on Mars. Whether people will be replaced by computers in the game of chess. What the future hold for our national park system. And whether they should take melatonin the next time they fly to Europe. These and many other interesting questions can be answered, or the debate fueled, by reading the articles compiled in Science Annual, Fall 1997.We hope you enjoy this new approach to current science news.

Contributors

Tina Adler

Sandra Blakeslee

Margaret F. Boorstein

Malcolm W. Browne

John T. Burns

David G. Fisher

George J. Flynn

Bil Gilbert

Denise Grady

Hans G. Graetzer.

Will Hively

Carl W. Hoagstrom

Jeffry M. Jensen

Jeffrey Kluger

Gina Kolata

Ralph L. Langenheim, Jr.

Warren E. Leary

Richard Monastersky

Andrew Pollack

Janet Raloff

Wendy E. Sacket

Payal Sampat

David M. Schwartz

Rose Secrest

Joseph L. Spradley.

William K. Stevens.

Gary Taubes

Russell R. Tobias

John Travis

Matthew L. Wald

Katherine Whittemore

Ted Williams

Corrina Wu

Contents

1 | The Animal and Plant Worlds

CONTENTS

HOW A WEED ONCE SCORNED BECAME THE

FLOWER OF THE HOUR

BY KATHERINE WHITTEMORE

The gaudy sunflower is the ornament of the nineties, turning up everywhere and on everything, including baseball players' faces

This all started some five years ago when my friend Allison moved to Florida. Allison loves sunflowers, but she doesn't see many down there in the limestone country of the Keys. Clever me, though, I decided that whenever I wrote Allison from Boston, where I live, it would be on greeting cards festooned with her favorite flowers.

At first, it wasn't easy to find what I was after. I browsed card stands for buttery photographs, scanned for Monets, Gustav Klimts or Georgia O'Keeffes. Usually there was a Van Gogh, whose famous painting *The Sunflowers* (1888) sold for nearly $40 million in 1987, but that was about it.

As time passed, however, sunflowers began turning up everywhere. It got strange. Not only did the card collections grow positively yolky with *Helianthus* (*helios* = sun, *anthus* =flower), but I'd go to the movies and count a trio of different sunflower T-shirts in line for popcorn (popped, increasingly, with sunflower oil). At salad bars, suddenly, sunflower kernels vied with croutons. One window at the Harvard Coop displayed boxer shorts flocked with sunflowers. A wineshop featured Georges Duboeuf chardonnay with bold sunflowers on the label. A store nearby offered umbrellas that opened into enormous...need I say it?

Pottery Barn bowls, Lillian Vernon doormats, totebags and jewelry at Boston's Museum of Fine Arts store. Calendars, notepads, journals, photograph albums. Sunflower hair conditioner by Herbal Essences, sunflower barrettes. Backpacks with sunflower-riddled scenes from the

THE ANIMAL AND PLANT WORLDS | **13**

Disney film *Pocahontas*. Bedsheets, hot plates, lamps. Sunflowers, an eau de toilette by Elizabeth Arden. Neckties. Suspenders.

None of this was lost on local florists, who yellowed right up, filling their display windows with sunflowers. At the neighborhood market, the cereal aisle proffered something called Sun Crunchers, its cheerful box adorned with…guess what? At an airport shop in California I found "Easy-Stitch Sunflower Pillows" on the cover of *Family Circle*, "Make Our Easy Sunflower Cake" on *Woman's Day* and "Sunflower Season: Reaching New Heights" on *Harrowsmith Country Life*. I'll say. New heights of runaway feel-goodism. "Sunflowers are a joyous crop," one writer gushed, touting such varieties as Sunbeam, Teddy Bear and Big Smile. I put the magazines back on the display rack and walked over to skim the card section. One, two, three…fourteen.

"Sunflowers have become a classic in the last five years," says Belinda Nemeth, a creative director at American Greetings in Cleveland. "They're happy. They're American, they're strong, they persevere against the elements." As such, sunflowers work best on get-well cards. But they're also one of the few flowers suitable for masculine cards, Nemeth notes. She backs this up by sending me scads of guy-themed samples, all brawny with sunflowers: "It's Father's Day!" "Just For You, Nephew," "My Husband, My Friend."

So now everyone's cashing in. W. J. Deutsch & Sons, in Armonk, New York, imports all that sunflower-labeled Georges Duboeuf chardonnay. "Why sunflowers?" I ask William Deutsch. "Have I got a story for you," he begins. "The label used to show a little purple thistle the French call a *chardon*. In France, that was fine, but over here sales were not too exciting. My daughter Susan suggested changing the image to a sunflower. Sales skyrocketed more than fivefold."

I visit the swank Manhattan offices of Elizabeth Arden, the cosmetics company, to get the goods on the scent called Sunflowers. Susan Arnot Heaney, the publicist (blonde, in a cherry-red suit), and Clare Cain, the fragrance's creator (blonde, in a lime-colored jacket), are thrilled with their success. Since its 1993 launch, the Sunflowers product line has been "blowing out the doors," Heaney says. Of course, the scent has absolutely nothing to do with the plant. "Real sunflowers either smell bad or not at all!" Heaney explains. It's their spunky image that counts.

> Modern archaeologists have found seed caches in Tennessee dating from almost 3000 B.C., leaving no question that the sunflower's home is North America.

Cranberries, blueberries, pecans, strawberries and sunflowers are among our primary native crops, but several centuries ago there was some confusion about where sunflowers originated. This was due mainly to a 16th-century Spanish explorer's description of sunflowers he saw in what he called Peru. Modern archaeologists, however, have found seed caches in Tennessee dating from almost 3000 B.C., leaving no question that the sunflower's home is North America.

Sunflowers do carry a strong Native American pedigree — as an old synonym, *Sola Indianus*, bears out. A number of tribes used different parts of the sunflower to treat rattlesnake bites, relieve chest pains and heal cuts. The Hopis made a purple dye from the seeds. Others used sunflower oil as a hair dressing and kneaded sunflower meal into breads. My favorite Indian sunflower recipe, from the Hidatsa of North Dakota, runs thus: parch seeds in a clay pot, pound them into a fine meal, roll it into a ball. Wrap the ball in buffalo-heart skin or storage. Perfect for long treks; kind of a Native American granola bar.

It was the Spanish conquistadors who "discovered" sunflowers in North America and took them back to Europe, along with corn, tomatoes, potatoes and gold. By the early 1500s, sunflowers were growing in the botanical gardens of Madrid. From there, they made their way across Europe to the Balkans and Russia.

In fact, Peter the Great collected some seeds on one of his European trips, and by 1880 Russia had 400,000 acres of sunflowers under cultivation; by World War I, more than two million. Such popularity grew, intriguingly, from a loophole. For the 40 days before both Easter and Christmas, the Orthodox Church of Russia issued a roster of high-fat foods that were banned. Sunflower oil was just novel enough to avoid inclusion.

Though it is a plant native to North America, other continents witnessed the significant cultivation of sunflowers long before the United States or Canada.

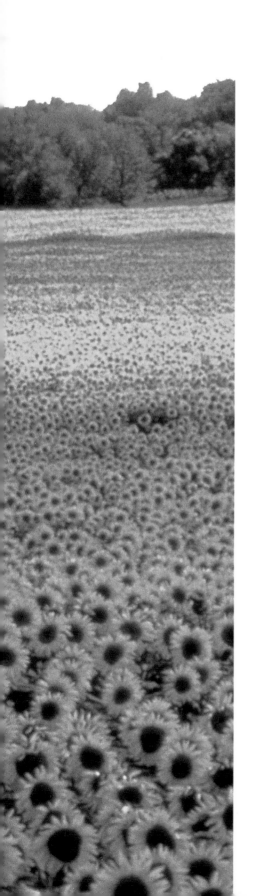

Today, nearly 85 percent of Russia's cooking oil comes from sunflower-crushing facilities. Until the Soviet breakup, the USSR was the number one producer of sunflower seeds in the world. As of last year, though, Argentina ranked first. The United States produced 1,817,000 metric tons of seeds, Russia 4,200,000 and Argentina 5,900,000.

The current cultural rage for sunflowers is by no means the first. Back in the 1870s and '80s, sunflowers were very big in Europe during the short-lived Aesthetic movement. They occurred "in every conceivable material from cast-iron and brickwork to embroidery," one book on the period observes. Van Gogh and Monet couldn't get enough of them, of course, and the British were especially taken. William Morris, the poet, artist and designer, splattered them on his wallpaper. William Blake penned an ode: "Ah, sunflower! weary of time./ Who countest the steps of the sun/ Seeking after that sweet golden clime/ Where the traveler's journey is done."

While he was still in his early 20s, the Irish writer, wit and dandy Oscar Wilde became a leading popularizer, if that is the right word, of "art for art's sake" and the Aesthetic movement's ubiquitous sunflower motif. When he gave a lecture in Boston, 60 Harvard students showed up to ridicule him, each wearing a lily in his lapel (a Wilde trademark) and carrying a sunflower. Wilde was caricatured in *Punch* as the head of a flower declaiming: "O, I feel just as happy as a bright sunflower!"

By the early 1880s at least one other magazine, *The British Architect*, had had it with artistic reform and sunflowers. "If there is nothing else to illustrate the fact," the editors railed, "the sickening repetition of the sunflower in all sorts of decorative work (as though it were the sum total of all beauty) would be enough to show how little the general public have yet derived from the increased study of art."

Back home, the sunflower's time had not yet come. A handful of farmers grew the plant for silage but that was all. "The sunflower 'tis rank and coarse/ 'Twould make a lovely bouquet for a horse" ran one aphorism. In fact, American books of the day snubbed sunflowers for their indelicacy, their immigrant loutishness. They were scorned as noxious weeds. Remember, those farmers only knew wild sunflowers, the ones that look more like black-eyed Susans, not the lush cultivated sort then developing in Europe. And sunflowers as ornamentals? You wouldn't find them in a flower shop, wrote botanist Charles Heiser Jr. in his book *The Sunflower*.

The life of a sunflower is full of aggravations, including mildew, wilt, rust, beetles, moths, midges, weevils and blackbirds, not to mention major droughts and, at the other extreme, too much rain.

"At best, you might see them used to camouflage a garbage can or a privy."

How did we get from derision to *de rigueur*? Think Russia by way of Canada. In the 1870s groups of Mennonites emigrated from Russia to the prairies of southern Manitoba. They brought sunflower seeds with them, and by the 1880s their Mammoth Russian variety was appearing for sale in American seed catalogs. Nothing much happened, though, until World War I, when the United States was scrounging for any source of oil and discovered that sunflower oil could be used for margarine and the manufacture of munitions.

Another long pause and then finally a sort of sunflower Sputnik era. Long story. The gist of it is, there's this research director at Cargill, the Minneapolis agricultural corporation, named Richard Baldwin, and an elderly Russian geneticist, V. S. Pustavoit. In 1965, Baldwin visits Pustavoit at the old man's labs in Krasnodar, by the Black Sea. Pustavoit is the man who figured out how to raise the oil content of sunflower seeds from 27 percent to 45 percent—yes, twice that of soybeans. The two scientists chat, and eventually Baldwin asks if he might take a few of those 45 percent seeds back home. Nervous silence. Pustavoit pictures himself eating fisheye soup in the gulag and says, "*Nyet.*" Baldwin is devastated, but a little bit later his interpreter casually asks Pustavoit for a few seeds "to eat in the car."

Shortly after that, plant breeders figured out how to hybridize sunflowers for disease resistance and higher yields. Those seeds and the ones Baldwin brought back from Russia became the foundation for the sunflower renaissance now in full swing.

Baldwin came home at the perfect moment. Midwestern farmers were desperate for ideas, since the Red River Valley of Minnesota and North Dakota was in the throes of a flax crisis. (And who can forget where they were when they first heard of *that*?) No longer were their fields lavender-blue with flax blossoms. Latex had put an end to that; paint manufacturers were cutting back on linseed oil, which is pressed from flax.

Yet there was still a flax infrastructure in place — crushing facilities and so on — that could be retrofitted for sunflowers. In the late 1960s, the Russians, desperate for foreign currency, began dumping much of their sunflower oil on the European market. But then they suddenly backed off and the Europeans, now hooked on the stuff, beseeched us,

The two basic classes of sunflower seeds are the oil-types, grown for their oil and meal, and the non-oils, or confections, grown for direct human consumption.

the true motherland of sunflowers, to help. We were happy to oblige, and come summer, the Red River Valley turned swaggeringly, luridly, blindingly yellow.

Fargo, North Dakota, the heart of the Red River Valley, is the nerve center of the sunflower business. Some very important sunflower genetic research goes on here at the Northern Crop Science Laboratory (NCSL), which is part of the U.S. Department of Agriculture.

The life of a sunflower is full of aggravations, including mildew, wilt, rust, beetles, moths, midges, weevils and blackbirds, not to mention major droughts and, at the other extreme, too much rain. Even bears. John Swanson, a farmer in Mentor, Minnesota, told me he's seen bear tracks in his fields. From the look of the damage, he figures they must lumber in, eat their fill and then, for fun, lie down and roll around, scratching themselves on the broken stalks.

At the NCSL, scientists are trying to create sunflower hybrids that can stand up to some of these enemies. Their work involves traditional breeding techniques as well as cloning, in which they extract the desired trait and genetically copy it into select sunflower DNA.

Take a midsummer drive across the Plains states, from Kansas to Montana to Minnesota, and the many sunflower fields you see will look fairly uniform, all the plants about the same height, each unopened head following the sun's path in the sky. (The French word for sunflower is *tournesol*, meaning it turns toward the sun.) But that's not the case in these Fargo experimental fields; they all look different. Geneticist Jerry Miller shows me a rust-resistant line from South Africa, something called Armavirskij 50 from Russia, and various shorts and talls from Romania, Algeria, Israel and Texas. "Beetles don't like this one," Miller says, pointing to a silverleaf variety. "If they lay their eggs on the stem, the eggs desiccate. Unfortunately, the midges happen to love it. You can't get everything in one plant."

Right now, the hottest thing in 'flowers (that's the shorthand, out here) is something called "high oleic" sunflower oil. "The industry wants to make an oil that can be legitimately labeled as being one of the lowest in saturated fats,"

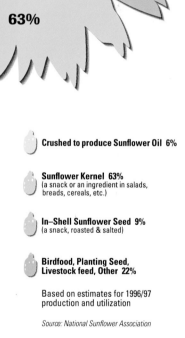

U.S. Sunflower Production Utilization

9%

6%

22%

63%

Crushed to produce Sunflower Oil **6%**

Sunflower Kernel 63%
(a snack or an ingredient in salads, breads, cereals, etc.)

In-Shell Sunflower Seed 9%
(a snack, roasted & salted)

Birdfood, Planting Seed, Livestock feed, Other 22%

Based on estimates for 1996/97 production and utilization

Source: National Sunflower Association

Miller explains. That's the holy grail. Sunflower oil has less saturated fat than soybean, olive and corn oils but more than safflower and canola. The challenge, therefore, is to find a way to lower its total saturates to 8 percent.

Sunflower seeds are becoming increasingly popular in the dugout. It has reached the point where baseball even has its own "official" sunflower supplier.

David & Sons, based in Fresno, California, makes sure every major - and-minor league locker room is well stocked.

Sunflower oil and seeds consistently rate high in consumer-appeal polls. This likability has prompted the National Sunflower Association (NSA) in Bismarck, North Dakota, to promote a bunch of sunflower-exploiting recipes —sunflower-pumpkin muffins, that sort of thing. The NSA is a "farmer-controlled, nonprofit commodity organization working to improve the status of U.S. sunflower producers and the industry in general," it says on the masthead of *The Sunflower*, a magazine the organization publishes.

Between the sunflowers growing in the fields and the sunflower muffins baking in your oven there is interposed this "infrastructure" I referred to earlier. It consists mainly of seed-processing facilities like Dahlgren & Company, in Crookston, Minnesota. The floors here resemble bald tires because over the years millions of errant sunflower oilseeds have been squashed underfoot. Just so you know—oilseeds are solid black, while edible seeds (also known as confection seeds) are striped. Both are used as birdseed. About 60 percent of the market is in oilseeds, another 20 percent is used for human consumption and 20 percent goes to the birds.

Dahlgren started processing confection seeds back in the late 1950s. The company sells its striped seeds as roasted kernels and as in-shells, and it even markets the discarded hulls for turkey bedding. "Contrary to the song," quips Kelly Engelstad, "turkeys don't like to be in straw." Engelstad, Dahlgren's president, is showing me around today, along with Don Lilleboe, a dry-humored editor at *The Sunflower*, who looks a bit like the actor Ed Harris. Lilleboe pens articles like "Tempted to Cut Nitrogen for 'Flowers in '95?" He answers most of my reportorial requests by exclaiming, "You bet!"

The Dahlgren plant smells warm and salty, and the din forces us to pantomime questions and answers. Huge chutes spit seeds furiously and an electric eye sorts impurities from the kernels. Other machines shake out bins of small, medium and large seeds. Any stray leaves or burrs ("trash" as farmers say, or "dockage") are whomped onto a sort of Velcro apparatus that holds them fast. Impact hullers smash the seedcovers, scootching out the little beige hearts, which are then zipped by pneumatic conveyors to the roasting plant. After roasting and salting, these kernels are packaged for sale in vending machines and stores.

The roasting plant is big and runs round the clock yet requires only about ten workers, some of whom are called master roasters. Engelstad tells me masters spend an average of five years learning their trade. It's an art; if you roast seeds a bit too long, you lose the entire 500-pound batch. Our host scoops up palmfuls of ready kernels for Lilleboe and me, all warm, gleaming, fragrant and salty. Sublime.

By the end of my stay, my lips feel permanently shriveled. Whether they're in-shells (also called "crack-and-spits") or shelled kernels (technically called "achenes"), I am eating sunflower seeds with a pathetic lack of self control. Engelstad sympathizes. "I can't go to a game without a bag of 'em," he confesses.

Neither can a lot of other people. Connie Hofland, the marketing director at the NSA, tells me no precise figures are available, but she guesses domestic sales for human consumption have more than doubled in the past decade. However, the seeds are a janitor's nightmare and a lawyer's dream (think liability) because they make the floors of theaters, gymnasiums and arenas dangerously slippery. This is why, in a sunflower booster town like Fargo, you can't buy the seeds at many indoor sporting events.

Roger Maris, the New York Yankee who in 1961 established a new home-run record for a single major-league season, is buried in Fargo not far from the NCSL. In Maris' day, chewing tobacco was perceived as the professional player's chaw of choice, but concerns about image and health are changing that. (In 1993, in fact, the minor leagues banned chewing tobacco outright.) So what to do about all those oral fixations? You guessed it. Sunflower seeds are becoming increasingly popular in the dugout. It was reached the point where baseball even has its own "official" sunflower supplier. David & Sons, based in Fresno, California, makes sure every major-and-minor-league locker room is well stocked.

A few years back, Larry Andersen, now a pitching

It was the Spanish conquistadors who "discovered" sunflowers in North America and took them back to Europe, along with corn, tomatoes, potatoes and gold.

coach with the minor-league Reading Phillies in Pennsylvania, improvised a bit of sunflower goofiness that has added a whole new dimension to the game. Andersen discovered that if he opened sunflower-seed hulls slightly, they would pinch his skin and stick wherever he put them. As a relief pitcher with the San Diego Padres, he began occupying his idle hours in the bull pen by putting them all over his face, a pastime that is now being taken up by other players. Doesn't it hurt? "Only the ones on the eyelids," Andersen insists.

Internationally, sunflower-seed preferences serve as a kind of cultural barometer. "The Spanish like the recreational aspect of crack-and-spits," Connie Hofland explains. Japan only imports shelled kernels. "The Japanese are not crack-and-spitters," Hofland says. "To them, in-shells are bird food. At one trade show we gave them some, and they wouldn't spit them out!"

The Russians outdo everyone with a kind of Khrushchev-shoe-pounding approach. It's said the average Russian can crack a steady stream of seeds on one side of his mouth, while dislodging kernels with his tongue and simultaneously spitting out empty hulls from the other side. "The Germans are our number one export market," Hofland says. Kernels. Not crack-and-spits. And the French? Kernels only. "They think crack-and-spits are uncivilized," Kelly Engelstad says, "As incomprehensible as corn on the cob."

It was August, wheat harvest time, when I dropped in one morning on Roger and Connie White, of Stirum, North Dakota. We chatted in the tidy kitchen of what they like to call the "Western White House." Roger is leather-brown and whip-thin; Connie, a little softer looking, wears sunflower earrings. The Whites devote 600 of their 2,500 acres to 'flowers. On the wall is a photograph of the farm surrounded on three sides by their yellow blooms.

"Seems we always get good 'flowers," says Roger. "They take the drought, they're reliable." This is the salient fact about sunflowers: they're remarkably tough, often require little fertilizer and don't need irrigation. They are able to scavenge nutrients left unused in the soil by shallower grains like wheat or rye (the roots of some sunflowers can go down as deep as eight feet), making them a fine rotation crop.

Unlike T-shirt makers and china painters, farmers don't get excited about sunflowers when they're at the glowing, smiley-face stage. Money is made at harvest time, in the late fall, when sunflowers are paper-bag brown, raspy, hangdog messes. (When Alf Landon, of Kansas, ran against FDR

Oilseeds are solid black, while edible seeds (also known as confection seeds) are striped. Both are used as birdseed. About 60 percent is used for human consumption and 20 percent goes to the birds.

for President in 1936, he wore campaign buttons in the shape of a sunflower, the Kansas state flower. "Sunflowers die in November," the Democrats quipped, and sure enough, Landon lost by a landslide.) "They're the homeliest things you ever saw," says Connie White. In old Russia, peasants used nailstudded paddles to rake the seeds free. The Whites use a special head on their wheat combine. "It snaps and crackles and sounds like a forest fire," says Roger.

Though their 'flowers almost always "come through real nice," as Roger says, the Whites have had to cope with stem weevils, too much rain and, most irksome of all, seed-eating blackbirds. The couple have tried to spook them with propane boomers, which emit periodic sound blasts. They've also hacked down the cattails in nearby sloughs; blackbirds tend to converge on wetlands, then forage from there. There was a time when the Whites would just plain shoot at them, more to frighten than to kill. "In the evenings, we'd get our guns," Connie recalls. "Roger would take his lawn chair to one end of the field, and I'd sit on the other, and we'd just shoot and shoot." A wee irony there. Last year, in this country alone, about 300,000 tons of sunflower seeds were sold to feed birds, up from 121,500 a decade ago.

I asked Sue Wells, director of the National Bird-Feeding Society, in Northbrook, Illinois, why birds are so fond of them. "It's the high oil content. Big birds like cardinals and grosbeaks can crack the hull of the striped seeds, and the little ones — chickadees, goldfinches — prefer hulled seeds." Aelred Geis, research director of the Maryland-based Wild Bird Centers of America (and known in certain circles as "Dr. Birdfeed"), concurs. "If I had to pick one all-around seed for birds it would be sunflower seeds — especially the black ones."

One morning I talked with Jay Schuler, who is the president of the seed company SIGCO Sun Products, in Wahpeton, North Dakota. The subject turned to birdfeed. "I guess you all have less children back East," he offered, grinning, "so you feel a need to adopt some birds." We silly birders account for a fifth of his business.

A few days later, my homebound plane lifted off the Fargo runway and I watched the fields below us blur into huge Mondrians — no primary reds or blues here but plenty of yellows. When I got back to Boston, I went through my mail. Bills, magazines, a card from Allison. "Hope you had a great time," she wrote, "and that you're not too sick of these!" She meant the picture on the front of the card. ∎

Sunflower oil is among the healthiest vegetable oils available. It ranks very high in percentage of polyunsaturated fat and is an excellent source of linoleic acid — one of the essential fatty acids required by the human body. The vitamin E content of sunflower oil is the highest of all leading vegetable oils.

NATURAL ALLIES

BY TED WILLIAMS

E very spring, when cowslips blaze yellow in Meadow
Brook and peepers jangle around the marshy fringes of
Poler's Pond, I lead an evening "woodcock walk" to the
Grafton Conservation Area, 50 miles west of Boston.
This year 20 participants and a reporter met at the
trailhead at 7:15 P.M. and, while robins whinnied and
song sparrows trilled, I read them Aldo Leopold's "Sky
Dance." Then, in the orange explosion of a Yankee sunset,
we hiked up the ancient cowpath and took our seats under a
dogwood stand.

The Conservation Area is 52-acre sanctum for such
suburban outcasts as foxes, owls, hawks, wild turkeys, and
eastern coyotes—a place of shade and shine where meadow
and woodland wildflowers bloom from early spring to late
fall, where ruffed grouse thunder out of old orchards tangled
with bittersweet, where butterflies dance through milkweed
silk that sails on the summer breeze and the breath of school
children.

Eight years ago when a developer was poised to replace
the living cloverleaves with the asphalt kind, to run a sewer
line up the cowpath and gouge out foundations for 50 houses,
my wife, Donna, and I organized a crusade to save our special place. Everyone, especially me, thought it was impossible. But we brought people here, showed them the wildlife
and the beauty, and somehow convinced our frugal community of 12,000 to cough up $1.3 million to buy the land.

I like to bring my woodcock watchers here half an hour
before curtain call so they can absorb the wildness of the
place, listen to church bells from old-Grafton center and
birdsong from hardwood groves, and gradually convince
themselves that the woodcock isn't going to show. When,
finally, he materializes out of the afterglow and utters his
first nasal "peeent," the excitement is tangible. Sometimes I
hear gasps when he launches into the azure sky, fluttering

> Hunters and anglers have a
> long history of protecting and
> restoring fish, wildlife, and
> habitat. Our 92-million-acre
> national wildlife refuge system
> was started by hunter Theodore
> Roosevelt.

and twittering between Venus and the moon, then warbling and falling like an oak leaf almost to our feet. When I explain to the woodcock watchers that I will hunt these birds in October with a 12-gauge shotgun and my soul mate, a 60-pound Brittany named Wilton, some of them are visibly shocked and disappointed.

More than 50 million Americans fish, and 15 million hunt, yet environmentalists have made scant effort to forge any lasting alliance with them to protect the land and water that sustain wildlife. "Environmentalists don't reach out to sportsmen," says Chris Potholm, a professor of government and legal studies at Bowdoin College in Maine. "If they did, they'd be invincible. Whenever sportsmen combine with environmentalists, you have 60 to 70 percent of the population, an absolutely irresistible coalition."

Consider the alliance between the Rocky Mountain Elk Foundation and the National Fish and Wildlife Foundation, an agency set up and funded by Congress to leverage matching conservation grants from the private sector. The latter is run by a former national Audubon Society lobbyist; the former by elk hunters. Working together (and with help from other sportsmen and environmentalists), the alliance has protected or restored 1.8 million acres north of Yellowstone National Park.

Consider also Trout Unlimited, perhaps the most effective force for environmental reform among sportsmen's groups. What has made Trout Unlimited so successful is that it is run by people who are not just sportsmen or just environmentalists, but both. On endangered species, grazing reform, mining reform, hydroelectric relicensing, clean water, forest practices, river dewatering—Trout Unlimited is on the front lines, suing every exploiter in sight and generally raising hell.

Such conservation-minded sportsmen predominate in Alaska, though you'd never know it from talking to state officials. Only three years ago the Alaska Department of Fish and Game hatched a plan to generate more moose, caribou, and hunting-license revenue by shooting wolves from aircraft. "We feel we are going to create a wildlife spectacle on a par with the major migrations in East Africa," effused Fish and Game's Wildlife Director David Kelleyhouse, known to his many critics as "Machinegun Kelleyhouse" because he once tried to requisition a fully automatic weapon for "wolf management." Supporting this 1920s-style theory of game production was then-Governor Wally Hickel, who explained

In the early 1950s bureaucrats targeted Echo Park in Dinosaur National Monument for a hydroelectric dam. Led by the Sierra Club's David Brower, sporting and green groups protested so loudly that Congress nixed the shortsighted proposal.

Elk in the Suisun Wildlife Preserve.

to me and other journalists at a Fairbanks "wolf summit" that "you can't let nature just run wild." Most journalists reported that the state was responding to Alaskan hunters. But, as usual, hunters got a bum rap; a statewide poll revealed that only 36 percent of them were in favor. Since then typical Alaskan hunters—who admire wolves and understand ecosystems—have joined with environmentalists to try to ban aerial wolf-hunting permanently. The Wolf Management Reform Coalition, as the alliance is called, has already gathered enough signatures to get such an initiative on the November 1996 ballot, and Alaskans are showing strong support.

Success stories of this sort don't raise Professor Potholm's eyebrows. Sixteen years ago he founded The Potholm Group, a national polling and strategic-advice company that has engineered some unlikely habitat victories in 55 state referenda. For example, it's hard to imagine a more hopeless task for the Great Basin Nature Conservancy than convincing the residents of that 83-percent-federally-owned bastion of property-rights fanaticism called Nevada to pass a $47 million bond issue for the purpose of acquiring *more* public land. Initial polls indicated that the 1990 referendum

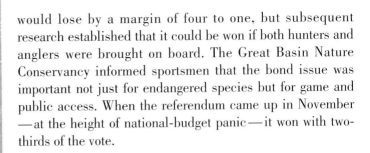

would lose by a margin of four to one, but subsequent research established that it could be won if both hunters and anglers were brought on board. The Great Basin Nature Conservancy informed sportsmen that the bond issue was important not just for endangered species but for game and public access. When the referendum came up in November —at the height of national-budget panic—it won with two-thirds of the vote.

More than 50 million Americans fish, and 15 million hunt, yet environmentalists have made scant effort to forge any lasting alliance with them to protect the land and water that sustain wildlife.

"We've won referenda in Nevada, New Mexico, Florida, Rhode Island, Maine, Minnesota, and Arizona because we were able to get environmentalists and sportsmen to cooperate," reports Potholm. "We can win environmental referenda anywhere if we get environmentalists and sportsmen working together. I can get the cowboys in Montana to vote to save the black-footed ferret if the environs will let them hunt elk on the land….The biggest mistake enviros make is they always look to the Democrats first. If I can get the sportsmen on board, then I get them to bring the Republicans."

Hunters and anglers have a long history of protecting and restoring fish, wildlife, and habitat. They saved game (and many species now classified as non-game) from commercial market hunting, a practice that had no more to do with sport hunting than gillnetting has to do with angling. At the beginning of the 20th century there were about 500,000 white-tailed deer in the United States; today there are 27 million. Only 41,000 elk survived in 1907; now there are a million. In 1910 antelope were down to 5,000; today there are at least a million. A century ago wild turkeys were close to extinction; last spring there were 4.2 million.

Our 92-million-acre national wildlife refuge system was started by hunter Theodore Roosevelt. And it was saved by hunter J. N. "Ding" Darling, the Pulitzer prize-winning political cartoonist of *The Des Moines Register* who, with his fellow waterfowlers, pushed through a law in 1934 to require duck and goose hunters to purchase a federal permit in the form of a stamp (to be pasted to the state hunting license that they also had to buy). Since that day duck-stamp money has gone to purchase national wildlife refuges.

In Darling's cartoons one of the bloated, cigar-chomping politicians commonly seen evicting bandaged, splinted birds and animals from their happy homes was President Franklin D. Roosevelt. Dumb, FDR was not; so he wrestled the camel's head inside the tent by hiring Darling to direct the Bureau of Biological Survey, progenitor of the Fish and Wildlife Service.

When the president broke his promise to fund the new national wildlife refuge system, Darling conspired with Senator Peter Norbeck of South Dakota to tack a $1 million appropriation to the duck-stamp bill. The hugely popular Norbeck spoke in such a heavy Norwegian accent that when he asked for something, his colleagues preferred to just say "yes" rather than undertake the daunting task of translation. No sooner had Norbeck taken the Senate floor than he removed his false teeth and, as Darling loved to tell it, "asked, in words totally devoid of understandable articulation, for an amendment to the bill allocating six million dollars."

"Aye," said the Senate, uncertainly. Darling had told Roosevelt to watch for the bill and sign it. Somehow, it appeared on the president's desk just as he was hurrying out the door to go fishing. On returning to the White House, FDR sent Darling this note: "As I was saying to the Acting Director of the Budget the other day, 'this fellow Darling is the only man in history who got an appropriation through Congress, past the Budget, and signed by the President without anybody realizing that the Treasury had been raided.'"

To raise money for wildlife management, hunters and anglers have successfully lobbied for excise taxes on fishing tackle and ammunition. Today, they are joining with other nature lovers to push for new excise taxes on an even wider range of outdoor products (such as backpacks, tents, birdseed, and field guides) that would provide an additional $350 million a year for ecosystem management. Leading the charge are the state game and fish directors who call themselves the International Association of Fish and Wildlife Agencies. Their initiative, "Teaming With Wildlife," has been endorsed by more than 1,000 environmental and sportsmen's organizations and businesses.

Formation of such alliances, however, has been painfully, dangerously slow. A major obstacle is the ease with which hunters are body-snatched by their worst enemies. They, much more than anglers, are paranoid because

Hunting and fishing have been a part of our national forest system since it was established in 1907.

they have been beaten up so savagely and so long—not just by the animal-rights advocates but by society in general. I cannot count the number of times I have been shrieked at by antihunters. Once I drove away with one slashing at me with her fingernails and literally hanging from my truck window. Now, when they demand to know if I have a hunting license, I ask them if they have a badge.

Hunting advocate Michael Furtman, writing in the April 1996 issue of *Midwest Fly Fishing*, offers this explanation: "After a decade of attacks by the animal-rights movement, defensive sportsmen were like a dog too long in its kennel—literally panting for kindly attention. Anyone that would pat us on the head would be rewarded with our undying friendship. That the person reaching out a hand—the wise-use movement—was intent upon taking that 'dog' to a medical research facility never occurred to most of us."

While environmentalists have been ignoring or alienating sportsmen, developers and their hirelings within the wise-use movement and Congress have been seducing them by dressing up in camouflage and flouncing around at photo ops with borrowed shotguns. For example, the 50 senators and 207 representatives of the Congressional Sportsmen's Caucus loudly profess to defend fish, wildlife, and sportsmen but consistently vote to destroy habitat. In the House, 83 percent of the CSC supported H.R.961, the bill that would basically repeal the Clean Water Act. By contrast, only 34 percent of non-caucus members supported the bill. Last year CSC members voted for fish, wildlife, and the environment an average of only 23 percent of the time (as recorded by the League of Conservation Voters) compared with 43 percent for the entire House and 47 percent for the entire Senate.

Leading the CSC in the Senate are Conrad Burns (R-Mont.: LCV score 0), John Breaux (D-La.: LCV score 29), Richard Shelby (R-Ala.: LCV score 0), and Larry Craig (R-Idaho; LCV score 0). House leadership consists of Don Young (R-Alaska; LCV score 0), Pete Geren (D-Tex.; LCV score 31); Toby Roth (R-Wis.; LCV score 8); and John Tanner (D-Tenn.; LCV score 31). These voting records make perfect sense when you check some of the funders of the caucus' money-raising tentacle, the Congressional Sportsmen's Foundation: Alabama Power, Alyeska Pipeline Service, Chevron, Dow Chemical, International Paper, Weyerhaeuser, Champion International, Mead, American Forest and Paper Association,

Vast as it is, the 7.5 million-acre Gates of the Arctic National Park was just one of 35 new conservation areas established by the 1980 Alaska Lands Act. Broad support was essential to passage, says the Sierra Club's Edgar Wayburn. "We could not have gotten so much without the hunters."

National Cattlemen's Association, Olin, and Phillips Petroleum.

Just before the last election Don Young—arguably the most vicious enemy of fish and wildlife in Congress—used his CSC connection to persuade *Outdoor Life* to ooze and gush about his self-proclaimed greenness. The 99-year-old publication told its 1.3 million subscribers that Young "is your kind of politician," that he "fights the good fight," and that "you'd be hard pressed to find a more fearless Washington advocate of the sportsman's life." There followed a lengthy interview in which Young berated the long-silent animal-rights activist Cleveland Amory and puffed and blew about the public's right to bear arms. This from the magazine that had produced Ben East—a giant in outdoor journalism, a heroic defender of wild things and wild places, and grandfather of Sierra Club Executive Director Carl Pope. (*Outdoor Life* is now under a new editor.)

Signs of success in preserving our natural wildlife.

Then there is the Wildlife Legislative Fund of America, a front for developers, wise-users, and right-wing ideologues that wangles voluminous space in outdoor media. When U.S. Fish and Wildlife Director Mollie Beattie (now deceased) moved to control such incompatible and illegal activities on wildlife refuges as overgrazing and jet-skiing, WLFA told sportsmen to send money so it could stop her from also banning hunting and fishing—something she had never dreamed of doing. The hook-and-bullet press swallowed it hook, line, boat, and motor. *Wildfowl Magazine* reported that non-hunter Beattie was plotting "to abandon waterfowl management on the refuges," and asked its readers to confirm the rumor that she was "wearing spandex shorts to work" just like Mariel Hemingway, last seen in an Audubon TV special "strutting around the Chincoteague National Wildlife Refuge in her spandex biking shorts and whining [about hunting being 'controversial'] like some PMS poster child."

When Beattie added 15 hunting programs and six fishing programs on refuges (something she had planned to do all along), WLFA bragged that it had "bloodied" the service and saved the refuge system for sportsmen. At this point,

WLFA's national affairs director, Bill Horn—who, as assistant secretary for fish, wildlife and parks under James Watt, had crusaded to open the Arctic National Wildlife Refuge to oil drilling and invited developers into the whole refuge system—set about drafting (or "helping to draft," as he prefers) H.R.1675, the "national Wildlife Refuge Improvement Act," for Don Young. When Horn, a lawyer, isn't working for WLFA, he offers counsel to such clients as Washington State property-rights zealots trying to block a new wildlife refuge and Florida condo developers seeking to restore subsidized federal flood insurance in order to build more profitably on coastal habitats.

The bait Horn and Young set out to attract sportsmen to their refuge bill was the elevation of hunting and fishing (already permitted on refuges wherever possible and appropriate) from "uses" to "purposes," thereby changing the official mission of the refuge system from protecting biodiversity to pleasuring humans. In the same vein, the bill would waive restrictions on military uses of refuges and require the Fish and Wildlife Service to get congressional approval to buy any new refuge over 500 acres with land and water conservation funds. On April 24—the day the bill passed the House—Mollie Beattie called it "the beginning of the end of the National Wildlife Refuge System as we know it."

Basically, WLFA attributes its victory to me. "More than any other factor," writes Vice President Rick Story in a letter to the 2,000 members of the Outdoor Writers Association of America, my "diatribe against the bill [in the May 1996 issue of the association's magazine] provided that much-needed surge of adrenaline which helped motivate our staff to continue plugging through the arduous last stages of the campaign to ensure the bill's passage.... Sportsmen and sportswomen nationwide did a fabulous job communicating their concerns to Congress." For once I agree with Mr. Story, at least with the last sentence. It's just that the House, as usual, didn't listen. Under the inspired leadership of the National Wildlife Federation, the Izaak Walton League of America, Trout Unlimited, and local hunting-and-fishing clubs in Montana, sportsmen and sportswomen nationwide were and are working closely with the environmental community to kill the bill. Now it looks as if the alliance will prevail. The refuge bill is expected to run into major trouble in the Senate; and in the unlikely event that it makes it through, Interior Secretary Bruce Babbitt will ask the President for a veto.

ven as the frightened hunter hears monster stories from the Congressional Sportsmen's Caucus and the Wildlife Legislative Fund of America, some environmentalists oblige by acting the part of anti-blood-sport bogeyman. The big green groups such as the National Audubon Society and the Sierra Club have never opposed hunting. In fact, they recognize the sport as a legitimate and necessary wildlife-management tool. But they are perceived as anti-hunting because of embarrassing behavior by some of their members. Take the position of certain state Audubon chapters on mourning-dove hunting. At the same time agribusiness destroys the habitat of upland gamebirds such as grouse, quail, and pheasants it produces vast swarms of grain-eating doves. Over 2 million hunters legally kill about 50 million doves a year in 37 states without even denting the population. In farming states like Indiana and Michigan there is every good reason to hunt mourning doves and no reason not to. For any sober, practical champion of biodiversity, dove hunting is the quintessential non-issue. Yet when I explained this in the March 1985 *Audubon*, as part of an eyewitness report on Indiana's first dove hunt, the editor was deluged with mail and wound up printing 49 letters, 26 of them irate. "Are robins next?" demanded one reader. "I would not object to destroying Ted Williams," wrote another. "We have an overpopulation of his breed." After 11 years I thought that Audubon chapters might have learned something, and maybe they have. But in 1995, when Michigan tried to legislate a hunting season for its superabundant doves, the Michigan Audubon Society (the second biggest chapter with 40 sub-chapters of its own) shouted the bill down. "Many, in these violent times, point to the irony of a proposed hunting season on the international symbol of peace," it seriously asserted.

"They didn't have to support the bill," remarks Wildlife Management Supervisor Richard Elden of the Michigan Department of Natural Resources, "just remain neutral and it might have passed. Michigan Audubon said its position was not an effort to oppose hunting, but it truly was. We have plenty of doves. They just plain opposed expanding legitimate hunting opportunity."

Such behavior plays into the hands of those seeking to discredit the entire environmental movement. "There are people out there day in and day out telling the public and Congress that environmentalists are anti-hunting," declares Paul Hansen, director of the Izaak Walton League of

New York's Adirondack Mountains have long been a mecca for hunters and anglers, who backed a constitutional amendment in 1894 that declared the state's extensive Adirondack holdings "forever wild."

America, a conservation group composed largely of hunters and anglers. "To my knowledge, the environmental groups haven't done a thing to clarify it. Some of their members might be anti, but institutionally none of them are — not Defenders, not Audubon, and not the Sierra Club. If there's one piece of advice I have for environmental groups it's this: Get right up front and say that you aren't anti-hunting."

The traditional refusal of most environmental groups to do this fuels sportsmen's paranoia and makes it difficult to educate them about environmental politics. I know because I've been attempting such education for 26 years. The very word "environmental" engenders suspicion in the hook-and-bullet set. Therefore, I am the "Conservation Editor" of *Fly Rod & Reel*. As "Senior Editor" of *Gray's Sporting Journal*, I took elaborate pains to explain how much gunpowder I've burned whenever I wrote something to augment the me-and-Joe stories. Even so, I received and published countless letters like the following: "Ted Williams has betrayed sportsmen everywhere" and "If you insist on bringing up controversial environmental issues, you do not become a sportsman's magazine but an environmental magazine. There are too many 'do gooder' magazines on the market today and few that give you the joy of remembering a good hunt or the one that got away. Please review your policy and let's keep *Gray's* a clean magazine." Or consider this, recently published in *Fly Rod & Reel*: "Dear Mr. Williams: You are a good writer, but I am getting tired of paying my money to hear your political agenda. From what little I know of the 'wise-use movement,' they appear to have taken a different (perhaps better) slant on managing our environment. Let me enjoy reading about your skillful exploits. Leave the politics alone."

Six years ago when Defenders of Wildlife tried to initiate dialogue with hunters by joining the Outdoor Writers Association of America, a large element of the association fantasized that Defenders was somehow anti-hunting and moved to throw it out. Such a prolonged stink was raised that Defenders voluntarily withdrew. "All we had in mind was an occasional exchange of views," read the good-bye letter. "Yours for diversity, biological and otherwise, M. Rupert Cutler, President." Joel Vance, who had just finished his term as OWAA's president, upbraided us in our magazine as follows: "For shame! We've run off a group that wanted to communicate with us...and we call ourselves communicators? Naah, we're just a bunch

It's no accident that hunters are welcome in Oregon's Three Sister Wilderness — for they helped pass the Wilderness Act of 1964.

of hypocrites who can't stand a contrary view."

So if environmentalists can excuse sportsmen for flee-
ing into the arms of their worst enemies, maybe sportsmen
can at least understand why reaching out to them hasn't
always been that easy.

But lately both sides have been doing a whole lot better. One of the brightest spots has been *Sports Afield* magazine, now in the hands of a fearless, enlightened editor
named Terry McDonell, who has been educating his readers
with such exposés as: "The Misguided War Over Refuges,"
"A Bad Deal for Sportsmen: What's Wrong With the
Contract With America," and "A Spring Sermon…Or
Siberia" (an essay on why sportsmen need to work with environmentalists). And yet only five years ago, under a different
editor, the magazine contributed $24,375 to the
Congressional Sportsmen's Foundation and ran a 15-page
supplement (largely paid for by gun and booze companies)
in which CSC members got to write articles on behalf of
their campaign contributors, one of the more nauseating
bearing Don Young's byline and entitled "Why Alaska
Sportsmen Support Opening the Arctic National Wildlife
Refuge."

I f only hunters, anglers, and environmentalists
would stop taking potshots at each other, they'd be
an invincible force for wildlands protection.

A year ago the 600,000-member Bass Anglers
Sportsman Society (B.A.S.S.) — a conservative, for-profit
organization with strong ties to the Republican Party — took
on a new role of environmental activist. Bruce Shupp, the
respected biologist B.A.S.S. hired to run its conservation
program, set about forging what promises to be a political
juggernaut — a sportsman-enviro alliance called the Natural
Resource Summit of America. The catalyst was the disas-
trous "clean water" bill and its mouthy House sponsorship,
which made the costly error of referring to B.A.S.S. on
national TV as "an environmental extremist group."

The summit's goals have evolved way beyond just sav-
ing the Clean Water Act to striving for solidarity on such
fronts as environmental law and natural-resources and public

lands policy. The third meeting of the summit, on March 4, was attended by such diverse groups as the Sierra Club, the American Fisheries Society, the Izaak Walton League, the American Sportfishing Association, The Wilderness Society, the International Association of Fish and Wildlife Agencies, and the Environmental Defense Fund. "The whole complexion changed yesterday," Shupp said on March 5. "We went in a new direction. We've got a product now. We're going somewhere. After 25 years of splitting apart we finally got our act together, and we're talking to each other."

Much credit for the new unity must go to the 104th Congress. For instance, Senator Pete Domenici (R-N.M.) has introduced a grazing bill so hideous as to accomplish the impossible—that is, forge an alliance not just between enviros and sportsmen, but between sportsmen and animal-rights advocates. Basically, the bill would reserve public lands in the West for the ranching industry. If agents of the Forest Service or BLM had to check compliance on a grazing lease, they would need permission of the permittee to set foot on the public's land. Eleven of the bill's 16 original sponsors are members of the Congressional Sportsmen's Caucus, but sportsmen haven't been fooled. Lonnie Williamson—vice president of the Wildlife Management Institute and past president of the Outdoor Writers Association—blasted the CSC and Domenici, calling the legislation "the Rangeland Rape Bill." Urging opposition to the bill in a joint letter to members of the Senate are 155 unlikely collaborators, including the Sierra Club and eight of its chapters, 11 Audubon Society chapters, Defenders of Wildlife, National Wildlife Federation, Republicans for Environmental Protection, Humane Society of the United States, The Fund for Animals, People for the Ethical Treatment of Animals, Izaak Walton League of America, California Bowmen Hunters and State Archery Association, and Sportsmen's Council of Central California.

Assisting Domenici in forging this new unity has been Congressional Sportsmen's Caucus Co-chair Senator Conrad Burns (R-Mont.), who is in his last election bid raised over half a million dollars from energy, mining, and agriculture interests. Burns has introduced a bill that would promote the sale and development of public land managed by the Forest Service, the BLM, and the Bureau of Reclamation. But Montana sportsmen-enviros, marching under such banners as the Montana Wildlife Federation, Billings Rod and Gun Club,

The big green groups have never opposed hunting. In fact, they recognize the sport as a legitimate and necessary tool.

and Anaconda Sportsmen's Association, are exposing Burns with a media blitz called "Keep Public Lands in Public Hands." The coalition's stated mission: "Save Montana's hunting heritage from the clutches of Conrad Burns and his crazy attempts to sell off our public lands." Stung by the bitter opposition from a group that had bowed and scraped for him in the past, Burns charged that the Montana Wildlife Federation "has lied about the bill" and dubbed the organization a "front group for [the] Democratic Party."

Meanwhile, in Yankeeland, my sportsman-environmentalist friends are being called the same thing whenever they complain about a Contract-on-America bill that would squander our nation's real wealth. Most of them belong to the grand old party of Abe Lincoln and Teddy Roosevelt, but unlike some of the new Republicans who allegedly represent them, they have a right to call themselves "conservatives."

On John Muir's birthday last April, Donna, Wilton, and I met one of them trudging out of the Grafton Conservation Area. Behind him on the cowpath were four women and a small boy. They'd read the story about Friday's woodcock walk in the morning paper and had hoped to see the show for themselves; but they said the woodcock had stood them up.

"You're ten minutes too early," I said. With

The 52-acre Grafton Conservation Area is a place of shade and shine where meadow and woodland wildflowers bloom from early spring to late fall.

that, we all filed back up to the dogwood patch, took our seats under a crescent moon that flashed through fast, pink clouds and, to the score of peepers, field sparrows, and distant church bells, watched a spectacular double sky dance by dueling males.

In the old days I used to lecture my generally anti-blood-sport woodcock watchers about what bird hunting means to me, and the words would always come out wrong. Now I just tell them how this wild, magic place came to be saved. We get along fine. ■

**IT WAS NECESSARY TO FIND A WAY TO GET THEM TO AND FROM
THE GREAT APE HOUSE,** where they have long had satisfactory quarters.
The O-Line, which actually was conceived long before the Think Tank,
was a spectacular solution to this problem.

NEW IDEAS IN THE AIR

AT THE NATIONAL ZOO

BY BIL GILBERT

In Washington, D.C., there is, to put it conservatively, an abundance of institutes, centers and foundations that are collectively referred to by inside-the-beltwayers as think tanks. These establishments have various agendas and reputations, but there is only one where crowds gather to watch the principals actually do their cogitating. It is located at the Smithsonian's National Zoological Park. There, for the past several months, a number of orangutans have been commuting more or less daily from their residence at the Great Ape House to a new hightech facility that is called, yes, the Think Tank.

To go between the two buildings, which are about 500 feet apart, the orangutans clamber up steel towers and then swing across a pair of heavy cables. They are separated from people watching on the ground by 35 feet of empty space. The orangutans make the traverse hand over hand, foot over foot and in combinations thereof, much as wild members of the species have been observed moving through tropical forests on swaying vines and branches.

The O-Line, as the overhead system is called, is now a dominant feature at the National Zoo. Somewhat as do carnival barkers or mimes performing outside a store, the O-Line trapeze artists irresistibly attract spectators and lead most of them into the Think Tank to find out what is going on.

NO MORE ROOM FOR MONKEY BUSINESS

After three years of planning and construction, and the expenditure of some $4 million, the former Monkey House—the National Zoo's oldest standing building—was converted into the Think Tank and opened to the public last fall. The general ambiance of the place is that of a progressive, well-endowed educational institution. This is the intended effect, according to Benjamin Beck, the project director. "We wanted," he says, "to present information about cognitive behavior in an atmosphere that encourages visitors to reflect on scientific methods as they might in a classroom or library."

Accordingly, the central gallery offers a series of interactive exhibits that amount to a continuous, multimedia lecture. The series opens with an essential academic qualification: since other species never testify directly as to how their minds work, all of our judgments about their mental processes are necessarily speculative. Whether a particular behavior is thoughtful depends ultimately on what the observer thinks thinking is. Opinions on the subject have been numerous and often contradictory, but presently most interested students define thinking more or less as it is defined at the Think Tank.

The O-line, as the overhead system is called, is now a dominant feature at the National Zoo. The O-line trapeze artists irresistibly attract spectators and lead most of them into the think tank to find out what is going on.

Thoughtful acts involve intent—a purposeful effort to achieve goals or solve specific problems. They demonstrate flexibility—the capacity to choose between various courses of action—as genetically programmed, instinctive, or innate, behaviors do not. Thinking also requires the ability to form and respond to mental representations of things that are not present.

With text, light and keyboards, interactive games and other state-of-the-art displays, the exhibits in the central gallery apply the foregoing definition to various animals. It is pointed out, for example, that salmon swimming upriver to lay eggs in the exact place where they were hatched years before are certainly purposeful. But the fish will die rather than spawn in another, more accessible and equally suitable place. Thus, by the Think Tank's definition, their behavior is innate, or instinctive, insufficiently flexible to be thoughtful. A chimpanzee selecting a stem to extract edible termites from their nest is offered as an example of a true thinker. Come heaven, hell or high water, beavers will build dams across narrow streams because they have been genetically programmed to do so. But if their dam is threatened by rising waters, beavers may respond thoughtfully by cutting spillways in it.

The Think Tank provides a variety of settings for research on animal cognition. In an elaborate terrarium, a colony of tropical ants cut and process leaves, then tend and harvest the fungus gardens that grow on the leaves. The ants do so with machine-like regularity and precision, demonstrating what the exhibit characterizes as complicated innate but thoughtless behavior. In a greenhouse-like enclosure, nine Sulawesi macaques, notably social monkeys from Indonesia, go about their regular business. Here observers are urged, on the basis of what they have learned elsewhere in the Think Tank, to decide if and in what circumstances the macaques are thinking.

STAGING AN EVENT FOR MAN AND APE

These and other exhibits in the Think Tank are artful and informative, but the main attraction is a glass-walled amphitheater where members of the staff and the Zoo's orangutans appear in "behavioral events" for the edification of visitors. The style and substance of the performances vary, but a recent one might theatrically be described as follows:

CAST: Benjamin Beck, biologist and project leader; Rob Shumaker, graduate student specializing in orangutan language use; Dan Shillto, graduate student specializing in orangutan self-awareness; Indah, 16-year-old female orangutan.

SETTING: Indah lolls against a wall with windows, outside of which runs an open, elevated counter, or stage apron. About 40 spectators are seated in front of and below the counter. Indah and spectators regard each other with what appears to be mutual curiosity.

ACT I: Beck enters from the right and explains that he, Rob and Dan are interested in whether orangutans are aware of the thought processes of people and can analyze or empathize with them. Pondering the matter earlier in the day, staffers devised an ad hoc experiment. Beck provides some background.

Since people at the Zoo are constantly unlocking and locking doors, Beck says, they carry sizable key rings. Misplacing them causes extreme vocational panic. Orangutans, who are known to be unusually observant creatures, seem to be well aware of how the key rings are prized by keepers. All of which suggested the behavioral event that then begins as Beck exits.

Rob enters from the left, ostentatiously twirling his key

ring. He greets Indah with a casual wave. She responds with a friendly expression and taps on the glass wall. A pencil drops from Rob's pocket. As he bends down to pick it up, he drops the key ring. Indah watches intently. Apparently unaware of what has happened, Rob blithely exits right, leaving the key ring where he dropped it.

Dan enters from the left and, feigning surprise, finds the key ring. He picks it up and shows it to Indah. His gestures and facial expression indicate he is puzzled. Indah stares at him while rubbing her hands together. Her gestures and facial expressions are seemingly pensive. After a bit of this byplay Dan strolls across the stage, places the key ring on a stood and exits.

ACT II: Beck re-enters from the right and asks the spectators if they think Indah is aware of all the business with the key ring. Those who respond agree that she is. Beck says the scientific point of this charade is to discover what, if anything, Indah thinks about the happening. If, for example, Rob returned and she tried to draw his attention to the misplaced key ring, this behavior would suggest Indah had reflected on the problem. Beck advises the audience that this experiment has not been conducted previously at the Think Tank or, so far as he knows, anyplace else. Therefore he has no better idea about what may happen next than the spectators do.

ACT III: Rob re-enters from the left and frantically searches the area where he dropped the key ring. He looks inquisitively at Indah, who stares impassively at him. Then her attention seems to shift to a woman in the audience who is wearing a brightly colored, sharply pointed stocking cap. Rob continues to behave in a distraught manner for several minutes. Then Dan enters, goes to the stool, picks up the keys and hands them to Rob, who pantomimes gratitude. Indah watches but appears to be only mildly interested in the exchange. She shuffles away from the glass and finds one of the pieces of burlap fabric that are provided for all the orangutans. She sits down, carefully covers her feet with the burlap and stares at the ceiling.

Beck returns and concludes the behavioral event by saying that science is a process of testing hypotheses. Negative results, he says, are sometimes as instructive as positive ones.

Backstage, Dan Shillto says that hypothesizing is the easy part of this research. New questions about the behavior of orangutans are constantly popping into his mind. The hard, crucial thing is coming up with ways to ask the questions that will engage the minds of the animals. Perhaps Indah is incapable of analyzing the lost-keys problem and responding to it as the researchers thought she might. Or she may have fully understood the happening but on reflection found it insufficiently relevant or interesting to merit any response.

Tracey Barnes, a volunteer at both the Great Ape House and the Think Tank, was involved in an incident that anecdotally supports the proposition that orangutans may try to influence human behavior, or even take advantage of it, after noticing something a person has done. A particularly cunning 19-year-old orangutan named Bonnie has a well-deserved reputation for keeping an eye on new keepers to see if they are careless about leaving desirable objects within reach or can be worked for special treats or privileges. "A few weeks after I started here," says Barnes, "I was fixing something in a narrow corridor outside Bonnie's place. She reached through the bars and tried to grab my tools. I told her to stop it and she did. Orangutans are very aware of our rules. When they are caught breaking them they appear to be contrite, but I am not sure they are."

Members of the staff and the Zoo's orangutans offer a variety of interactive exhibits and "behavioral events."

After being admonished by Barnes, Bonnie picked up a piece of burlap and held it over her face. From time to time she peeked out to make seemingly apologetic and comical faces at Barnes, who was amused until she looked down and saw Bonnie's foot edging toward the toolbox. "It seemed pretty clear to me she was intentionally trying to distract and deceive me."

Orangutans have been an important part of the Think Tank idea from the very beginning. The National Zoo has nine of the animals, all captive-bred, and it is responsible for maintaining them properly throughout their lives, which may last 50 years or more. Presently the youngest is a 5-

year-old male, Chang. The eldest and sire of four of the others is Junior, a 30-year-old.

What can best, if anthropomorphically, be described as boredom may cause serious behavioral problems for mentally complex and active animals in zoos. Consequently, zookeepers are eager to provide interesting devices and activities that will, as they say, enrich the lives of their charges. Once this may have been unwittingly accomplished by the animal shows that were commonly staged at zoos, mainly to attract and amuse visitors. Those entertainments fell out of favor because they were deemed exploitative. Today zoos are encouraging animals to extend their natural talents and abilities. Thus elephants paint pictures (*Smithsonian*, December 1990) and play musical instruments, sea lions cavort through the water like porpoises and orangutans go to "school" at the National Zoo's Think Tank.

In their native Borneo and Sumatra, orangutans spend most of their time high up in trees and adults appear to lead rather solitary lives. In research laboratories and zoos, as well as in the wild, the orangs' cognitive behavior has been less well studied than that of more terrestrial and social chimpanzees. However, many students who have worked with all of the great apes have the impression that, though their minds seem to work in somewhat different ways, orangutans are at least the cognitive equals of the others. Benjamin Beck, whose research specialty is tool use, shares this opinion. He says that if a keeper leaves a screwdriver within reach of a chimpanzee, the animal is likely to examine and fool with it for a time and then move on to something else. In the same circumstances, an orangutan may rather pointedly and perhaps deceptively ignore the tool at first. Later that night, when the keeper has gone home, the orang might use the screwdriver to dismantle its cage and escape. "'Reflective,' 'contemplative,' 'insightful,' 'deliberative'— these are words I associate with orangutans somewhat more than I do with chimps," says Beck.

When Beck and his colleagues were planning the Think Tank, they realized early on that, due to space limitations, not all of the Zoo's nine orangutans could be permanently located there. That being the case, it was necessary to find a way to get them to and from the Great Ape House, where they have long had satisfactory quarters. The O-Line, which actually was conceived long before the Think Tank, was a spectacular solution to this problem.

The overhead cables are supported by eight 45-foot-tall towers. One of those towers is erected within the orang-utan yard at the Great Ape House; another is erected in the outdoor enclosure at the Think Tank. Except when the O-Line is closed because of inclement weather, the animals are free to climb these two towers whenever they please during the day. At the top of each of the six intervening towers is a platform where the orangutans can rest and reflect as they travel between the two buildings. To prevent them from descending and roaming about in the Zoo grounds or else-where, a barrier of charged electrical wires is fixed just below each platform.

The O-Line was experimentally opened in September 1994. The adventuresome Bonnie was the first to travel its length. She was followed shortly by her son, Kiko, and another female, Iris. Several months later, an 18-year-old male named Azy got into trouble. Touching the charged wires, he became disoriented and forced his way over them to the ground. A veterinarian on duty that day was able to subdue the 250-pound animal with a tranquilizer gun. The O-Line was closed for repairs and modifications. Fortunately, Azy did not suffer any real injury, but since his shocking experience he has not had anything to do with the cables, a decision that appears to reflect well on his thought processes. Several other orangs have investigated portions of the O-Line and are expected, in their own good time, to become regular commuters.

Swinging along the cables, the animals look down on the roof of the Reptile House, an ornamental duck pond, a number of trees, bushes, Zoo paths and pedestrians. People at the Think Tank believe this mode of travel is a uniquely enriching experience, since no captive orangutans else-where have such a facility.

As far as her travel and housing arrangements are con-cerned, Indah, of the "Lost Keys" skit, is a special case. Behind the demonstration area in the Think Tank, there is a holding area. Indah was brought there for a physical exami-nation which, in the case of an orangutan, requires that the animal be anesthetized. When the procedure was completed, Indah declined to leave even though she had access to the O-Line. Therefore she has remained a full-time resident in the Think Tank, along with Azy, who was moved there last fall.

Indah, Bonnie, Iris and Kiko receive praise and small edible treats when they take part in demonstrations or research projects. Otherwise they are not pressured to perform or, in the case of the commuters, to show up at all. They volunteer eagerly, apparently more for the excitement of the thing than for the insignificant rewards. They seem to enjoy their interactions with the staff.

Many animals are known to employ external objects very much as we do tools; which of them are thoughtful tool-users remains a speculative matter. In this regard, much attention has been paid to primates, who manipulate many objects as well as or better than people do and often appear to do so purposefully, innovatively and imaginatively.

Orangutans will stack boxes to facilitate reaching previously unreachable things. They selectively collect leaves and use them to ward off the sun or rain somewhat as we use parasols. Those swatches of burlap given to the animals at the National Zoo serve as leaf substitutes. They use them as portable tents or blankets, and occasionally as nets or lassos for dragging objects into their cages. Orangutans use sticks as probes, rakes and levers; they sometimes bend, break or chew on them to manufacture more efficient or specialized utensils. The National Zoo's orangutans have discovered that, with the right sort of stick, they can jam open the valves of watering devices so they flow continuously. Having done so, they entertain themselves by filling buckets under the taps and playing messy water games. They also will put biscuits in a hat or bowl, add water and make gruel, all on their own initiative.

In public behavioral events, the orangutans obtain cereal nuggets by using bamboo rods to drag them under the windows. This is a fairly simple demonstration, but most spectators seem to be convinced that it is an example of thoughtful tool use. The Orangutan Language Project being carried on at the Think Tank is a much more complicated proposition for both the animals and the people.

Lions roar, roosters strut, fireflies flash and most, possibly all, other animals transmit specific information about their conditions and intentions. If and when any of them use language as we define it—communication by means of abstract symbols and syntax—remains a complex question for behaviorists. In this matter, primates again have been of special interest. To date, much of the work has involved chimpanzees; their ability to learn and use sign language and other abstract symbols has been well documented. One long-term orangutan study has been documented. That project used sign language, but it involved only a single animal.

Rob Shumaker, the Orangutan Language Project coor-

> Three themes of the think tank are tool use, language and social interaction. A fourth, unstated, is wonder.

Orangutan on the O-line, now a dominant feature at the National Zoo.

dinator at the Think Tank, hopes to expand on previous primate studies to investigate the specific capabilities of orangutans. As a first step, he has introduced the participating animals to sets of plastic flash cards. On each of them is a boldly printed geometrical figure—in essence, a "word" symbolizing a thing, condition or concept. Some represent general nouns—"chow," "banana," "bag," "burlap." Others represent proper ones—"Rob," "Indah" and so on. All of the Think Tank people and orangutans have been assigned distinctive symbols. There are also flash cards for adjectives and numbers (zero to nine). Shumaker is now teaching the orangutans, in public view, to recognize the symbols and their assigned meanings. He is also showing them how to indicate that they recognize images projected on a screen—a picture of an apple, for example—by tapping corresponding symbols on a panel located directly below the screen. Right answers are rewarded with praise and edible tidbits. Incorrect responses are not rewarded. The entire session is conducted in a positive and encouraging manner. All sessions end with success. If the answer has been wrong, another choice is given until the orang gets it right.

To date, Indah has proved the most apt pupil. She now understands the symbols for "banana" and "apple," and is learning "grape." Impressively, Indah has learned how and why to use the send key on her computer. Before the project began, many anticipated that Bonnie, the notably inquisitive and ingenious orangutan, would be the outstanding student. Although she is still highly motivated, she has often been frustrated, somewhat like a child who has excelled without much effort in most undertakings but is dismayed and discouraged when she cannot cope quickly and easily with a problem.

Primates manipulate many objects as well as or better than people do and often appear to do so purposefully, innovatively and imaginatively.

Based on the experiences of other primate researchers and the progress the National Zoo orangutans have made, Shumaker would not be surprised if, within a year or so, Indah and perhaps others will comprehend a dozen or more of the abstract symbols. But he is less interested in the size of their vocabulary than he is in whether orangutans have or can develop a sense of syntax sufficient to support inter-species dialogues:

"Indah, where is the bag?"

"Rob, which bag?"

"Indah, where is the big red bag?"

"Rob, there is the big red bag."

Shumaker thinks that such exchanges may be possible via computer but are not likely to occur for some years.

Posted prominently on a large red sign at the entrance to the Think Tank is a message that reads: "This exhibit is about animal thinking. It contains some things you may agree with, some you may disagree with and others that may even trouble you. Come, explore and see what you think."

Most visitors pass by without stopping, as if this were a pro forma warning against eating, drinking or shouting in the building. But in fact the sign has been carefully worded and placed, as a low-key acknowledgement that questions about animal thinking are central to one of the oldest and bitterest disputes in the annals of what is commonly called Western civilization. In centuries past, anyone suggesting that orangutans might use tools and language thoughtfully would have been drummed out of polite intellectual society as a charlatan or lunatic, if not pilloried as a dangerous shaman or blasphemous heretic. Even 20 or 25 years ago a scientific exhibit devoted to thinking animals would have been generally considered unseemly.

At the heart of the matter is an ancient conviction, which holds that man is not *a* but *the* rational animal. Respectable philosophers and theologians have long contended that a thinking being must be a human one. Ergo, other animals did not and could not think because they were obviously not human. Concerned scientists supported this orthodox position by demonstrating in various ways that animals were organic machines driven by unalterable instincts, as mills are turned by water and sailing ships are moved by wind. Their behavior might be complex, one scientist acknowledged, but it was devoid of decision making or reflection.

For many the issue is by no means dead and settled, which is why the warning sign stands at the entrance of the Think Tank. It reverberates in current confrontations between creationists and evolutionists; biblical dominionists and animal-rights advocates; cognitive and mechanistic ethologists. There has, however, recently been a notable shift of learned opinion on the subject. Previously many professional thinkers staunchly defended the no-they-don't dogma. Now those in the intellectual mainstream generally agree that some animals sometimes think, as we define it, but they probably do so differently from people and, as measured by human criteria, not as well. Centuries before savants came to this conclusion, many farmers, hunters, trappers, casual naturalists, animal trainers and pet-lovers had already done so. To a greater extent than is usually acknowledged, the accumulated observations of those untutored but commonsensical students of animal behavior served as the foundation for contemporary scientific investigations.

In one exhibit at the Think Tank devoted to the cognitive abilities and accomplishments of people, it is noted that "humans are thinking specialists." Few would argue with the truth of that. But though it is nowhere remarked on, the Think Tank by its very existence demonstrates another human attribute that may be even more singular than our thoughtfulness. The Think Tank celebrates what has been called our yearning to know other bloods. Among us this yearning is so universal, in time and place, that it probably should be considered innate or instinctive. ∎

The jaguar, though rarely seen,
is a resident of the sky islands,
and fiercely protected by the
cowboy environmentalists

'SKY ISLANDS'

BY WILLIAM K. STEVENS

DOUGLAS, ARIZ.

Warner Glenn's dogs picked up the jaguar's scent when the big spotted cat was almost within sight of the canyon where Geronimo surrendered 110 years ago, here in one of the most unusual landscapes of North America: an archipelago of magnificent mountain forests and grasslands rising from the desert like islands from the sea. They are called sky islands, and they are home to one of the richest panoplies of living creatures on the continent.

Jaguars are rarely seen, though, and when the roaring predator was brought to bay after a five-mile, three-hour chase, it was a highlight of Mr. Glenn's life. Tall, lean and leathery at 60, he is a fourth-generation cattle rancher who gets up at 4 A.M., wears chaps to work, guides hunters, is a registered Republican and displays a full-length poster of John Wayne in his house. But Mr. Glenn is a different sort of cattleman—a cowboy environmentalist and a leader of a group of ranchers who are writing a remarkable new chapter in conservation here on the Arizona-New Mexico border.

So instead of shooting the jaguar that day last March, as ranchers have almost always done, he took photographs and let him go. Since then Mr. Glenn has been as fiercely protective of the cat as of the landscape in which it was tracked down. The jaguar "is here because he likes what he's found—plenty of game and not very many people, and that's the way we'd like to keep it," he said during a break in a trail ride on horseback to the top of the Peloncillo Mountains, one of the sky islands, from where he traced the cross-country route the chase had taken.

At a time when bitter conflict often convulses the range, Mr. Glenn and some of his rancher neighbors have taken the initiative in creating a working alliance with conservationists and government agencies, their former adversaries. Spurred by a common interest in improving the health of the range and preventing it from being cut up into subdivisions, the Malpai Borderlands Group, as the alliance is called, and its new allies aim to cooperate in managing nearly a million acres of ranch land, divided into more than 30 ranches, for ecological as well as economic values. Only in this way, the ranchers believe, can ranching be sustained in the long term.

Biologically and climatically speaking, one can go from the desert almost to mountain tundra on a single drive of perhaps two hours up a single sky island.

Already, the once-hostile groups are working together in a science-based effort to prevent overgrazing, restore the landscape, preserve endangered species and rejuvenate grasslands by reintroducing necessary ecological processes like cleansing fires.

This distinctive alliance has been forged on behalf of an equally distinctive landscape. From the top of the Peloncillos on that trail ride a few days ago, a September sun illuminated the blue peaks of three other sky islands:

the Chiricahua Mountains, onetime stronghold of Geronimo's Apaches, 30 miles to the north; the Animas range just to the east and outliers of Mexico's Sierra Madre a few miles to the south.

In all, there are some 40 sky islands in southern Arizona and New Mexico and northern Mexico, where they rise as high as about 10,000 feet above sea level and 6,000 feet above the desert "sea." Neither Rockies nor Sierra Madre, they are a geological and biological province all their own. Here, plants and animals from the northern United States and Mexico both reach the limits of their distribution. In the lower elevations, eastern species mix with western ones.

All mingle with some 60 species found nowhere else, in many instances having survived here while mountain ranges farther north were wiped clean of life by Ice Age glaciers. Many are rare. Isolated from similar species on other sky islands as effectively as if they were in the Galapagos, they represent especially potent raw material for evolutionary change. One such creature is the endangered Mount Graham red squirrel, the focus of a long-running political struggle over whether to destroy some of the squirrel's habitat to erect a complex of astronomical telescopes on the Pinalenos Mountains sky island.

Last light of day on the Animas Mountains, Gray Ranch. New Mexico.

This variety has turned the sky islands into "probably the richest area of this size in the United States" biologically speaking, said Dr. Wade C. Sherbrooke, the director of the American Museum of Natural History's Southwestern Research Station in the Chiricahua Mountains.

The United States section of the archipelago is home to about 265 species of birds, more than 75 reptile species, as many as 120 varieties of native grass, 20 percent of all known North American ant species, about the same proportion of bee species, 75 varieties of reptiles and 90 species of mammals, said Dr. Peter Warshall, an independent ecologist who has extensively studied the sky islands. About 175 species are considered imperiled.

The region is said to be the most diverse sector of the United States for ants, reptiles and mammals. Big wide-ranging predators like the Mexican wolf, grizzly bear and ocelot have long since been extirpated, but the region still teems with mountain lions, black bears, ring-tailed cats, bobcats, coatimundis, mule deer and a local subspecies of small white-tailed deer called the Coues' deer. And the occasional jaguar.

Biologically and climatically speaking, one can go from the desert almost to mountain tundra—or from Mexico to northern Canada—on a single drive of perhaps two hours

In all, there are some 40 sky islands in southern Arizona and New Mexico and northern Mexico, where they rise as high as about 10,000 feet above sea level and 6,000 feet above the desert "sea."

along winding roads up a single sky island. The journey takes a visitor upward through distinct "stacks" of different ecological communities.

On just such a drive in the Chiricahuas, Dr. Warshall pointed out the stacks. From semidesert grassland, where tarantula spiders nearly the size of a man's palm scuttled by, the road ascended to the spectacularly beautiful Cave Creek Canyon, hemmed in by volcanic stone towers stained and weathered to shades of lemon, salmon, ocher and rust.

There, starting just above 5,000 feet, the mountainside was dominated by a dense mixture of evergreen oaks and pines, most of them characteristic of Mexico. Mexican birds like the painted redstart flitted through the branches in response to Dr. Warshall's call. Along the creek itself, bird-watchers from around the world come to spot a wide variety of species, including the trogon, a bird found mainly in Mexico that some believe to be the most elegant in North America.

Higher up, the trees changed gradually to towering ponderosa, a species of northern North American pine, then to a forest of Douglas fir, later to a mixed forest of Douglas and white fir, and finally to high-altitude Canadian or Alaskan spruce. Near the top, a foraging black bear and her two cubs claimed the visitors' attention by sending rocks clattering off the mountainside.

For more than a century, cattle have grazed both the grassland valleys of the region and mountainside pastures up to 9,000 feet. In the late 1800's, hundreds of thousands of cattle roaming the open range devastated the grasslands. Today, although things are better, most ranchers are finding it difficult to bring the land back from that low point, said Jora Young, a Nature Conservancy official who has studied the situation for a book she is writing. The Conservancy is a key player in the Malpai conservation experiment.

At the same time, natural fires have long been suppressed, allowing brush like mesquite to take over fire-resistant grasslands formerly swept clean by flames.

Still, the region's ecology is remarkably intact. "It's not pristine, but all the pieces are there, on the landscape, in the order they're supposed to be," said Ben Brown, a wildlife ecologist who is program director for the private Animas Foundation. The foundation owns the former Gray Ranch, which, with more than 300,000 acres, is the biggest chunk of the Malpai group's territory.

The sky island journey takes a visitor upward through distinct "stacks" of different ecological communities.

10,000 ft.

Ecosystem
Characteristic of
Northern Canada

Aspen and
Douglas Fir
(cover highest slopes)

Grizzly Bear

Oak Tree

5,000 ft.

Elegant
Trogan

Mexican Wolf

Desert Level

Ecosystem
Characteristic
of Southwestern
United States

Cactus

Tarantula Spider

Desert Grass

0 ft.   **Sea Level**

Now the challenge is to restore natural processes like fire and, above all, to fend off creeping subdivision—today's chief threat in the eyes of the Malpai group. Already, development has eaten away at the Santa Catalina sky island outside Tucson and has begun to encroach on others farther out in the country. It is even nibbling at the seemingly remote Chiricahuas: "Crown Dancer Ranch Estates," reads a sign, advertising lots for sale, near the mouth of Cave Creek Canyon.

That is too close for comfort for the Malpai ranchers, whose territory includes the Peloncillo and Animas sky islands, the next two over from the Chiricahuas. As it happens, that is also a major concern of the Nature Conservancy and other environmental groups.

This common concern was long masked by a pattern of hostility and distrust among ranchers, conservationists and Federal land managers. The basic source of the conflict is that while cattlemen have assumed control of their ranches, the ranches themselves are cobbled together from both public and private land. Typically in the West, environmentalists have attacked both the ranchers and public agencies for misusing the land, while the ranchers have felt themselves losing control.

The leaders of the Malpai group, including Warner Glenn, his wife, Wendy, and a neighbor, Bill McDonald, came to see this constant headknocking as getting them nowhere. About six years ago, they began to think cooperation might be better. Early in the game, Mr. McDonald, a 44-year-old, fifth-generation rancher, said to John Cook, a Nature Conservancy vice president, that "if we don't join with the environmentalists, we're dead."

Public opinion has turned against the ranchers in the debate over public lands, Mr. McDonald explained the other day, adding that joining forces with their adversaries would enable the ranchers to "get off the defense." In the end, the Malpai ranchers hope, the resulting alliance will allow them to keep their ranches intact for the long term while improving the land, the cattle forage—and the environment—at the same time.

At the ranchers' invitation, Mr. Cook is co-executive director, along with Mr. McDonald, of the Malpai group.

In 1992, a wildfire on government-owned ranch land brought a confrontation of ranchers and government officials. The discussions led to a cooperative arrangement among the ranchers, the Forest Service and other government agencies to use fire as a land-management tool. Some 30 ranchers—there were only four holdouts—subsequently signed on voluntarily to an area-wide fire management plan.

That is a more significant achievement than it might seem at first glance, since the fire plan embodied the principle behind a nascent movement toward managing whole ecosystems and landscapes in a coordinated fashion, balancing the needs of nature with those of the economy. The fire plan bore an important result in June, when 6,000 acres of public and private land interwoven in checkerboard fashion were burned in the region's first prescribed fire after 80 years of deliberate fire suppression. A second prescribed burn involving 9,000 acres is being planned.

Neither Rockies nor Sierra Madre, the sky islands are a geological and biological province all their own. Here, plants and animals from the northern U.S. and Mexico reach the limits of their distribution.

In another innovation, the Malpai group has set up a program called "grassbanking," in which a rancher whose grasses have been depleted by grazing and drought is allowed to graze his cattle on another ranch while his land recovers its health. In return, he signs a conservation easement, held by the nine-member Malpai board of directors, prohibiting subdivision of his land in perpetuity. So far four area ranchers have joined the program. Their cattle now graze on the former Gray Ranch.

Some ranchers are also working to restore the range by replanting native grasses and fencing in and restoring riparian areas.

Almost from the start, the Malpai ranchers took a step long anathema to many of their brethren: they invited biologists onto their land. Many ranchers have been "scared to death," in Wendy Glenn's words, that an inquisitive scientist would find an endangered species whose discovery would prevent them from using the land.

To Warner Glenn, people who refuse scientists are "dumber than a post, really, because there is some stuff we damn sure need to know" about the landscape if good decisions about its care and use are to be made. As it turns out, many ranchers have been "charmed" upon learning from scientists about the biological treasures on their land, says Ben Brown of the Animas Foundation. ∎

The sky islands are home to about 265 species of birds, more than 75 reptile species, as many as 120 varieties of native grass, 20 percent of all North American ant species, about the same proportion of bee species, 75 varieties of reptiles and 90 species of mammals. About 175 species are considered imperiled.

FROM THE HIPPO'S GAPING JAWS

BY DAVID M. SCHWARTZ

Deep inside Tanzania's Ruaha National Park, biologist William Barklow

sounds out the complexities of "river horse" communication

Imagine a rusty old trombone, dented and pitted with the ravages of age. Now imagine its owner, a jazzman past his prime, totally bereft of finesse but still bursting with gusto. He inflates his lungs and lets loose a wild ear-splitting shriek, then quickly lunges the brass slide to its full length, belting out a cadence of percussive low-register grunts, brassy Bronx cheers. Four, six, eight of them before, winded, he quits.

There, for your mind's ear, is a rough approximation of what Bill Barklow is listening to on this July morning. It is one solo in a repertoire that has captivated him since he made its acquaintance eight years ago. The sounds emanate not from trombones but from hippopotamuses congregating at pools in the Great Ruaha River of central Tanzania. Whenever hippos congregate, Barklow has found, they communicate. And how! He has measured the bellow of a territorial bull hippo—an elocution suggestive of our wayward trombonist—at a deafening 115 decibels. The volume is equivalent to a heavy-metal rock band playing 15 feet away. Yes, hippos are big talkers, but it is not the size of their sounds that fascinates Barklow. It is how they cope, acoustically speaking, with the two media of their amphibious environment—air and water. "What impresses me most about hippos," says Barklow, rocking back on his haunches and regarding his study subjects with binoculars, "is that they have to deal with these two separate acoustic environments—when it has taken other animals so long to perfect a communication system in just one medium."

Though it is one of Africa's most conspicuous and vociferous animals, the hippopotamus has received surprisingly scant attention from biologists. Little is known about its social life or behavior, and before Barklow began his studies in the late '80s, no one had investigated its remarkable vocalizations. "Here we have hippos interacting underwater and making sounds, and hippos interacting above water, making other sounds," says the Massachusetts biologist, who studied loons before he turned to hippos, "yet I think they can decode everything they hear." How long it will take Barklow to decode what the hippos hear is another matter. He spent 20 years working on loons in Maine—his recordings of their hauntingly beautiful calls have graced records and films, including *On Golden Pond*—but he thinks the loon communication system is simple compared with that of the amphibious behemoths. "It is the most complicated acoustic system I know of." He believes he has made a discovery about its basic nature: hippos seem to possess a unique ability to hear and emit sounds in stereo—both above and below water at the same time.

Three thousand years ago, when the Greeks encountered these massive mammals lolling in the Nile Delta, they named the species *hippopotamos*, or "river horse." With bulls growing up to 15 feet long, 5 feet high and 8,000 pounds in weight, hippos are the second-largest terrestrial mammals. Only elephants are larger.

Gregarious and generally aquatic during the day, hippos are solitary and terrestrial at night, hauling themselves out of the water to feed. They can walk five miles in search of grass and sedge, which they tear from the ground with wide, fleshy lips. One night's take can be 100 pounds, but in light of their size, it is not a particularly gluttonous feast. Nocturnal activity is necessary because hippos have a very thin epidermis (the protective outer layer of skin), leaving them vulnerable to desiccation. Hence, they spend the daylight hours in water or mud. The myth that hippos sweat blood derives from a pinkish, oily skin secretion that helps to protect them from the sun's rays.

Although feeding always occurs on land, most everything else—courtship, copulation, birth and nursing—takes place underwater. A hippo can dip below the surface for five minutes at a breath because the hemoglobin in its red blood cells, like that of cetaceans (whales, dolphins and porpoises), latches onto oxygen with unusual tenacity. While hippos appear to be great swimmers, they actually move underwater by walking or running along the bottom. Whether in aquatic

While hippos appear to be great swimmers, they actually move underwater by walking or running along the bottom.

or terrestrial mode, their speed belies their bulk: they've been clocked in short dashes at 30 miles per hour.

Herds typically space themselves out at intervals of about a hundred yards, each herd with roughly 10 to 100 animals. Cows are guarded vigilantly by a single highly territorial bull. When a show of tusk is not enough to deter transgressors, a territory holder will lock jaws with a challenger in vicious, sometimes lethal, battles. (In older males, razor-sharp canines can grow more than two feet long.) As a result, the hide of every experienced bull hippo is well gashed, sometimes so badly it looks like Arabic graffiti. The comical, huggable hippo of cartoons and children's books is, in reality, a bellicose beast of murderous temperament.

It is not surprising that hippopotamuses would evolve an ability to speak to one another. It saves energy and even lives to be able to advertise location, social status and mood, and to communicate concise messages convincingly, especially "Get the hell outta here!" Since hippos pass their days in water so murky that visibility is measured in centimeters, the use of vocal, rather than visual, cues would be the most effective.

Mt. Maru from Arusha Game Park, Tanzania.

Bill Barklow had never thought about any of that before he made his first trip to Africa in 1987. Although he was on a commercial safari, he had an opportunity to break away from the group and spend an afternoon alone at a hippo pool. He settled in for a few hours of uninterrupted observation. "The pool was enchanting," he recalls, "lined with palms and papyrus, like the Nile in ancient Egyptian wall paintings, but nothing much was happening with the hippos. After a little while, I was bored." There were a dozen of them, and they spent most of their time underwater. Sometimes they would rest in what he calls their "amphibious position"—ears, eyes and nostrils above water, but mouth, throat and everything else below. But activity picked up later in the afternoon, and so did the hairs on the back of his neck when one hippo spotted him, stared for about ten seconds, then let out a thunderous blast so concussive that he could actually feel it. Other hippos who had been underwater began to surface and they, too, called. Barklow was thrilled by that seemingly unremarkable event, and it would change the course of his career.

Acoustically, water and air do not mix. Water is 800 times denser than air, and because of this great density difference, virtually no sound travels from one medium to the other. How then, did animals who had been completely submerged know to surface when the blast was given? Or was the timing a coincidence? He saw it happen again. It certainly seemed that underwater hippos were hearing above-water sounds. If so, can underwater hippos make sounds that can be heard above the surface? Could they have a repertoire of underwater sounds no human has ever heard?

On his fourth African trip, he is still trying to answer some of those questions. He is positioned about 15 feet from a busy hippo pool at a bend in the river, hunched over a speaker adapted for underwater use. It is wired to a digital audiotape player powered by a car battery and lashed to a tripod crudely fashioned from three branches. The whole speaker assembly is cantilevered at the end of a 15-foot pole. Barklow starts the tape player, and for an instant, the incongruous tones of soprano Kathleen Battle singing La Traviata resonate across the river. He chuckles and hits the "stop" button. "Just a test." (He prefers to test his equipment with Verdi rather than hippo music because the real hippos quickly get used to hearing the recorded hippos and stop responding.) While he runs final tests, his field assistant (and wife), Lori-Ann LeBlanc, readies the video camera she will use to record the behavior of unsuspecting hippos confronted with potentially threatening sounds. Barklow hoists the long pole and shimmies it through his hands, extending it over the water. It bows like a fishing pole as he lowers the dangling speaker into the water. Next into the drink goes the hydrophone, an underwater microphone that is the size and shape of a hockey puck. It too hangs off a

Gregarious and generally aquatic during the day, hippos are solitary and terrestrial at night, hauling themselves out of the water to feed.

long pole, wired to a tape recorder and Barklow's headphones. The hydrophone will pick up the sounds broadcast through the speaker and any hippo response.

Barklow scans the water for an animal in the amphibious position, his first experimental subject of the day. He wants to see if hippos resting at the surface will respond to underwater broadcasts of previously taped territorial bellows. If they do, it would be strong evidence that they can hear underwater even when their ears are above the surface. It is the reciprocal of the situation he observed eight years ago, when underwater animals seemed to respond to above-water sounds.

Nine times out of ten, before Barklow can target an appropriate animal and coordinate his playback with LeBlanc's videotaping, the prospect sinks out of sight. As any field biologist knows, designing experiments is one thing, but getting them to work is another. In several hours today, Barklow manages to deliver only three broadcasts to hippos in the amphibious position, and not one of the broadcasts has been greeted with anything other than total indifference.

The bellow of a territorial bull hippo has been measured at a deafening 115 decibels. The volume is equivalent to a heavy-metal rock band playing 15 feet away.

This time, he focuses on "Sleepy," an animal whose eyes seem to be perpetually at half-mast. With Sleepy in the amphibious position, LeBlanc starts running video, and Barklow hits "play." Almost instantly, several tons of hippo lurch through the water, emitting a brief *huff*. The moving animal then encounters three compatriots and dips underwater. Barklow is triumphant. "We woke up Sleepy! Wouldn't you love to know what's going on?"

Between African research trips, Barklow has been trying to figure out the anatomy of hippo hearing and sound production. An amphibious hippo, resting with only the top of its head above water, trumpets its sounds into the air through flared nostrils. By the laws of physics, this same sound emission cannot pass into water. If it entered the water through the animal's submerged mouth, bubbles would be visible, but Barklow has never seen such bubbles. Perhaps there is another way for hippos to get sound into the water. Dolphins give off some of their underwater repertoire through a fatty area on the forehead called the "melon." It can transmit sounds into water because its density is very close to that of water. Barklow investigated hippo heads for an analogous structure, and found one—a roll of fat in the throat, just beneath the larynx. Since the larynx is the source of all hippo vocalizations, this is the perfect location, and it has the same density as water.

There remained the question of whether a hippo could hear and localize underwater sounds. As any scuba diver knows, hearing sounds underwater is no problem. What's difficult is telling where they come from. Airborne sounds can be localized because they arrive at one ear sooner than the other. Brain processing "tells" the animal that the first ear to hear the sound is the one closest to it. To face the sound, we simply turn until it arrives at both ears simultaneously. But when sounds are waterborne, it's a different story. Waterborne sounds, conducted through our entire skulls, arrive at both ears at essentially the same time, and from every direction at once. They seem to be coming from the middle of the head.

Barklow looked again at cetaceans. In the 1960s, Ken Norris of the University of California, Santa Cruz, drew on studies noting that the middle and inner ears of porpoises are suspended by ligaments from the rest of their skull. This would cut down considerably on random bone conduction. Examination showed that each middle ear contacts a tube of fat that runs alongside the inner surface of the lower jaw to an unusually thin dish-shaped area. Norris hypothesized "jaw hearing": sounds from the water are conducted through the thin part of the porpoise's jaw, up the fat tubes inside the lower jaw, to the ears. Since the sounds arrive at the ears independently of one another, they can be localized.

After having observed hippos communicating underwater in Africa, Norris visited the Smithsonian's mammal collection and found a huge hippo skull collected by Teddy Roosevelt. Norris was struck by a dramatic similarity to cetacean skulls: each hippo jawbone possessed a saucer-shaped area as thin as a dime. Could hippos also be hearing with their jaws? The evolutionary distance was not so great as one might imagine. Hippos are artiodactyls, or even-toed ungulates, a group that includes pigs (generally regarded as their closest cousins), while cetaceans are believed to have evolved from an artiodactyl ancestor. Norris saw what could be a deep significance in the similar jawbones. "Here's an

The myth that hippos sweat blood derives from a pinkish, oily secretion that helps to protect them from the sun's rays.

animal, the dolphin, that's descended from ungulates and it hears through its jaw," he says. "And here's another animal, the hippo, which is an ungulate, and it has a structure suggesting that it, too, may hear through its jaw!"

When Bill Barklow looked at hippo skulls, he confirmed the thin dishlike areas of the jaws. He also examined the ears and found that, like the cetaceans but unlike most other mammals, a hippo's middle and inner ears are suspended by ligaments, not embedded in the skull. He saw three attachment points for each middle ear: two that he had expected—to the canal coming from the outer ear and to the hearing sensors of the inner ear—and one that he found very significant. It went to a part of the skull that directly contacts the lower jaw. Here was anatomical ammunition for Barklow's theory that hippos have a second set of ears. "A hippo resting in the amphibious position could be keeping track of both worlds at the same time. Its external ears are above the surface, listening for airborne sounds, and its jaw is a foot below the surface, monitoring the water. It could work!" Barklow is now collaborating with an otolaryngologist

Hippos are among African animals causing the most human fatalities.

in search for fat channels or some other means of sound conduction from the hippo jaw.

Meanwhile, support for a whale-hippo connection has come from unexpected quarters. Jerold Lowenstein, an immunological researcher at the University of California, San Francisco, has compared the blood serum proteins of whales with those of many ungulates, including cattle, pigs and gazelles. He found them more similar to those of hippos than any other group, suggesting a closer evolutionary relationship between the two than was previously suspected. But DNA studies have failed to confirm Lowenstein's finding, and it remains a tantalizing but inconclusive tidbit of information.

There is little agreement as to which African animal causes the most human fatalities, but hippos are often mentioned for top honors. They are certainly more deadly than many feared predators, including lions.

Whether hippos ultimately prove to have their closest evolutionary affinity with whales, pigs or something else, there's no doubt that in historical times they have had little affinity with humans. The two species have rarely coexisted easily. Although the modern species of river hippo has always been limited to the African continent, it once ranged from Cairo to Capetown. It has since been eliminated or sharply reduced in much of its range and is now concentrated in east-central and southern Africa. Generally considered to be the biblical behemoth, hippopotamuses were displayed as curiosities in Roman circuses, according to Pliny the Younger. Stripped and dried, their thick hides made formidable shields for Roman warriors.

For a period around the turn of the 18th century, hippo tusks found favor among dentists, who used them to make artificial teeth. Unlike those made from elephant ivory, these did not yellow. But the invention of porcelain enamel changed all that, and the market for hippo tusks dwindled. It has recently taken an unexpected and unwelcome turn upward. The 1989 ban on the trade in elephant ivory has helped those pachyderms but not hippos, whose ivory has surged in demand. From 1988 until 1991, exports of raw hippo ivory more than quintupled. Not surprisingly, hippo populations have correspondingly dipped. In 1994, an aerial census in eastern Zaire showed only 11,000 animals where 23,000 had lived in 1989. An estimate by Keith Eltringham of Cambridge University puts the world hippo population at about 157,000.

"It is a cause for concern," says Eltringham, who chairs the hippo specialty group of the International Union for the Conservation of Nature. "People worry about elephants, but most conservative estimates put elephant populations at over half a million, three times more than hippos. And because of the hippo's strict requirements—it needs both water and grazing—it is actually much more vulnerable." Although not in immediate danger of extinction, hippos are seriously threatened by the loss of grazing lands due to encroachment of rapidly growing human populations.

Of course, hippos have never gone down without a fight. When applied to human interlopers, their tusks have the same effect as the scimitars they resemble, and the strength with which they can be applied is legendary. Accounts of African travels are peppered with horrific tales. In *Wild Beasts and Their Ways*, the Victorian explorer Sir Samuel Baker describes a hippo charging the paddle wheeler on which he was traveling. "Not content with breaking several floats off the paddlewheel, it reappeared astern, and, striking the bottom of our iron vessel, it perforated the plates in two places with its projecting tusks, causing a dangerous leak." While filming hippos underwater in Kenya's Mzima Springs in the 1960s, Alan and Joan Root were attacked by a subadult male. Joan was shaken but unscathed, but Alan received the brunt of the animal's anger. "He got my leg right into his mouth, so that the left-hand canines were slicing through the calf while my foot and ankle were between his right-hand molars," Root later wrote in a dispatch from Nairobi Hospital. "My calf was bitten right through and chomped three or four times, fortunately all more or less in the same place. The hippo then shook me like a rat.... My most vivid recollection here is deciding that my leg had had it and that feel of the hippo's whiskers on the back of my thigh as I was shaken about. He then dropped me and went off." But even Root was lucky compared with several hundred people a year who do not survive close encounters of the hippo kind. There is little agreement as to which African animal causes the most human fatalities, but hippos are often mentioned for top honors. They are certainly more

For a period around the turn of the 18th century, hippo tusks found favor among dentists, who used them to make artificial teeth.

deadly than many feared predators, including lions.

Not only their ferocity has been underestimated, but also some of their benefits. More than just interesting natural curiosities, hippos play a critical role in African river ecology. Many waterways would be virtually lifeless were it not for hippos —or, more exactly, their dung. Hippo dung forms the nutrient base of an aquatic food chain that begins with microscopic plant life and culminates in fish, crocodiles and predatory birds. Their daily migrations also affect vegetation. One researcher has suggested that grazing hippos are responsible for riverine forests through their constant mowing of grass, which suppresses fires. The hippos do not consume trees, but the fires would. Aquatic vegetation cannot establish itself where hippo herds move about. When poachers decimated the hippo population of the Okavango River in Botswana, channels clogged, interfering with water movement and the region's flooding cycle.

In one remembered episode, humans and hippos developed a positively chummy relationship. In the mid-19th century, at the height of an English craze for exotic animals and natural history specimens, the viceroy of Egypt sent a male hippopotamus calf to the London Zoo. Named Obaysch for his native island in the White Nile, he was the first of his species displayed in Europe since Roman times. People lined up by the thousands each Saturday to visit him at his sumptuous quarters in Regents Park. *Punch*, the English humor magazine, chronicled every event in the life of H.R.H. (His Rolling Hulk). Silver models of Obaysch sold briskly, as did sheet music for the hit tune "Hippopotamus Polka," which depicted on its cover an elegant lady dancing with a distinguished-looking hippo in evening dress.

Of course, it's unlikely that *Punch* or anyone else listened to Obaysch the way Bill Barklow is listening right now to the hippos of Ruaha National Park. He keeps a wary lookout for crocodiles as he sidles over to a large boulder that juts into the river's sharply cut bank. The site offers good views of the hippo pool and enables him to drop the hydrophone into the water just ten yards from all the action. Above water, the herd is bellowing in unison, and the choruses are being answered by other herds, the noise passed down the watercourse like a bucket in a fire brigade. The phenomenon is called chain chorusing. On an earlier visit, Barklow and a crew of students traced and timed a chain chorus that traveled five miles downriver in about four min-

Hippo dung forms the nutrient base of an aquatic food chain that begins with microscopic plant life and culminates in fish, crocodiles and predatory birds.

utes. "I know of no other animal that uses its whole herd in this way," he explains. "Chain chorusing lets the group broadcast its size and location. The bigger it is, the more noise it can make. Since a big group is probably controlled by a big, experienced male, this is a potent advertisement for unattached females and a warning to other males."

For all the acoustical variety of groans, grunts, honks, rumbles and bellows that can easily be heard at a hippo pool, Barklow is even more intrigued by what the animals have to say underwater. In 1989, on his second African trip, he was probably the first person ever to hear the cacophony of underwater sounds made by hippos: soft flutters, plaintive moans, staccato clicks, eerie squeals and more. He is recording these sounds today, trying to tie them to the animals' behavior.

"About 80 percent of their vocalizations are given underwater," he says, "and the underwater sounds are the ones we know the least about. They probably indicate a level of social organization no one has ever suspected. Some of the answers are in there..." He nods toward a metal box the size of a briefcase. It contains hundreds of hours of stereo sound recordings from both above and below the surface, and corresponding video recordings of the animals'

Hippos in pool at Lake Manyara Park, Tanzania.

Hippos seem to posess a unique quality to hear and emit sounds in stereo—both above and below water at the same time.

behavior above water. Later, in his lab at Framingham State College near Boston, he will run the sound recordings through a computer program that produces visual representations called sound spectrographs, which allow him to analyze the sounds.

QUERY: DO HIPPOS ECHOLOCATE?

The hydrophone is picking up clicks now. They come in clusters, each a rapid-fire delivery called a "click train." Like so many of Barklow's hippo findings, click trains have a provocative counterpart in cetaceans: dolphins use them to locate underwater objects through echolocation. "Do hippos echolocate?" he asks. "Possibly. But possibly they just click to give their location in murky water. They could be saying, 'Here I am, don't bump into me!'" He has plans for an experiment at the Toledo Zoo's Hippoquarium, where the behemoths can be viewed underwater. Barklow will place oil drums in the tank at night and listen with hydrophones to see if the click trains increase as soon as the residents start running into the unexpected obstacles. Once they learn where the drums are, he'll shuttle the drums around to see if the hippos resume clicking.

The clicks are still a mystery, but the clacks have been solved. Occasionally, Barklow has heard an underwater clacking sound quite distinct from click trains. "I knew something interesting was going on," he says, "but I had no idea what it was." While clacking, the hippos seemed to be involved in intense underwater activity. An agitated animal or two would surface in churning water, then head right back down. Barklow mentioned the observation to Stephen Krueger, a zookeeper in Toledo. With help from Bubbles and Cupid, the Hippoquarium's resident couple, Krueger figured it out. Through the exhibit's glass walls, Stephen Krueger saw the two engage in ritual tusk clashing—not combat, but courtship. Mouths agape, they circled in a gyrating dance, turning, twisting, arcing through the water, jousting all the while with their teeth. After 15 to 30 minutes, they copulated. Hydrophones confirmed that sparring tusks create the clacking sounds that had perplexed Barklow on the Ruaha. In July, Krueger last witnessed the hippo courtship dance. Bubbles' calf is due in mid-February.

I had certainly seen my fill of hippos in Tanzania, but I was enticed by the prospect of underwater viewing. For all its barrel-shaped heft, I was told, an underwater hippo is a graceful beast indeed. "You cannot imagine how agile and athletic they are," said Jeff Jewitt, then public relations director for the San Diego Zoo, where a new exhibit, "Hippo Beach," has the nation's second underwater hippo viewing chamber. Since opening last May, it has become the zoo's most popular exhibit in recent memory. I had to see it.

I parked myself on a bench in front of a two-inch-thick wall of glass designed to stop 8,000 pounds of hippo flesh hurtling at 15 mph. The two leviathans bounded effortlessly across the bottom. They galloped, gamboled, cantered, pirouetted—then rested, one's head on the other's shoulder. They even looked happy. I thought of gymnasts, hurdlers, astronauts walking on the Moon. Eavesdropping on the excited chatter of my bench mates, I learned that the graceful hulks brought ballet dancers most often to mind. Ballet dancers? Happy hippos as ballet dancers? Could it be that those cartoons and children's books weren't so far off after all? ▪

Hippos seem to posess a unique ability to hear and emit sounds in stereo — both above and below water at the same time.

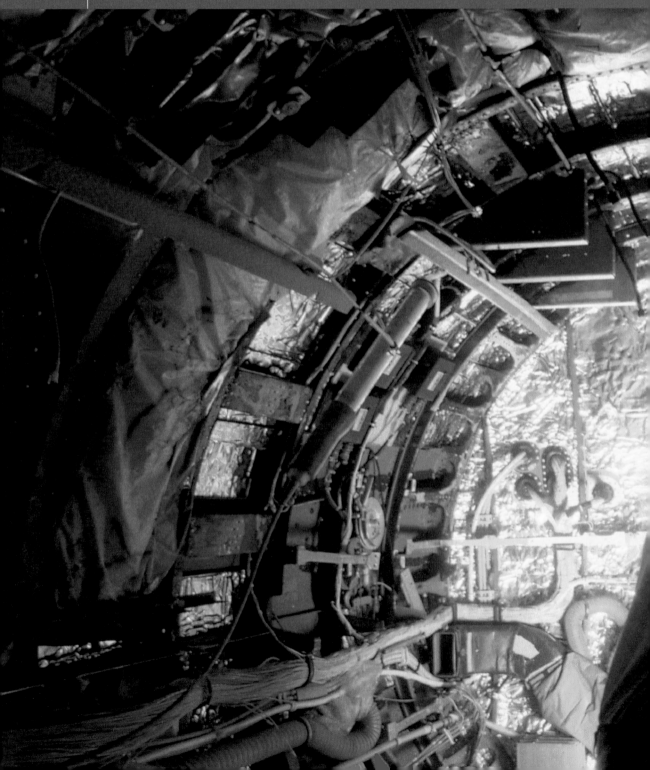

CONTENTS

The Caltech nose is the
brainchild of chemist
Nate Lewis.

The Electronic Nose

BY GARY TAUBES

Can't tell a *Chateau Margaux* '82 from an '84? Can't stop worrying whether you turned off the gas? Need to check the smell of your new car or your old cheese, your perfume, your brake fluid, your breath? Get a new nose. On a chip.

Scientific endeavors rarely proceed without unforeseen complications. Before Erik Severin took his baby blue Mazda GLC wagon down to Monterey Park, for example, he inquired about fish at his local Ralph's supermarket. He was told that if his experiment required something that would rot with a pungency worthy of the cliché, he would do best with a saltwater fish, which Ralph's did not have in stock. So Severin, a graduate student at Caltech, drove to Monterey Park, where he knew of a Chinese grocery by the unlikely, albeit appropriately Californian, name of Shun Fat. From bins of saltwater fish he chose a small kingfish, paid 69 cents, and brought it back to the Noyes Laboratory at Caltech.

Severin installed the kingfish in a glass jar with two glass tubes attached. He arranged for a stream of air to pass through one tube, circulate around the kingfish, absorb its aroma, and proceed out the other tube, over what is technically referred to as an array-based sensor apparatus, although Severin and his labmates call it the prototype electronic nose, or sometimes the noselet. "I set the fish on a heating element and let it rot for days," says Severin. Fortunately, his sense of smell is not as keen as some. "People would come in, their eyes would start tearing up, and they'd say, 'My God, this is awful.'"

The experiment's denouement, according to Severin, was a qualified success: the electronic nose could easily distinguish between kingfish fresh and kingfish rancid, but not between, say, two-day rot and three-day rot. Still, Severin and his colleagues have high hopes for the nose. Since their noselet experiments, they've built a more sophisticated smelling device—the supernose. Using computerized switches, the supernose can automatically control details like the concentration of the aromas, how fast they flow by, and which odor follows which. "I used to have to stick close to the noselet, changing the jars, adjusting valves, and so on," says Severin. "I had trouble finding five minutes to run to the bathroom. Now, with the supernose, we set it up, press a button, and leave the nose running for days." Someday, the researchers expect, their supernose will be able to tell a Merlot from a Beaujolais, a Heineken from a Budweiser, or anything that human noses, or even dog noses, can do effortlessly.

THE SUPERNOSE POINTS THE WAY TO AN ABSURDLY INEXPENSIVE NOSE ON A CHIP—AN ELECTRONIC SNIFFER THAT WILL COST NO MORE THAN THE AVERAGE KINGFISH. SUCH NOSES WILL SERVE AS SENSORS AND AROMATIC ARBITERS IN USES SO WIDESPREAD THAT THEY MAY SOMEDAY DO FOR ODORS WHAT THE COMPUTER CHIP HAS DONE FOR PRETTY MUCH EVERYTHING ELSE.

Until half a dozen years ago, such an olfactory accomplishment seemed safely beyond the reach of technology. With the Caltech achievement, though, the science of electronic noses appears to be in for a paradigm shift. The supernose points the way to an absurdly inexpensive nose on a chip—an electronic sniffer that will cost no more than the average kingfish. Such noses will serve as sensors and aromatic arbiters in uses so widespread that they may someday do for odors what the computer chip has done for pretty much everything else.

The Caltech nose is the change-of-life child of a chemist named Nate Lewis, who became famous in his field not just for the preternaturally early development of his chemical insight, but also for his ability to bring to bear on any single project a merger of disparate scientific talents, effecting a kind of cross-pollination of ideas and then publishing the final word on that particular research. His reputation attracted the brightest graduate students and postdocs in the country, whom he would unleash on problems of his choosing, further enhancing his reputation.

By 1992, however, Lewis was showing signs of a midlife crisis. He had spent the first 15 years of his career, as he puts it, "trying to coax semiconductors into acting like artificial leaves to produce stored chemical energy from sunlight." Now he was contemplating 30 more years spent doing the exact same thing. He was ready to try something new.

Lewis had his epiphany walking along a beach in

Ventura, California, after a conference. "I was thinking," he says, "that we know how people touch; we know how people see; we know how they hear. We don't really know anything about how they taste or smell. That's pretty interesting. And in science it's good to choose a problem hardly anyone knows anything about."

The olfactory system in humans is still the subject of much debate. Simply put, what we smell is nothing more than stray molecules of substances, known as odorants, that waft through the air and settle into molecular receptors inside our nostrils. The odorants induce an electric signal in the receptors that is carried through neurons into the olfactory bulb, which sends signals into a brain structure known as the olfactory cortex, which passes them along until they eventually reach the hippocampus, a primitive brain structure associated with memory in mammals. (That association may be why the smell of lilacs on a spring morning can evoke with such passionate insistence the uncomplicated days of youth.)

All of this, however, goes far beyond the problem that Lewis, or anyone else hoping to model the nose, had to worry about. His main question was first electrochemical and then, perhaps, computational: How do odorants induce an electric signal in the neurons in the nose itself, and how is this signal decoded?

A typical approach of chemistry to detecting and identifying odorants would be to build what are known as lock-and-key receptors. Odorant molecules would fit into receptors like keys into locks, with each molecule specific to its own receptor and vice versa. But because a mind-bogglingly vast variety of molecules stimulate our nostrils, such an approach would be hard for researchers to implement. And it didn't seem nature could work this way, either. "It's probably true," says Lewis, "that male dog noses, for instance, have lock-and-key receptors for pheromones, which are sex attractants. But it's unlikely that dogs develop lock-and-key receptors for cocaine when they're trained to smell it out at airports. So how do they do that?" Then there was the problem of complicated odors: What happens with a scent like Coca Cola's, a blend of perhaps 100 different odors that add up to a scent similar to but distinct from Pepsi's? Could a nose really be expected to have 100 different lock-and-key receptors for each variant odor in each brand of cola?

As Lewis figured it, the nose had to generate some olfactory signal, even for molecules it had never encoun-

The world is already full of designer sensors, such as smoke detectors and breath analyzers, that look for a single chemical. These can be considered one-trick noses.

tered before. The brain and nervous system might respond by realizing they were faced with a new smell entirely, or something that smelled like almonds, or brussels sprouts, or lilacs—new, but not entirely new.

The only way the nose could send such complex, coherent messages (or the only way Lewis could envision it doing so) was if it was engaged in a game of pattern generation and recognition. Receptors would not be specific but promiscuous, so to speak. Each receptor would respond to each odorant molecule with a signal. The signals would vary form receptor to receptor and from odorant to odorant, so each incoming odorant would generate its own particular pattern of signals from all the different receptors. This pattern would be transmitted to the pertinent parts of the brain, where the process of recognition would take over. ("Aha, lilacs!") This scenario had the added benefit of assigning the learning problem to the brain, where it seemed to belong, rather than to the nose.

The array-based sensor apparatus, dubbed Pinocchio, at the California Institute of Technology.

Now Lewis had only to find chemical substances that could be used as electrochemical sensors to mimic the promiscuous reactivity of the receptors. Each odorant would induce a reaction in each chemical sensor, and that reaction would induce a stronger or weaker electric signal. Taken together, a collection of these chemical sensors, each different, would transmit a pattern specific to whatever odorant had set them off.

Imagine, for example, an artificial nose made with four chemical sensors, confronted by a succession of odors. Fresh fish might induce a strong signal in sensors one and three, a weak signal in sensor four, and not much reaction at all in sensor two. Rotten fish might induce a similarly strong signal in sensor one, little or nothing in sensors three and four, and it might send sensor two off the charts. So the hypothetical nose would have little trouble telling fresh fish from rotten fish. Then along comes an expensive designer cologne, which coincidentally generates nearly the identical reaction in all four sensors as fresh fish (depending on the fish). Now the nose would do well to have a fifth or sixth sensor, so that the odds that the cologne would invoke a different pattern from fresh fish would be greatly increased. Given enough of these sensors, the electronic nose might generate a different pattern for every possible odorant, including those that had never come its way before.

What chemicals, wondered Lewis, should he use to make those sensors? For years he had been collaborating with a Caltech chemist named Bob Grubbs, an expert in materials technically known as organic conducting polymers, and less technically as plastics that conduct electricity. Unlike most metals, these plastics can be easily dissolved into a liquid form and then painted onto substances. "They're metallic, but they don't react like metal," says Lewis. "You can dissolve them and spin them wherever you want or paint them on."

Lewis figured he might be able to use these conducting polymers to make his electronic receptors. A polymer molecule is just a long chain of single molecules known as monomers—for instance, polyacetylene is a long chain of single acetylene molecules. In a conducting polymer, electrons move freely down these chains. When two chains abut, electrons can hop from one to the other. The fewer points there are at which the chains touch, the more resistance there is to an electric current.

I f stray molecules—odorants, for instance—were to waft over the polymers, some would nestle in the gaps between polymer chains and thus be absorbed into the material the way water is absorbed into a sponge. Moreover, different molecules would be absorbed differently by different conducting polymers, just as a sponge will absorb a lot of water but only a little gasoline. The absorption would cause the polymer to swell like a sponge, pushing the chains apart and decreasing the number of spots where electrons could hop from one chain to another. This would show up as an increase in resistance to the flow of electricity. And that change in resistance could be measured easily. After a few seconds the odorants would float out of the gaps between polymer chains the way they had floated in.

The key to Lewis's scheme was that a specific odorant would cause different conducting polymers to swell to different extents. Grubbs had already made a handful of conducting polymers for Lewis by chemically attaching different molecules to the backbone of the polymer. This wasn't par-

Using computerized switches, the supernose can automatically control details like the concentration of the aromas, how fast they flow by, and which odor follows which.

ticularly easy to do, and the number of different conducting polymers they might eventually make was limited, but they provided what Lewis called "four or five tweaks" that would react in different ways to any passing odorant.

"Chemists have some intuition in these things," says Lewis. "We know like likes like, for instance; so we know something with lots of water in it will like to interact with something else that has water in it. And if it has lots of benzene in it, then it doesn't like water, it likes benzene. Things in between are going to be in between. So we knew what our first four or five guesses were going to be. We want something that has a charge on it; something that has a benzene in it; something that has grease in it; something that has water in it. We can make the conducting polymers pretty different and see what's going to happen. And maybe if we can make these polymers different enough, then if we give them a vapor, they'll swell, and they'll become more resistive and they'll be differently more resistive, so we'll get our pattern."

> THE NOSE COULDN'T HANDLE THE BEER HEAD. WHENEVER THE RESEARCHERS TRIED TO PASS AIR THROUGH THE BEER, IT WOULD BUBBLE UP, OVERFLOW THE VESSEL, AND CLOG THE GAS-FLOW PIPES.

This was a brilliant idea, one of those eureka moments in science. It has a downside, however, as often happens with brilliant ideas. It had been done. One night, Lewis did a computer search of the scientific literature to discover whether any of his peers or predecessors had had similar thoughts. British scientists, he found, had already written books on electronic noses made of six or seven different conducting polymers. In fact, as he learned later, several firms were planning to sell them commercially, for upwards of $50,000 a nose.

"So we didn't have the invention of an electronic nose," says Lewis, "and we didn't have the first way to think about doing it from a resistor or electrical measurement. That was all out there." What they did have was Lewis, who still believed there was something interesting to be done with electronic noses, and his students, who had ideas of their own.

When Lewis had first returned from Ventura, he had approached Michael Freund, one of his postdocs, and said, "Let's build a nose." Freund began his nose project with the conducting polymers from Grubbs but was a little leery of them because they have an annoying sensitivity to air. In the real world, they fall apart and lose their conductivity within a few hours, leaving researchers no choice but to work with them in an airless environment, such as a vacuum chamber. So Freund made one sensor from Grubbs's polyacetylene, just to see if it would work, and then considered a second kind of conducting polymer, known as polypyrrole. Polypyrrole did fine in air but didn't come in multiple variations like the polymers Grubbs had already designed.

Then Freund had *his* eureka moment. All he had to do was take his polypyrrole and mix it with various different kinds of insulators, as if he were swirling different sauces — strawberry or butterscotch or fudge — into vanilla ice cream. Insulators are substances that resist the flow of electricity; like conducting polymers, they will absorb different chemicals at different rates. Mixing them into the polypyrroles was a simple way to mimic the different conducting polymers. Now he would have a single conducting polymer with different insulators swelling in it.

Freund put his idea to work in the very first noselet. After mixing his insulators with his polypyrrole, he would paint a little swath of each variation on a glass slide, connect electrodes to each side of the swath, run a current through, and then detect how the resistance changed when he passed vapors over it. His first experiments were with various solvents from around the lab—methanol, ethanol, acetone, benzene, tetrahydrofuran, and so forth. "It was clear," says Freund, "that they responded differently to different solvent vapors. Some of the sensors' resistances would go up, some would go down, some would go down and up, or up and down. But if you looked at them all, you would see one pattern with ethanol, another with methanol."

Freund also showed various patterns to Lewis without telling him what they were. "I very quickly trained Nate to distinguish between different solvents from their different patterns," he says, "so I knew a computer would be able to do it."

Lewis, Californian that he was, wanted to see whether his incipient nose could distinguish between wines and other alcoholic beverages. Freund gave it a whirl, first with beer, but the bubbles from the head stymied him. Whenever he tried to pass air through the beer, it would bubble up, overflow the vessel, and clog his gas-flow pipes. Freund moved on to wines and liquors, which the noselet had little trouble telling apart, although it failed to differentiate between individual wines. And then Freund left to take a position at Lehigh University before he perfected the apparatus. "Nate was talking about fish when I left," says Freund, "so I'm glad I got out of there."

The Caltech nose still had a major evolutionary step to go through before it could change the face of artificial smell research. Lewis was talking to Grubbs about how to make the sensors even more variable. One of the two — neither remembers who — realized that despite all the work on conducting polymers, they didn't really need them after all. "Anything would work," says Lewis. All they had to do was mix any conductors with any insulators, and if the insulator would swell, then it would change the resistance differently to different odorants. By using nonconducting polymers for their insulators, they could even make the mixtures conveniently paintable.

"You can take little particles of carbon as the conducting part, or little balls of gold, or little balls of silver," says Lewis. This time you can think of the insulators as different flavors of ice cream, with various conductors mixed in like nuts or chocolate chips. "It can be almost any conductor in any insulator. So now you start thinking about how many different things can be made this way. Our first arrays now have 17 off-the-shelf polymers as insulators. But 17 probably isn't enough. We want a million different sensors. Now we think we can do that. It's not hard to envision a computer chip with these little wells, and you have the sensors in the wells, and a set of wires going in and out, and you measure the resistance. So reading a million resistances on a chip — no problem. The British had the idea right. We just took it much further by broadening what could be used as a sensing material."

Even 17 sensors, however, would allow for an unfathomably large number of possible patterns — too many to analyze easily. Or as Lewis says, "Sometime after we made the polypyrrole nose, we realized we had more signals than we knew what to do with."

Fortunately, the problem was not hard to solve, because Lewis, Freund, and company were lucky enough to be working at a place like Caltech. They went to talk to Caltech biophysicist John Hopfield, the father of a system of computing known as a neural network. At the time, Hopfield was working on computer programs that might simulate what the brain does in processing signals from the olfactory bulb.

Hopfield had his researchers teach Lewis's chemists

The Caltech nose can be trained to recognize what's normal — the everyday smells, or what scientists would call the baseline — and then alert users to anything different.

how to run the necessary computer programs. Neural networks are artificial-intelligence programs wired rather like the interconnected neurons of human brains. Like people, they can learn as time goes by, so they can be trained to recognize patterns. The network would "just sit there saying, "What does this smell like? What does that smell like?"" explains Lewis. It would take the input from all the different sensors, recognize how the patterns evoked by different odorants were similar and how they differed, and then record them for future use.

The more odors the network sniffed—the more patterns that came its way—the more it would recognize. Eventually it would learn which patterns are similar, suggesting that the smells were similar. "You can train the software in a neural network to take the patterns and find the differences," says Lewis. "You just need enough sensors sending enough signals so that no two things have the same pattern and seem to smell alike."

By early 1996, Lewis had created one of his signature teams to flesh out the electronic nose. It helped that he had access to Caltech's remarkable intellectual resources. He set his electrochemists to work with biologists, neural network experts, computer scientists, chip designers, and even some physicians in Galveston, Texas, who participated through electronic mail.

Lewis has great dreams for his nose. For starters, his nose on a chip should cost less than a dollar to manufacture and sell, which is a reasonable markdown from the $50,000 plus of existing electronic noses. That one dollar should buy the neural network hardware on a chip, the signal conditioning on a chip, and the million sensor dots. The Microdevices Laboratory at Caltech's Jet Propulsion Laboratory (JPL) is currently building Lewis his miniature nasal device. "Once we get the elements right," says Lewis confidently, "the rest of it should not be very stressful."

With the nose in hand, uses should come by the snoutful. The world is already full of designer sensors, such as smoke detectors and breath analyzers, that look for a single chemical. These can be considered one-trick noses. The chemical in question reacts with another chemical on a film, prompting a reaction that changes either the electrical or optical properties of the film, and that in turn sets off an alarm. But a carbon monoxide sensor won't smell a Freon leak from the refrigerator or a methane leak from the stove, and a breath analyzer won't tell you if your house is on fire. Lewis's nose, says Minoo Dastoor, who manages environmental and biomedical technology at JPL, "is a fundamental technology advance. Instead of looking at the response of one specific chemical to one individual sensor, you're looking at the response of one specific chemical to a whole array of sensors."

The Caltech nose can be trained to recognize what's normal — the everyday smells, or what scientists would call the baseline — and then alert users to anything different. Lewis foresees people using his sensors for all kinds of sniff tests: "Cadillac wants the leather in its various cars to smell the same. It doesn't need to know what's in the leather, it just wants it to smell like it did yesterday. Give this thing the pattern, and it will tell you whether the leather smells right. Cheese makers want their cheese to smell the same, too. Or perfume. Or brake fluid, which smells funky when it goes bad. Train the nose to recognize good brake fluid and it will signal you if it gets out of sorts. The same nose, trained differently, might smell a bad batch of gasoline in your fuel tank or warn people if they're getting carbon monoxide inside the car."

"THE BRITISH ALREADY HAVE A NOSE FLYING ON THE RUSSIAN SPACE STATION, WHICH I'M CONTINUALLY REMINDING NASA. THIS FACT HAS NOT ESCAPED ME, AND I HOPE IT DOESN'T ESCAPE NASA EITHER."

Lewis and Dastoor have convinced NASA to fly the artificial nose on the space shuttle, probably in 1998. NASA is seriously interested, says Dastoor, in incorporating the nose in the life support systems of the planned space station. As Lewis says, "These space stations seem to stink when something goes wrong. I hear the shuttle can smell like crazy, and the Russian space station, MIR, is worse. They don't know if the vapors are bad for astronauts or not." And besides, he says, "the British already have a nose flying on MIR, which I'm continually reminding NASA. This fact has not escaped me, and I hope it doesn't escape NASA either."

What intrigues Lewis even more than the commercial applications is the science that can be done with his nose. In his search through Caltech for people who could help him understand the olfactory system, he met up with a computational neurobiologist named Jim Bower, and the two bonded instantly. Bower makes biologically realistic models of mammalian nervous systems and has a particular interest in the olfactory system.

"I spent most of the last ten years," says Bower, "trying to convince people that the olfactory system recognizes odors based on tremendous receptor complexity, that what you really want to do is not detect specific features that you know about to begin with, but to sample as broadly as possible. That the main objective of the nose is to generate some signal no matter what the stimulus. I pent ten years trying unsuccessfully to persuade people in my field to think about it this way. And then I have a lunchtime conversation with this chemist, and he's already seen for himself that this is how it has to be."

Bower and Lewis are collaborating, using Lewis's nose to make predictions about how humans and rats might smell. The idea is to measure when the nose has trouble distinguishing between two odors, and then seeing whether humans and rats have the same trouble. If the electronic nose turns out to be drastically different from the human or rat nose, the researchers can readjust it by retraining the neural network. "If we can predict on the output of Nate's nose what odors are hard to distinguish," says Bower, "it means we're starting to understand something about the complexity of the human olfactory recognition problem."

The experiments may also help Lewis understand what it is about a molecule that determines its odor. "Suppose you could look at a molecule," he says, "and compute anything you want: How wide is it? Where are its electrons? How will it swell a polymer? You still can't say what it will smell like." But once the researchers start understanding the patterns generated by the molecules in the electronic nose, they can start comparing those with the various features of the molecules. They can find molecules with similar physical features and give them to humans, rats, and the electronic nose, to see whether different noses perceive them the same way.

The possibilities are endless, in part because of the ridiculous simplicity of the electronic nose once it reached its final incarnation. Indeed, Lewis says one of his friends, an astrophysicist from the University of California at Berkeley, insisted that Lewis's vaunted nose was "just a high school experiment." Lewis responded, "I know, and I'm proud of that." Lewis and the astrophysicist, however, may even have been overestimating the complexity. "It's so easy," says Severin, "that a junior high school student recently heard Nate lecture, and he went and did a science project on it." ∎

IF CARS TRAVELING AT THESE SPEEDS LIFT OFF THE GROUND

OR VEER FROM THEIR HEADING BY EVEN A FEW DEGREES,

the vehicles could tumble or roll uncontrollably, destroying car and driver.

GROUND TESTS LOOM FOR ULTIMATE HOT RODS,

Supersonic Cars

BY WARREN LEARY

ALMOST A CENTURY AGO, A FRENCHMAN SET THE FIRST OFFICIAL SPEED RECORD WITH A CAR WHEN HE BLAZED THROUGH A COURSE AT NEARLY 25 MILES PER HOUR.

Records have come and gone since then, but competing teams of highly innovative car designers are about to go after the last major speed hurdle on land: breaking the sound barrier by hurtling across a dry lake at dizzying speeds of 760 miles an hour or more.

And they predict that they are on the verge of achieving their goal.

With the vehicles just inches off the ground, buffeted by forces that no one can foretell with certainty, the risks are as staggering as the potential glory.

Several groups around the world have built or are designing and building jet-powered cars that they say will break the land speed record of 633.47 miles an hour. They plan to go on to attack the sound barrier with jet engines that previously propelled fighter planes and sleek configurations designed to knife through thick, ground-level air.

"It can be done and that's what we are going to do," said Richard Noble, the 50-year-old British sportsman and car enthusiast who has held the land speed record since 1983. Mr. Noble is the leading force behind one of the most prominent contenders in the race, a sleek, twin-jet machine called the Thrust SSC, which stands for supersonic car.

The other major player is Craig Breedlove, 59, the dean of land speed racing who has returned to the sport after gaining international fame by repeatedly smashing records 30 years ago. With a new car bearing the same Spirit of America name of his earlier speedsters, Mr. Breedlove says he wants to bring the speed mark back to the United States and raise the ante past 700 miles an hour. Then, he says, it

will be time to aim at the mark of about 760 miles an hour, roughly the speed of sound at sea level.

"We are going for the record and we've built an incredible car that can do it," Mr. Breedlove said. "There are unknowns and it won't be easy. But if it were easy, everyone would be doing it."

The unknowns that these cars face are considerable. Cars that accelerate to hundreds of miles an hour in seconds always face tough problems with stability, control and braking. But approaching or reaching supersonic speeds presents a new set of aerodynamic problems that raise risks in areas that are unknown.

As aircraft, and presumably cars, go from subsonic to supersonic speed, they pass through a critical transonic period where air rushes past different parts of the vehicle at varying speeds, producing pressure and shock waves that influence lift and drag, engineers say. No one is sure how supersonic shock waves will affect ground vehicles pressing against the sonic wall. And automobile designers are particularly concerned about how these shock waves will behave in the critical area between the bottom of the car and the ground.

If cars traveling at these speeds lift off the ground or veer from their heading by even a few degrees, the vehicles could tumble or roll uncontrollably, destroying car and driver.

"Reaching supersonic speed on the ground is certainly possible, but the big question comes down to controllability," said Dr. James M. Luckring, director of the transonic-supersonic aerodynamics branch at the Langley Research Center of the National Aeronautics and Space Administration. "Can you control the vehicle as it goes from transonic to sonic speeds?"

The transonic regime "is inherently messy and always a problem, even for aircraft," Dr. Luckring said. As vehicles pass through the transonic domain, some of the air flowing over surfaces goes supersonic while other flows are still subsonic, causing turbulence, uneven lifting, increased drag and other problems that can throw it out of control. "And when you talk about experiencing these effects really close to the ground, you're getting into an unknown area," Dr. Luckring said. "These guys are going beyond the limits of what we know."

While acknowledging these risks, both Mr. Breedlove and Mr. Noble say they are confident that their cars, which were designed using very different approaches, can make

Opposite page: (above) Spirit of America driven by Craig Breedlove; (below) Richard Noble with the Thrust SCC.

the high-speed dashes safely.

"You simply can't anticipate everything and there will be unknowns and risks," said Mr. Breedlove. "There is risk associated with anything worthwhile."

Both the Thrust SSC and the Spirit of America, which have taken several years to design and build, began low-speed test runs in the last two weeks. Each car is facing tight deadlines to see if it will be ready for high-speed record runs before early November, when seasonal rains usually render desert raceways useless.

Mr. Breedlove is testing his car, a thin, dart-shaped vehicle painted red, white and blue, at the Bonneville Salt flats in Utah, and says he will use this legendary racecourse for as many high-speed trials as possible. Record-breaking runs require having a straight, flat course that is at least 11 to 12 miles long, and Bonneville, because of salt mining and other changes, no longer offers a good track of that length.

After the Bonneville tests, the plan is to take the Spirit of America to the Black Rock Desert in northwestern Nevada, the largest dry lake in North America, which offers an ideal, hard clay race surface. Mr. Noble also plans to take his car to Black Rock after it finishes its early test runs at Farnborough Airport near London and high-speed tests on the al-Jafr Desert in Jordan.

The contenders to become the fastest vehicle to run on land continue intense testing to see if the differing approaches of their designers produce a winner.

Mr. Noble, relying heavily on Ron Ayers, formerly chief aerodynamicist for the British Aircraft Corporation, has produced a complex, twin-engine craft whose design was forged through supercomputer simulations, wind tunnel tests and running scale models at supersonic speeds on a rocket sled.

This resulted in a big, black car with a thin fuselage sandwiched between two rounded engine enclosures that each contain a military surplus Rolls-Royce Spey turbojet. The engines in the 7-ton, 54-foot-long vehicle, which has a Kevlar, carbon-fiber composite body, combine to generate 50,000 pounds of thrust and 100,000 horsepower. The craft, which has the driver sitting at the midpoint of the car near its center of gravity, has a short, vertical tail with a triangle-shaped horizontal stabilizer.

Mr. Breedlove, who says wind tunnel and computer tests cannot accurately simulate what happens to a car running on the ground, relied on his experience and that of his team to design a simpler vehicle that can be more readily modified based on speed trials. "You test a little, tinker a little and gradually work yourself up to a point where you are ready to increase the envelope," he said. "It has to crawl before it walks, walk before it runs."

The Spirit of America is a slender, aluminum-alloy craft that places the driver at the tip of its pointed nose, ahead of two air scoops that feed the single jet engine that powers it. The General Electric J-79 engine, which formerly powered a Navy F-4 Phantom II fighter, delivers about 23,000 pounds of thrust and 45,000 horsepower.

The 4-ton, 44-foot-long car has a tricycle wheel arrangement with the two rear wheels, encased in aerodynamic fairings, set out and back from the fuselage. The front wheel, which is behind the driver, is actually three solid aluminum wheels set close together that have special, filament-wound graphite tires designed to withstand a speed of 850 miles an hour.

Mr. Breedlove said that both his car, which is chiefly sponsored by Shell Oil, and that of Mr. Noble had enough brute power to attain record speeds, but that the differences were in the details that would keep the cars stable and land-bound during high-speed runs. The cars will be subjected to multiple shock waves, coming off the bow, fairings, leading edges and other surfaces, as well as an anticipated pressure wave as they approach and exceed the speed of sound, he said.

To minimize buffeting and lift that could make the car go airborne, Mr. Breedlove has built his car very low to the ground. It is only six inches off the ground at the nose and eight inches at the rear, and has an elliptical cross section designed to carry any wind shearing or vertical shock waves off to the sides, he said.

"We have a minimum interface area to the ground which we think will keep us out of trouble," he said.

Mr. Noble, who has held the land speed record for 13 years, said his higher technology approach to design was the way to make a record-breaking car that was safer, more reliable and more stable than competing vehicles. "This is a very complex car," he said, "but, as Ron Ayers says, Thrust is actually a research vehicle before it is a record-breaker." Agreeing with Mr. Breedlove that wind tunnel tests could not reliably predict the performance of a car traveling on the ground, he said his team had devised a new test method that seemed to work.

Since the first official land record was established in 1898, when Gaston de Chasseloup-Laubat drove an electric car 24.5 miles an hour, it has been topped 55 times through newer technology.

Mr. Ayers used a computer program normally used to test aircraft and ran calculations through a supercomputer that evaluated configurations of a car moving from subsonic to supersonic speed. The team then made models of the car and repeatedly ran it on a rocket sled at speeds of 820 miles an hour. Before running the tests, the researchers filled in the track under the sled to simulate the hard surface of a dry lake.

he supersonic cars reach their top speed in four or five miles,

pass through the recorded measured mile, then take about five miles to stop mainly

by cutting power and deploying braking parachutes.

"When we brought the data together from the two types of tests, it was extraordinary how well the data matched across many cases," Mr. Noble said. "If they hadn't matched, we wouldn't know what to believe. But the tests ended up validating each other."

Mr. Noble declined to discuss his results or the exact configuration of the bottom of the Thrust SSC, citing competitive reasons. However, he said: "We believe we know exactly what happens underneath the car at supersonic speeds and that the fullscale car will replicate the rocket tests. We don't think it will be as violent as people think it will be."

The four-wheel Thrust SSC, which is steered by its two rear wheels, rides about 10 inches off the ground. But, among many innovations, the vehicle has a hydraulic suspension system that allows it to raise its rear up and down to vary ground clearance. "This is a revolutionary car," Mr. Noble said.

But the proof of cars like these is racing them. Since the first official land record was established in 1898, when Gaston de Chasseloup-Laubat drove an electric car 24.5 miles an hour, it has been topped 55 times through newer technology. Britons held the record almost exclusively until 1963, when Mr. Breedlove captured the honor for the first of five times within a two-year period.

Attaining a land speed record involves running a car through a measured mile, and then turning it around and racing it through the same course in an hour. The record is determined from the average speed of the two runs and must be certified by the Federation Internationale Motocycliste, an international group based in France.

Driving a jet car that accelerates from zero to 600 miles an hour in less than 30 seconds requires a flat, clear track and impeccable timing. The cars reach their top speed in four or five miles, pass through the recorded measured mile, then take about five miles to stop mainly by cutting power and deploying braking parachutes. As Mr. Breedlove puts it, "It's much more difficult to stop than to get going."

Mr. Breedlove, the first man to break the 400-, 500- and 600-mile-an-hour barriers on land, will drive the Spirit of America as it chases Mr. Noble's record.

When Mr. Noble decided to challenge his own record and set the supersonic goal several years ago, he says he realized he could not organize the project and raise money for it while training to drive the car. So he enlisted a Royal Air Force pilot, Andy Green, who has flown Toronado and Phantom fighters, to drive the Thrust SSC.

No matter who is driving the cars, there is substantial risk. Neither of the main contenders has ejection seats or escape capsules in case something goes wrong, and each is relying on the drivers or computer monitoring to shut down the cars at the first hint of trouble.

"There is danger and you can't anticipate everything," Mr. Breedlove said. "If the car leaves the ground, then you can have a fatal problem. You do everything you can to avoid that."

Two other race groups have built jet cars to challenge the current record: a group based in the Seattle area headed by Gary Swenson and Richard Kikes, who have a car named American Eagle One, and an Australian team headed by the racer Rosco McGlashan, which is testing a car called Aussie Invader 3.

Mr. Swenson said a lack of sponsorship would keep him from going for a record this year, but he expressed doubt that anyone could crack the sound barrier safely.

"You create a physical wave when you break the sound barrier," he said, "and if you do it on the ground, it will literally explode the vehicle off the ground. There is no way to land safely." ∎

 **The Micro Car**
Actual size: 1/1000
the size of a real car

 Match Stick

 Standard Paper Clip

 House Key

 Pocket Change

#2 Pencil

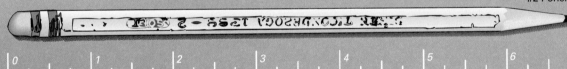

JAPAN'S MICRO-MACHINE PROJECT

DRAWS ENVY AND CRITICISM

BY ANDREW POLLACK

Japanese companies made their mark in the world automobile industry with the compact car. Now they are hoping the "micro-car" will position them as leaders of one of the most promising industries of the future.

As tiny as a grain of rice, the micro-car is a replica, at one one-thousandth the size, of the Toyota Motor Corporation's first automobile, the 1936 Model AA sedan. The minuscule vehicle has 24 parts, including tires, wheels, axles, headlights and taillights, and hubcaps that carry the company name inscribed in microscopic letters. The motor, which is itself made of five parts, is only 0.7 millimeters in diameter and can propel the car at speeds of up to 5 centimeters, or about 2 inches, per second.

Developed by the Nippondenso Company, a Toyota affiliate, the micro-car is a demonstration of Japanese micro-machine technology, the making of mechanisms with parts as small as a speck of dust. Already the world's masters of miniaturization, Japanese companies, backed by their Government, are now hoping to make complete machines the size of insects.

Some scientists envision that micro-machines could revolutionize fields like manufacturing and medicine. While the micro-car itself might not be a big seller, Nippondenso has already used the same manufacturing techniques to build a prototype of a capsule that can crawl through tiny pipes in a power plant or chemical plant like an inchworm, hunting for cracks. The company, Japan's leading manufacturer of auto parts, also hopes to make microscopic radars, gyroscopes and other components that could be installed in real cars, making them safer and easier to drive. The instruments' tiny size would make them light and easy to fit into engine compartments and dashboards.

The Olympus Optical Company and others are devel-

> As tiny as a grain of rice, the micro-car is a replica, at one one-thousandth the size, of the Toyota Motor Corporation's first automobile, the 1936 Model AA sedan.

oping extremely thin catheters and endoscopes, devices that could thread themselves like an artificial snake through narrower blood vessels and body cavities than is possible today. They would be equipped with micro-cameras, micro-scissors and other devices for performing diagnoses and surgery without having to cut open a patient.

Scientific instruments that now take up a table top could be shrunk to a size that could be worn on a wrist. Seiko Instruments wants to develop wristwatches that can monitor the wearer's blood pressure and other vital signs and inject medicine through a micro-syringe.

But whether the Japanese can achieve these goals is open to question because some scientists elsewhere say Japan has adopted a fundamentally wrong approach.

The heart of Japan's effort is the Micromachine Technology project, involving 26 companies with financing by the Ministry of International Trade and Industry. The 10-year program, now at its midpoint, has a total budget of 25 billion yen, roughly $250 million.

The United States Government is spending even more, having increased its support substantially in recent years. The Defense Department's Advanced Research Projects Agency, the main sponsor of such work, spent $35 million in fiscal 1995.

But in the United States, and to a large extent in Europe, research is concentrated on making what are known as microelectromechanical systems, or MEMS, using the techniques now employed with semiconductors, like silicon, to make the integrated circuits, or microchips, that are at the heart of computers. As a somewhat oversimplified example, an accelerometer can be made by etching a structure resembling a tiny diving board on a silicon chip. The greater the acceleration, the more the diving board bends.

Japan, however, while not completely ignoring the semiconductor-based technology, is emphasizing the miniaturization of conventional manufacturing techniques like machining, grinding and electroplating.

Japanese scientists argue that their broader approach will allow them to make micro-machines from a wider variety of metals and ceramics, providing more strength and versatility than offered by silicon and a few other materials that can be used with the semiconductor-based approach. And complex machines, like the micro-car, cannot be made with the semiconductor approach, which involves using physical

The micro-car is assembled by a technician with tools usually used by biologists to handle cells, so each micro-car costs more to build than a luxurious real car.

and chemical processes to create structures on flat wafers.

"It's two-dimensional technology," said Toshio Fukuda, a professor of engineering at Nagoya University. "We human beings live in a three-dimensional world."

Some Americans agree. Jay Lee, program director for materials processing and manufacturing at the National Science Foundation, says the United States is putting too much emphasis on the semiconductor approach and is in danger of losing the future market to the Japanese.

But other American experts argue that the Micro-machine Technology program is at risk of becoming another fifth-generation computer project, a big Government effort here that set overly lofty goals, then failed to deliver any-thing wanted by the market.

Etching structures into silicon chips, these experts argue, represents a leapfrog approach to miniaturization, while the Japanese approach is incremental. The semicon-ductor approach allows mechanical devices to be integrated on the same chip with the electronic circuitry needed to control them. And, as with transistors, thousands or even millions of micro-mechanical devices can be fabricated on a single thumbnail-sized chip, lowering costs.

Japan's approach, right now at least, requires making the micro-machines by hand. The micro-car, for instance, is assembled by a technician with tools usually used by biolo-gists to handle cells, so each micro-car costs more to build than a luxurious real car.

"I think they're spending a lot of bucks where they're not getting a big return," said Richard S. Muller, a professor of electrical engineering at the University of California at Berkeley. "They are not applying the test at the very begin-ning: is this something that will be reasonably cost-effective?"

Moreover, the semiconductor approach is already resulting in practical applications. The biggest so far has been tiny pressure sensors used in automobile engines, which are made by constructing a silicon diaphragm on a chip and measuring how much the diaphragm bends. Accelerometers to control the release of car air bags are also in use.

In a development that could cut into Japan's domi-nance of the market for making flat television screens, Texas Instruments Inc. has developed a chip-sized device for dis-playing video images. Each chip contains thousands of alu-minum mirrors, each 16 microns on a side, which can tilt individually into on and off positions, reflecting colored light onto a larger screen. A micron is a millionth of a meter, or

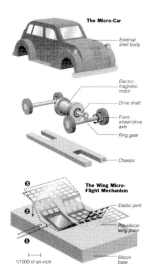

The Micro-Car

External shell body

Electro-magnetic motor

Drive shaft

Front-wheel-drive axle

Ring gear

Chassis

The Wing Micro-Flight Mechanism

Elastic joint

Polysilicon wing plate

Silicon base

1/1000 of an inch

A Tiny Wing That Flaps on Command

Scientists have also devel-oped a three-dimensional microstructure of a wing (based on the origami paper folding process) that can be driven by an electric current. When electricity is directed between the plates and the base (1), the center plates move down toward the base (2), causing the outer plates, representing the wings to bend upward (3). The fre-quency of the current can be alternated to regulate the speed at which the wings flap.

Sources: Denso Corporation, University of Tokyo

Scientific instruments that now take up a table top could be shrunk to a size that could be worn on a wrist.

about a hundredth of the diameter of a human hair.

Even some scholars in Japan say the Government is not paying enough attention to the silicon approach. "The silicon technology should be included in the project," said Hiroyuki Fujita, a professor at the University of Tokyo's Institute of Industrial Science who is Japan's master of clever silicon micro-machines. One mechanism he has made consists of hundreds of flagellating cilia, each half a millimeter long, on a chip. By controlling which cilia move and when, it is possible to make a micro-conveyer system to transport small objects in a future micro-factory.

Where conventional technology ends and micro-machines begin is somewhat fuzzy. The smallest gears in a watch, made with what is considered conventional machining technology, are less than 1 millimeter, or 1,000 microns, in diameter.

But Japan's micro-machine project aims at developing not just tiny components but entire machines that would be a cubic centimeter in size or smaller.

The project has three target applications—the pipe-inspection machine, medical devices that can be threaded through blood vessels, and a micro-factory small enough to fit on a desk and more energy-efficient than a conventional factory. The micro-factory could be used to manufacture tiny parts for watches and cameras or for other micro-machines.

In the project's first five years, companies working individually have developed a variety of minuscule motors, batteries, solar cells, generators, pumps and machining techniques that one day could be used to make micro-machines or micro-factories.

Hitachi Ltd. built a tiny hydraulic machine, containing a micro-pump 7 millimeters in diameter, that could stamp letters less than 10 microns wide on a sheet of aluminum.

Seiko Instruments developed a microscopic drill for making holes less than a micron wide in a metal or for micro-electroplating, depositing a microscopic dot of one metal on another. Both techniques use electrochemical reactions controlled by a scanning tunneling microscope, an instrument with a fine tip that rides over the surface of a material and can "feel" molecules.

Olympus is experimenting with metals that change shape when heated to make narrow endoscopes. The thinnest such devices now in use are 0.5 millimeters, still too big, for instance, to fit into the blood vessels of the brain.

For its second five years, the national project will work on integrating these pieces into complete machines, which will run into the problems of physics on a very small scale. When Nippondenso researchers tired to lubricate the micro-car to prevent wear and tear, for instance, the car stopped moving as if glue had been poured on its gears. Nippondenso also found that since the car was so light and the wheels so small, the friction between wheel and road that propels a real car did not work well for the micro-car.

Many experts predict that micro-machines will have to adopt tricks from insects and earthworms, which have evolved to operate at the micro-scale through the contraction and expansion of muscles.

Hirofumi Miura, a professor of mechano-informatics at the University of Tokyo, has built some micro-mechanical insects that can actually fly an inch or two up a guiding pole. His mosquito "bugbot," for instance, has wings that are made from silicon coated with magnetized nickel, so they flap when placed in an alternating electromagnetic field.

"If we release the silicon mosquito from the silicon chip, it flies off and we cannot find it again," Professor Miura said. "It's very small, like dust."

Still, it is a long way from robo-bugs to practical applications, and it is unclear what those applications might be.

To come up with inspiration and publicize its work, the micro-machine project has held contests in which schoolchildren are asked to draw their ideas for miniature machines. Among the wining entries: an artificial bee to pollinate flowers and a machine that shimmies up a human hair to repair split ends.

"These girls and boys already have the ideas," said Takayuki Hirano, executive director of the Government's Micromachine Center. "They should develop the applications. Our obligation is to develop the technologies."

Indeed, by the time Japan's project ends in 2000, it is unlikely to have produced a practical pipe-inspection machine or other complete micro-machine. Still, the project is likely to result in a host of new sensors, gears and other components that will make Japanese watches, cameras, printers and tape recorders even smaller and more versatile than they are today. ∎

Japan's micro-machine project aims at developing not just tiny components but entire machines that would be a cubic centimeter in size or smaller.

Kinder, Gentler Push for Metric Inches Along

BY MALCOLM W. BROWNE

T o some it has seemed as insidious as the supposed
dangers of creeping communism or water fluorida-
tion. To others it is the future cornerstone of
America's competitive edge as an industrial power.
It's the metric system, and even after more than a
century of debate, Americans cannot make up their
minds what to do about it.

Moribund for several years, the Federal Government's
efforts to sell Americans on metrication are undergoing a
mild revival, and opponents are organizing a response. But
whichever turn the debate may take, no one expects major
changes in the way people measure things any time soon.

The pace of change is illustrated by an extract from a
report by the Massachusetts Board of Education discovered
and published by Chemical & Engineering News:

"By admission of its few opponents, even, the complete
adoption of the metric system is at least assured. The pressure of public opinion has now made it necessary for every
teacher to teach the system."

That report was written in 1879, and every dozen or so
years since then, metric system supporters have made similarly unrealized predictions.

The Government agency chiefly responsible today for
promoting acceptance of the metric system is the National
Institute of Standards and Technology, formerly the National
Bureau of Standards. The institute is conducting a modest
publicity campaign, with a series of "town meetings" held
under the rubric — "Toward a Metric America" to explain
the merits of metrication to civic leaders, teachers and manufacturers. In the past two months, meetings were held in
Atlanta and Cambridge, Mass., and meetings are scheduled
in Seattle, Chicago, Dallas and San Jose, Calif.

Ralph Richter, an official of the institute, said in an
interview that no new money had been appropriated for the

Senator Claiborne Pell

campaign, and the agency was avoiding the hard-sell
approach sometimes taken by the Federal Government in
the past.

But gentle though the institute's effort may be, it is
seen as a red flag by opponents of the metric system. Seaver
W. Leslie, an artist who lives in Wiscasset, Me., and who
heads a loosely knit organization called Americans for
Customary Weight and Measure, plans to revive the publication of the group's anti-metric newsletter, called The
Footprint.

"Our newsletter hasn't come out in a year or so
because we felt that most Americans had come to realize the
folly of adopting faddish European units of measure," Mr.
Leslie said. "But we'll have to respond to the Government's
new propaganda campaign."

The anti-metric group has the support of the writer
Tom Wolfe and several other prominent writers and artists.
Mr. Leslie argues that customary measures are native to
America, saying that even pre-Columbian Anasazi architects recognized the foot as a fundamental unit of length and
the cup—the amount of blood in a human heart—as a convenient unit of volume.

Most scientists and engineers argue strongly for metrication, however, contending that the United States, alone
among other industrial nations, is isolated and handicapped
by its continued use of customary measures.

Sen. Claiborne Pell, Democrat of Rhode Island, a long-
standing supporter of the metric system, has frequently tried
to enlist all Federal agencies in a drive to achieve metrication. In a letter to President Clinton three years ago, he
wrote: "I am sure that you will agree that in order for this
nation's businesses to be truly competitive with the rest of
the world, we must play by the same rules."

But ordinary Americans have resisted change, and
they are not alone in continuing to use inches, pounds,
quarts and degrees Fahrenheit. Even some scientists argue
that the metric system, with origins in 17th-century France,
is badly outdated and that if the United States is to change
its customary system of measurement, the change should be
to an entirely new system more compatible with modern
computers.

The National Aeronautics and Space Administration,
which presides over some of the most advanced technology
in the world, is still far from embracing the metric system
wholeheartedly.

The space station NASA plans to begin building next year (at a cost of about $13.8 billion) will contain some metric fasteners and other odds and ends, but, for the most part, major components made by commercial manufacturers in the United States will be based on old-fashioned customary measures.

"We got pretty well into the space station design using inches and pounds, said Richard Weinstein, NASA's manager of engineering studies. "We'll accommodate the metric system where we can, but we simply cannot start over. The expense would be prohibitive."

Because the space station is supposed to be an international effort with Russia as one of the partners, the design of the station creates large problems meshing metric and nonmetric components in mechanical and electronic linkages, Mr. Weinstein said. But building adapters and special interfaces is cheaper than abandoning customary measures completely and starting from scratch.

While the Commerce Department has repeatedly warned that American competitiveness in international markets suffers because of this country's adherence to customary measures, manufacturing groups do not seem unduly worried. A spokesman for the Manufacturing Institute, a branch of the National Association of Manufacturers, said that metrication was not seen as a big issue.

The National Association of Manufacturers cites statistics from the International Monetary Fund describing the United States as the world's largest industrial exporter. The study reports that from 1985 through 1993, American exports increased 8.6 percent a year. America's closest competitors, both metric nations, were Japan, which increased exports by only 2.3 percent a year, and Germany, which had an increase of 1.8 percent a year.

Thomas J. Carr, an official of the American Automobile Manufacturers Association, said that Americans' failure to adopt the metric system "is really serious, largely because the Government hasn't gotten down to business." For example, most automobile transmissions are now designed using metric specifications, but they must frequently be mated to nonmetric engines, he said.

Despite progress toward automotive metrication, Mr. Carr said, he doubted whether even 50 years from now all cars manufactured in the United States would consist exclusively of metric parts.

Pre-Columbian Anasazi architects recognized the foot as a fundamental unit of length and the cup — the amount of blood in a human heart — as a convenient unit of volume.

Efforts to convert the United States to the metric system have repeatedly failed ever since the birth of the nation. In the early 1800's, the United States Coast and Geodetic Survey began importing and using meter and kilogram standards from France. In 1866, Congress authorized the nationwide use of the metric system, and it supplied each state with a set of metric weights and measures. In 1875, the United States became one of the original 17 nations signing the agreement that created the International Bureau of Weights and Measures, based on the metric system. In 1893, the United States adopted the metric system as its fundamental system of standards, thereafter defining feet, pounds, quarters and other customary measures in terms of their metric equivalents. Further initiatives toward metrication were started in 1960, 1965, 1968 and 1975, when Congress passed the Metric Conversion Act.

That act failed to specify a time limit for conversion, however, and the United States Metric Board created by the act reported in 1981 that it lacked a clear mandate to enforce the conversion. In 1982 the board was disbanded.

But the fight was not over.

In 1988 Congress passed the Omnibus Trade and Competitiveness Act, which specified the metric system as the "preferred system of weights and measures for United States trade and commerce," to be implemented by all Federal agencies by the end of the fiscal year 1992. But NASA is still measuring rockets by the inch.

Among the opponents of a hasty conversion of road signs and Federal construction projects to the metric system is Senator Byron L. Dorgan, Democrat of North Dakota, who argues that metric conversion would be unduly expensive in many cases.

Some opponents have labeled metrication as anti-American or worse. Typical of the many attacks against the metric system broadcast on the Internet is an essay by Allan Hjerpe titled "Communism, Marxism, Fascism and the Metric System." Writing of the Reign of Terror during the French Revolution, Mr. Hjerpe concludes that the metric system and mass murder have been inseparable ever since.

Physicists themselves sometimes invent customary measures for things that are only later assigned metric equivalents.

For example, particle physicists commonly use a unit called the "barn"—an area roughly the size of the surface of an atomic nucleus. It was so named because, relatively

The metric system is based on the meter, named in 1793, and defined at that time as one ten-millionth of an arc of distance from the Equator to the North Pole.

speaking, it is "as big as a barn," and therefore easy to hit with a particle projectile. A barn is defined as equal to 10^{-24} square centimeters so it has been accepted (with some reluctance) into the metric system.

The metric system is based on the meter, named in 1793, and defined at that time as one ten-millionth of an arc of distance from the Equator to the North Pole. That distance was measured and marked off on a metal bar in Sévres, France, which was then copied onto bars distributed around the world as standards.

But the definition of the meter has long since been changed to meet the needs of ever more accurate measurement. Since 1983, the meter has been defined as the distance light will travel through a vacuum in one-299,792,458th of a second. (Time can be measured this precisely using an atomic clock.)

But some scientists regard such an arbitrary number as "messy."

"This seems to me an absurd number to choose—its only merit is that it preserves the meter as the basis of the international system," wrote Dr. W. G. Rees of the Cavendish Laboratory at Cambridge University in England in a comment published by the journal Nature. Dr. Rees proposed instead the creation of a new fundamental unit as the basis of worldwide measurement: a unit defined as the distance traveled by light in exactly one billionth of a second. That distance would differ from the length of an old-fashioned English-American foot by less than one-fifth of an inch, Dr. Rees wrote, "and this, I feel, opens the way to a rehabilitation" of the old customary units.

Arguments over metrication will continue, and the adoption of the meter as America's preeminent measurement standard will face a long, uphill battle. Even the National Institute of Standards and Technology declines to guess how many decades it might take, but a memorandum circulated among employees of the agency in 1982 hinted at the difficulty of moving toward metrication.

"We have, for a period of approximately two years, stocked in the storeroom a large variety of metric fasteners," institute employees were told. "However, due to a lack of demand for these fasteners, it is necessary to drop them from our inventory." ∎

Most scientists and engineers argue strongly for metrication, contending that the United States, alone among other industrial nations, is isolated and handicapped by its continued use of customary measures.

E LECTRIC CARS HAVE SEEMED FOR YEARS TO BE OVER THE HORIZON,

OR MAYBE THE RAINBOW.

Now they are, in fact, around the corner.

NEXT WAVE OF ELECTRIC CARS:

Hybrids

BY MATTHEW L. WALD

WASHINGTON, MAY 12 — A motley collection of electric and hybrid vehicles will buzz, whirr and hum their way over 64 miles from Chesapeake to Annapolis in Maryland on Tuesday, about 50 in all, depending on how many have run out of juice, shorted out a component or otherwise broken down along the way in the eighth American Tour de Sol race, which began in New York City and will end here on Thursday.

The cars in the race are better than they ever have been. For many of the vehicles, the minimum demand of the race, up to 71.4 miles a day over a mixed city, suburban and interstate route, is hardly a challenge. The leading entry hopes to go 300 miles on a single charge, farther than many conventional cars go on a tank of gas.

By coincidence, the competitors in the annual race, a seven-day road rally for electric and hybrid vehicles, are heading for a finish line between the Capitol and the White House as President Clinton and Congress are maneuvering about whether to cut the gasoline tax by 4.3 cents a gallon. The best of the electrics have an energy cost of less than 2 cents a mile, compared with about 5 cents a mile for a typical car at current gas prices.

Electric cars have seemed for years to be over the horizon, or maybe the rainbow. Now they are, in fact, around the corner. General Motors will begin leasing a zippy two-seater electric, the EV1, through its Saturn dealerships in California and Arizona later this year. Chrysler will market the Epic, a five-passenger minivan based on the Plymouth Voyager and Dodge Caravan, and Ford will market an electric version of the Explorer, converted by an independent contractor.

Toyota announced last month that it would sell an electric sport-utility vehicle in the second half of 1997, and Honda said it would lease an electric four-passenger car in

> The Pentagon is a big backer of hybrid research and development because battlefield vehicles running on electricity would be hard for an enemy to hear or to find with heatseeking weapons.

the spring of 1997 that, like G.M.'s entry, is built from the ground up, not adapted from a gasoline design.

Behind the first wave of mass-manufactured electrics are models with far better batteries—promised soon by Japanese manufacturers. Beyond that is a second wave of technology, demonstrated in force in the Tour de Sol this year: hybrids, combining the best features of electrics and internal combustion engines. No major company has announced a plan to sell one commercially, but engineers say they could open up a new realm of choices for consumers who want fuel economy, environmental satisfaction or maybe even old-fashioned car virtues like faster acceleration and better handling.

The road that electric car development has taken to get to this point has had its share of political potholes.

For years, electric car research had been pushed by California, which had planned since the early '90s to require that 2 percent of the cars sold in that state in the 1998 model year produce "zero emissions," which would mean electric cars. New York and Massachusetts adopted the same rules. But in March, under heavy lobbying from the auto and oil industries, California backed off, settling instead for an expanded pilot program.

But as the auto industry's lobbyists have been fighting off the requirement, its engineers have been putting prototypes on the roads. Whether electric cars can be priced competitively has still to be demonstrated, but technological competition from amateurs and from startup companies has made it hard for the Big Three to claim that they are being asked for the impossible.

One major change in this year's race is that not all the entrants are purely electric. Many of the cars, covered with bold stickers advertising university and high school teams and corporate sponsors, are hybrids that have small internal combustion engines, some borrowed from motorcycles and others from even less likely sources. In some hybrids, the engines turn the wheels directly; in others, they charge the batteries or make current for electric motors. In either case, they provide extra horsepower for acceleration and hills, allowing them to perform like sports cars.

More and more engineers with experience in hybrids —including some at Ford, G.M. and Chrysler—argue that hybrid vehicles can include the strengths of both electric and internal combustion drives. Like an electric, a hybrid can be built to use no energy at idle and to recapture energy

For years, electric car research had been pushed by California, which had planned since the early '90s to require that 2 percent of the cars sold in that state in the 1998 model year produce "zero emissions," which would mean electric cars.

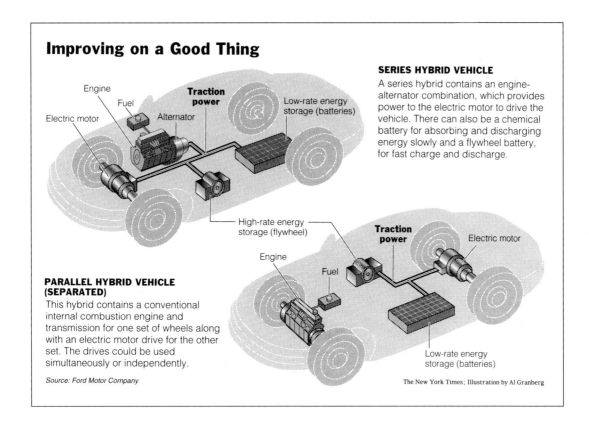

Improving on a Good Thing

Engine

Fuel

Electric motor

Traction power

Alternator

Low-rate energy storage (batteries)

SERIES HYBRID VEHICLE

A series hybrid contains an engine-alternator combination, which provides power to the electric motor to drive the vehicle. There can also be a chemical battery for absorbing and discharging energy slowly and a flywheel battery, for fast charge and discharge.

High-rate energy storage (flywheel)

Engine

Fuel

Traction power

Electric motor

PARALLEL HYBRID VEHICLE (SEPARATED)

This hybrid contains a conventional internal combustion engine and transmission for one set of wheels along with an electric motor drive for the other set. The drives could be used simultaneously or independently.

Source: Ford Motor Company

Low-rate energy storage (batteries)

The New York Times; Illustration by Al Granberg

when it decelerates, by letting the car's momentum turn the wheels, which drive the motors, briefly turning them into generators that produce a current to flow into the battery. As a result, hybrids can get 40 or 50 miles for the equivalent of a gallon of gasoline or even more.

And hybrids can use liquid or gaseous fuels that pack a large amount of energy into a small package, as conventional cars do. In addition, marrying the two —made easier in recent years by advances in power electronic circuitry, the circuitry that allows large amounts of electric power to be handled precisely— allows the internal combustion engine to keep running in a steady, narrow range where it gets the most efficiency and runs the cleanest.

It also permits a smaller internal combustion engine because it no longer has to perform solo in the hardest job: accelerating thousands of pounds of mass from a standstill to highway speeds in a few seconds. A hybrid can get acceleration help from an electric motor.

The Pentagon is a big backer of hybrid research and development because battlefield vehicles running on electricity would be hard for an enemy to hear or to find with heatseeking weapons. If those vehicles carried diesel engines to recharge the batteries, their range could be very long, and less fuel would have to be delivered to the battle zone.

Although conventional cars meet consumers' needs and expectations, they contribute heavily to air pollution, getting, on average, 27.5 miles per gallon, as optimistically measured by the Environmental Protection Agency.

A major cooperative research project between the Big Three auto makers and the Federal Government, the Partnership for the Next Generation Vehicle seeks to do the same work more cleanly, with three times the fuel efficiency. That will require something different.

"It seems like every major auto manufacturer has come to the conclusion that if we're able to market a vehicle that will meet what consumers want from their vehicles — in comfort level, performance, range and things like that — the only way you're going to be able to do that is with a hybrid," said Robert P. Larsen, manager of the technology engineering section at the Argonne National Laboratory's Center for Transportation Research, part of the Department of Energy. In related contracts, some of which predate the partnership, Ford, G.M. and Chrysler are each scheduled to deliver hybrids to the Energy Department in about two years.

One of the most important elements of an electric car, or a hybrid, is the battery. In the electric cars scheduled to come to market soon, Toyota and Honda plan to use nickel metal-hydride batteries, the kind that now dominate the laptop computer market. Most of the others are planning to use lead-acid batteries, but they have shown strong interest in nickel metal-hydride or other advanced technologies. Experts assume that before electric cars become popular, they will have batteries that store far more watts per kilogram of battery weight than lead-acid batteries can.

For the hybrids, other major questions remaining to be solved include how to yoke together electric and internal combustion systems.

One method is the series hybrid, like the University of Texas in El Paso's entry in the Tour de Sol, the HY!BRID, which has a Dodge Neon body with a 150-kilowatt (200-horsepower) electric motor and an old engine from a Geo converted to run on natural gas at a constant 3,000 revolutions per minute.

Among the pure electrics in the Tour de Sol, the favorite for the distance prize — and perhaps the efficiency prize, too — is the Sunrise, a four-passenger sedan with an all-composite body designed around its nickel metal-hydride batteries, built by the Solectria Corporation.

Prof. Carroll Johnson, the team's faculty adviser, sees the vehicle as a prototype for buses, which start and stop frequently and could benefit from having electric motors to capture the energy in stopping and to save wear and tear on the brakes, a major expense in heavy vehicles. A hybrid bus, he said, could do without its 3,000-pound diesel engine and run instead on two 100-pound electric motors and an engine like those in much smaller vehicles, like three-quarter-ton pickups, which weigh about 800 pounds. The hybrid would need a 400-pound generator, but it would not need a transmission.

The best of the electrics have an energy cost of less than 2 cents a mile, compared with about 5 cents a mile for a typical car at current gas prices.

But Prof. Michael R. Seal, adviser to the team from Western Washington University, in Bellingham, said that people who started by building a series hybrid usually tried a parallel hybrid next, like the ones his team is entering. In a parallel hybrid, the internal combustion engine and the electric motor pull together when the driver pushes down hard on the accelerator, but in the series hybrid, he pointed out, the engine runs independently of the driver, according to how the vehicle's control unit decides it should run.

"It's a most unpleasant thing," Professor Seal said. "We're not used to engines screaming away wide open, particularly when we're sitting at a stoplight, and that will happen because it's got to catch up from its last acceleration."

Chrysler, which has donated car bodies and travel expenses for nine hybrid teams, is showing off one design of its own, although it is not far enough along to run on public roads. Chrysler's Dodge Intrepid ESX carries batteries, a control unit and two 100-horsepower electric motors under the hood, with a 75-horsepower, 3-cylinder diesel engine in the rear. The batteries are lead-acid, but instead of the flat plates used in conventional car batteries, these have been wound into spirals with much greater surface area.

A conventional lead-acid battery is a little like a jug of wine; it may hold a lot but its narrow neck means that it can deliver what it has only slowly. The spiral battery is more like a peanut-butter jar; the volume is small but it can be filled or emptied quickly, which is exactly the load-leveling job that is required for fast starts or to accept current back from the motors in deceleration. Engineers refer to the quantity of electricity stored per kilogram of battery as the energy density; the speed of delivery is called the power density.

The relatively small diesel runs between 2,000 and 2,600 revolutions per minute, its "sweet spot" where it gets the best fuel efficiency, and therefore has good energy density. But Chrysler and others are also looking into fuel cells, devices that make current by combining hydrogen carried on board with oxygen from the air. These have poor power density, working well only at a steady state. That makes them unsuitable to run a car alone, but they have excellent energy density. To balance that weakness, several companies are working on flywheels, which could be spun up quickly to capture the excess energy during deceleration or quickly tapped for their mechanical energy.

But driving the ESC is a bit odd. As Professor Seal predicts, the car moves on electricity when the driver presses the accelerator pedal, but the diesel starts up when it wants to, which can be disconcerting.

Among the pure electrics in the Tour de Sol, the favorite for the distance prize—and perhaps the efficiency prize, too—is the Sunrise, a four-passenger sedan with an all-composite body designed around its nickel metal-hydride batteries, built by the Solectria Corporation of Arlington, Mass. Last year, it set a record at 238 miles, but this year, it has improved batteries and Solectria's president, James D. Worden, is hoping for 300. Before the Sunrise, which Solectria built with grants from the Pentagon and other government and private sources, Mr. Worden also set the distance record in 1993, with a converted Geo Metro that went 214 miles.

Toyota's electric vehicle, RAV4-EV, is powered by a transverse-mounted permanent magnet motor.

According to Solectria, interest in electric cars is quickening because of the plans by G.M., Ford and Chrysler. Solectria says that it has sold 215 vehicles since 1991—converted Geo Metro's or Chevy S-10 pickups—but that it might sell 100 this year alone. A spokesman, Mark L. Dockser, said that "the market has become more real" because of the interest by the Big Three auto makers.

Solectria would like to sell the Sunrise and says it could do so for $25,000 each if it could sell 20,000 a year. But at least for the near future, the company is a tiny converter, not a mass manufacturer. Still, advocates say that the Tour de Sol leads by example. ■

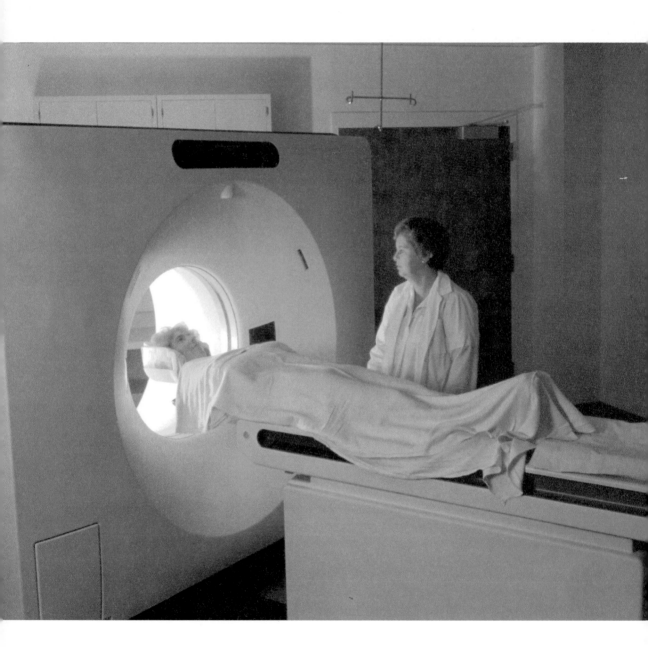

New Method of Mapping Brain

BY SANDRA BLAKESLEE

The technique causes thumbs to twitch and emotions to surge.

A psychiatrist presses a small, hand-held device over a patient's skull. There is a clicking sound and the patient feels what has been described as a "clawlike" sensation or skin being "drawn up." Usually it is not uncomfortable.

But bizarre experiences may follow. If the device—a powerful, fluctuating magnet—is placed on a spot over a person's left ear, experimenters say, his right thumb will begin to waggle. Move the magnet back an inch and he gets a vivid sensation of the thumb moving, but his eyes tell him that it remains still. When the magnet is placed at the back of his head, say on the left side, he will perceive a huge blind spot in his right eye.

Researchers say the device also produces mood changes—several hours of sadness, or happiness, depending on whether it is placed over the right or left eyebrow. In other experiments, researchers say the magnet has temporarily relieved depression, reduced the jagged movements in people who have Parkinson's disease and eradicated phantom limb pain in amputees.

Although it may sound like something advertised on late night television, the technique, called transcranial magnetic stimulation, or T.M.S., is being taken seriously by a small group of neurologists and psychiatrists around the world who are using it as a research tool.

All the results are preliminary, and so far the technique has been used only on a very small number of patients with brain disorders, but it shows early promise in two areas.

First, it can help map the normal brain. With a single pulse of the magnet, the magnetic stimulation produces functional brain "lesions," small regions of tissue that are temporarily paralyzed. Scientists can use these so-called lesions to locate many behaviors, feelings, sensations and mood centers. Second, the technique may also someday help treat certain brain disorders. Researchers using the technique say that with repeated pulses of energy, the magnet literally jump-starts sluggish regions of the brain, much the way electroshock therapy does, restoring normal function for hours to weeks.

Researchers say the magnet has temporarily relieved depression, reduced the jagged movements in people who have Parkinson's disease and eradicated phantom limb pain in amputees.

Researchers stress, however, that T.M.S. is highly experimental and if used incorrectly can induce brain seizures in healthy people. The technique ex-ploits the natural interplay between magnetism and electricity, said Dr. Mark George, an expert in brain imaging at the Medical University of South Carolina in Charleston. For example, Dr. George said, if a steady electric current is run through a coil, it will generate a magnetic field, which can be very powerful. Such electromagnets are used to pick up entire automobiles in scrap-metal yards. When the electric current is turned off, the car falls off the magnet.

Similarly, if a coil of wire is moved through a magnetic field, it will generate a flow of electricity, Dr. George said. Such magnetos are used to generate currents for the ignition of internal combustion engines.

Transcranial magnetic stimulation exploits the fact that neurons are essentially tiny electrical devices. When a nerve cell is activated, it passes a flow of electrons down its length. Upon reaching the nerve end, the electrons induce the release of chemicals that pass to neighboring nerve cells. Thus stimulated, those cells fire an electric current and the process continues, carrying coded messages throughout the brain.

People knew about the electrical nature of nerve cells hundreds of years ago, Dr. George said. They thought it would be neat to stimulate such cells externally by applying an electric current directly to the scalp. But the skin and scalp rapidly diffuse directly applied electrical currents, he said. Moreover, it hurts.

Some people also tried putting magnets next to the scalp, Dr. George said. But that did not work because the fields were simply too weak to produce an effect. Even if an ordinary magnet were strong enough to penetrate the brain, he said, it would not fluctuate; without some form of motion or change, no electric currents are induced to flow inside the brain.

Nevertheless, there are some who make extraordinary claims that magnets exert healing effects on the brain or psyche, Dr. George said. Most experts consider these claims to be totally without merit.

About 10 years ago, British physicists devised a way to get magnetic energy into the brain in a way that generated electric currents inside nerve cells, Dr. George said. They ran a strong electric current through a wire coil, turning it on and off every one ten-thousandth of a second, producing a rapidly fluctuating magnetic field that readily passed through the scalp and skull and into the brain.

This changing magnetic field prompts the flow of electrons through nerve cells. Although the nerve cells are stationary, the magnetic fields are changing rapidly enough to naturally induce a current to flow, Dr. George said. The magnets generate fields measuring 1.5 to 2 tesla, which can penetrate the brain by a fraction of an inch. But it is enough to reach the all-important layers of the cerebral cortex, he said.

The magnetic forces are different from those found in familiar magnetic resonance imaging (M.R.I.) machines, which emit strong, steady magnetic fields. Because the fields are not fluctuating, they do not cause brain cells to fire. Furthermore, the fields emitted by electric power lines bear no resemblance to T.M.S. Those fields are tiny, in comparison, and are no different from the earth's background magnetic field.

In experimenting with the magnetic stimulation technique, researchers have found that they can induce paradoxical effects. A brief, strong magnetic stimulus makes nerve cells fire a rapid train of electrical pulses, Dr. George said. Thus activated, the cells no longer accept signals from within the brain. Like a telephone with a busy signal, they are off line, their function blocked temporarily. Take away the magnet, and the cells immediately return to normal. But if cells are stimulated repeatedly, something else happens, Dr. George said. After showing inhibition, they rebound and become more active than before. The effect can last several days or months.

Researchers stress that T.M.S. is highly experimental and if used incorrectly can induce brain seizures in healthy people.

As a first step in probing the effects of T.M.S., researchers are making brain maps. Different brain regions specialize in specific behaviors and movements. Thus when a single magnetic pulse is applied to a key language area on the left side of the head, people momentarily lose the ability to talk, said Dr. Eric Wassermann, a neurologist and brain imager at the National Institute of Neurological Disorders and Stroke in Bethesda, Md. They are aware of the loss but cannot overcome it until the magnet is turned off.

Similarly, if a magnetic pulse is applied to another part of the head, people can no longer remember a short list of items recently committed to memory. In this case, they are not aware that they forgot the items.

Three studies have shown that the magnet can affect mood in normal people. When repeated pulses are delivered to an area above the left eyebrow, people feel sad, said Dr. Alvarel Pascual-Leone, a physiologist at the University of Valencia in Spain. One man said he felt the way he did at his grandmother's funeral a month earlier. Others reported feeling apathetic and depleted of energy. But when the area above the right eyebrow was stimulated, subjects said that they felt happier and more energetic. In both cases, the effects wore off after a few hours.

In other experiments, Dr. Pascual-Leone is trying to map the acquisition of new motor skills in the human brain. For example, the brain map for the right index finger should expand after a person learns to read the bumps and notches of Braille text. But how quickly does this happen? What happens to adjacent "fingers" in the brain's internal map of the hand?

To find out, Dr. Pascual-Leone recruited novice Braille students and attached an electrode to the muscle that controlled their right index fingers. He then laid out a grid on their scalps, over the region containing the map of the right index finger. A pulse of transcranial magnet stimulation over some points in the grid would cause the finger to jump, as the muscle was activated by nerve impulses from the brain. If the map expanded, more points on the grid would elicit this response.

In the experiment, the technique was used before and after class each day for one year. In the first six months of learning, the area of the brain that elicited finger responses expanded dramatically in the hours after class, Dr. Pascual-Leone said. But by the next day, it always returned to a

Transcranial magnetic stimulation can produce mood changes — several hours of sadness, or happiness, depending on whether it is placed over the right or left eyebrow.

smaller, pre-instruction size. After six months, however, the map for the right index finger took on the larger size, whereas maps for adjacent fingers shrank somewhat, Dr. Pascual-Leone said. Moreover, the brain's index finger map no longer expanded after Braille class.

"It's not just the finger map that expands" during the six months, Dr. Pascual-Leone said. "You are activating a whole network for Braille reading. The finger map is a small window into that larger network which has expanded."

Repeated magnetic pulses appear useful in treating phantom limb pain, Dr. Pascual-Leone said, as shown in experiments with people who lost one arm. In amputees who do not experience such pain, the brain map of the stump is larger than the map of the intact limb. But in those who suffer pain, the brain map of the stump has not grown, he said. It is same size as the intact arm region.

"This opens an interesting question," Dr. Pascual-Leone said. Would it be possible to increase the size of the brain map representing the stump? Repeated magnetic pulses were applied to the brains of 36 amputees suffering from phantom limb pain. In 31 people, the pain went away for days to months, he said. Experiments are under way to see if more frequent stimulation can permanently alter the maps.

People with various brain disorders may be helped by the technique, Dr. George said. For example, clinically depressed patients have decreased metabolic activity in the left frontal lobe and amygdala, two regions involved in planning and emotions.

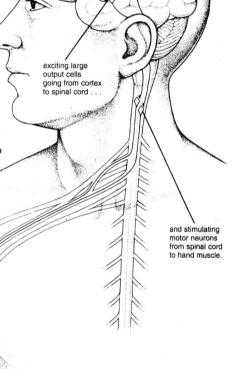

Strong pulsing electric current in coil

Coil

Neurons in cortex are excited by current . . .

Fluctuating magnetic field at right angle to induced electric current in brain

exciting large output cells going from cortex to spinal cord . . .

and stimulating motor neurons from spinal cord to hand muscle.

Magnetism as a Window on Mental Processes

A highly experimental technique called transcranial magnetic stimulation uses fluctuating magnetic fields to produce functional brain "lesions," small regions of tissue that are temporarily paralyzed. Scientists can use these so-called lesions to determine the brain areas involved in specific behaviors, feelings, sensations and moods. Magnetic stimulation of a particular brain area, for example, activates a specific nerve signal that makes the index finger jump. Researchers also hope that repeated magnetic stimulation, which sets up an excited flow of nerve signals, can someday treat mood disorders by jump-starting the brain.

"We don't know what explains it, but when the hypometabolism goes away with drug therapy, talk therapy or electroconvulsive therapy, people get better," Dr. George said.

Transcranial magnetic stimulation can be used to jump-start the same brain areas, he said. In experiments at the National Institutes of Health, severely depressed patients got T.M.S. every morning for 20 minutes over two weeks. They were later given a sham treatment in which the magnet was held over their head and made clicking sounds but no field was emitted.

The sham treatments had little or no effect on their depression. But repeated stimulation to the left frontal lobe made many people feel better, Dr. George said, while stimulation of the right side had little or no effect. This is opposite to what happens in normal people, he said, possibly because people who are severely depressed have a different brian chemistry or circuitry.

However the technique works, some depressed patients who did not respond to any other treatments said that they felt well for the first time in years, Dr. George said. But not everyone responded that way and the effects tended to wear off, he said. Experiments are continuing.

The magnetic technique could someday be an alternative to electroconvulsive therapy, in which a huge electric shock is delivered to the brain under general anesthesia, but it is too soon to tell, Dr. Pascual-Leone said. The challenge will be to find the right target in the brain for each person as well as the best dose of magnetic stimulation.

Even then, the technique may only superficially treat brain circuits involved in depression, said Dr. Harold Sackeim, chief of biological psychiatry at the New York State Psychiatric Institute. The areas that show low metabolism may be riding on top of permanent deficits in wider brain circuits, he said. Thus magnets may provide temporary relief from depression but would have to be used repeatedly in many people.

Dr. Sackeim said he worried that "T.M.S. is getting a lot of hype." Early experiments are promising, he said, but they have been few in number and not well controlled. "I would be delighted, but very surprised, if the effects of T.M.S. last more than a few days," he said. If there is any benefit, he said, it will come from combining the new technique with drugs and other treatments. ∎

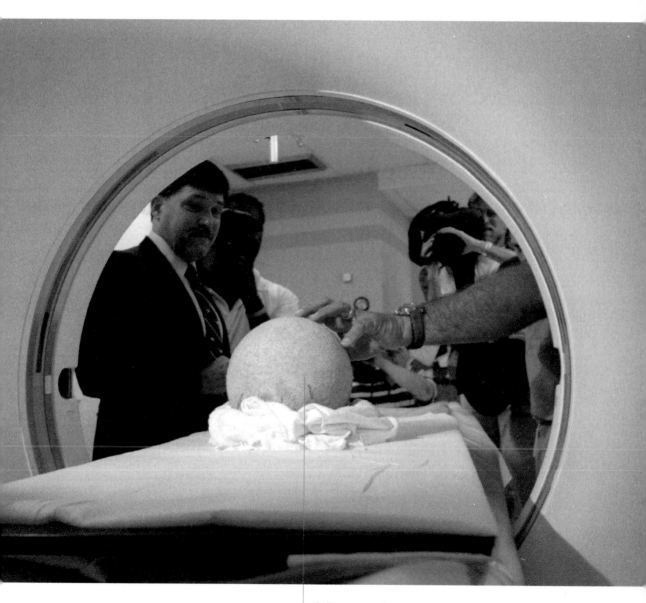

A dinosaur egg is x-rayed under a CAT
scan and is sent through an MRI .
Scientist's scanned the 80-million-
year-old egg to see if there was a
dinosaur embryo inside.

800 yards

Jurassic Cretaceous

330 yards

B470

B3022

WINDSOR CASTLE

The Holm Park

Golf Course

The Long Walk

Frances Rd.

X

Site of exploratory oil drilling 800 yrds. from the castle, 330 yrds. deep.

Drilling for Oil Under Windsor Castle

BY RALPH L. LANGENHEIM, JR.

On January 5, 1995, Queen Elizabeth II granted royal permission to Canuk Exploration Ltd. to drill a wildcat well on the grounds of Windsor Castle. The well site is 800 yards southeast of the castle and 200 yards east of the Long Walk, between the royal household cricket ground and royal household golf course. A sixty-foot-tall, truck-mounted, mobile drilling rig will drill the test well. Although shielded by a fence and surrounded by trees, the derrick will be clearly visible to passersby in the Great Park and from the Queen's private apartments. How could such a thing come to pass?

The answer lies in imposition of strict environmental standards on petroleum exploration and production and in the technologic response to those standards. Simple economics have long brought an end to permanent derricks on drill sites. The characteristic forests of derricks seen in active or abandoned oil fields before the Second World War are no longer to be seen. When a well is completed on land, present-day portable derricks are moved to the next drill-site, leaving nothing but a valve assembly or a pump if the well is a producer. Dry holes leave nothing at all above the soil's surface. Where surface conditions required unobtrusive operations, noisy, smelly, surface pumps servicing producing wells are replaced by quiet, odor-free, pumps within the well bore. Pumps, pipelines and tanks gathering oil and sending it to market can be hidden below ground and covered by appropriate vegetation. They are as invisible as the gas and water pipes serving upper-class residential areas. Electric lines bringing power to the pumps will be less obtrusive than those in most residential districts because they too may be buried. Finally, within the last decade, it has become possible to drill horizontally for thousands of feet. In this way

APPLIED SCIENCE AND TECHNOLOGY | 123

reservoirs underneath buildings or natural features that cannot be disturbed can be tapped from drill-sites completely out of sight from places like Windsor Castle.

Geologists and drillers have uncovered at least seven oil fields and one gas field in the Weald Basin, a broad, dished down fold filled with Jurassic through Tertiary rocks between the Thames estuary and a broad upfolded strip, the Weald Anticlinorium, north of the Isle of Wight. In addition, at least four wells struck oil in subcommercial quantities. As a consequence Windsor Castle is in a newly-developed, active petroleum-producing area. Oil in the basin chiefly occurs in limestone beds of middle and late Jurassic age that are between about 150 and 170 million years old. These sedimentary rocks were deposited in the sea at a time when dinosaurs roamed the earth. The oil is trapped in a series of folds that formed during the middle of the Tertiary period, about 30 million years ago. The oil and gas appear to have been "cooked" out of older Jurassic shale deposited between about 190 and 210 million years ago and which contained organic debris capable of generating oil. When this shale had been buried deeply enough, liquid and gaseous hydrocarbons formed from the heated organic debris. Thereafter, the oil and gas migrated upwards into the younger rocks that were never buried deeply enough to heat up sufficiently for hydrocarbon generation. Although petroleum production in the Weald Basin is dwarfed by that in the North Sea, not to say the Persian Gulf, the Weald and nearby Wessex Basins are the most prolific onshore oil-producing regions in the United Kingdom. The largest field, Wytch Farm in the Wessex Basin, contains an estimated 350 million barrels of recoverable oil ó a significant resource.

The Windsor Anticline, on which the Castle stands, is the northernmost anticline in the basin. Here Cretaceous chalk, the same rock that you see in the White Cliffs of Dover, is brought to the surface. At a depth of 1,000 feet, a basal Cretaceous sandstone, the Lower Greensand, rests on an ancient topographic surface truncating the Weald Basin's principal oil-bearing layer, the Great Oolite. As a consequence, an inclined, porous and permeable layer known to contain oil elsewhere in the area is truncated by a porous and permeable sandstone on the crest of an upfaulted anticline. These features together comprise a favorable structure that could trap and hold oil. All of these "structural" features have patiently been worked out by seismic exploration

Although petroleum production in the Weald Basin is dwarfed by that in the North Sea, not to say the Persian Gulf, the Weald and nearby Wessex Basins are the most prolific onshore oil-producing regions in the United Kingdom.

as part of continuing exploratory effort in the basin. The inverted bowl-like cap of the anticline encloses a potentially productive area of between 2,000 and 4,000 acres, enough to include an oil field of about 2 to 4 square miles. Depth to the top of the Lower Greensand at the crest of the structure is less than 1,000 feet. Assuming a reservoir rock as much as 130 feet thick, the known thickness of the Lower Greensand in water wells 26 kilometers north of Windsor Castle at Slough, the Windsor Anticline might contain as much as 100 million barrels of recoverable oil. This would be worth about $2,500,000,000 at present prices. In addition, more oil might be trapped in the Great Oolite or in underlying Paleozoic rocks. According to Desmond Oswald, owner and director of Canuk, three is probably one chance in eight that the Windsor anticline holds a commercially viable hydrocarbon accumulation.

After obtaining an exploratory license, Canuk completed geological and geophysical exploration without arousing opposition. Announcement of the plans to drill a test well, however, not only ignited opposition from the usual environmentalists opposed to drilling any oil wells anywhere, but also from preservationists legitimately concerned with protecting an important national heritage: Windsor Castle and Windsor Great Park. Dennis Outwin, Mayor of Windsor and Maidenhead, warned of creating a "Dallas on Thames" replete with Stetson hats and "nodding donkeys" (pumping jacks) that would irreparably damage the Queen's reputation and cause tourists to avoid Windsor Castle. Local residents complained of the noise and noxious odors of an oil field. They also worried about the heavy truck traffic required to take the oil to the refinery. A unnamed geologist in the British Geological Survey warned of possible subsidence damaging the castle and Dr. John Marshall, a geologist at South Hampton University, called attention to subsidence in the oil fields of the North Sea. Don Beer, chairman of the County Council's Development and Waste Regulation Committee, however, stated, in regard to the test well, "This is something we have got to do. I think it is imperative that we know whether there is oil or not." In any event, the Berkshire County Council approved the drilling plans, and the Queen assented to the plan.

Supporters of the project point out that the Wytch Farm Field produces its 90,000 barrels of oil per day in an environmentally sensitive area using "in hole pumps" that rise no more than five feet above the land's surface and that

The Windsor Anticline might contain as much as 100 million barrels of recoverable oil. This would be worth about $2,500,000,000 at present prices.

are quiet and non-polluting. The oil is removed by pipelines that are no more obtrusive than the gas and water lines that criss-cross all of thickly populated Britain. Surface installations at Wytch Farm are allegedly so inconspicuous that Cameron Davies, Director of International Projects for Oil Management Services Ltd., wrote in a letter to the The Times (Dec. 10, 1994): "If anyone were to drive to the Studland Peninsula, an area of outstanding natural beauty having a number of sites of special scientific interest, they would be hard put to find Wytch Farm, let alone smell or hear it." Finally, it has been pointed out, that royalties from production on crown land would go to the government, benefitting the populace as a whole. The Royal Family, as owners of Windsor Castle, would receive recompense only for use of the land surface and damages thereunto.

This is something we have got to do. I think it is imperative that we know whether there is oil or not.

At this point, drilling the exploratory well will take less than two weeks, given the shallow depth. After the exploratory test is completed, the drilling site, consisting of space to park the drilling truck, and access track, and a working area probably less than 25 feet in diameter will be restored to its prior condition. If an exploitable amount of oil is found, the company then must apply for a development and production permit. Canuk, if successful in finding oil and gaining permission to develop an oil field, plans to tap the reservoir through horizontal drilling. By this technique the drill site may be as much as a half-mile or more distant from the reservoir. Given the shallow depth, however, it may be necessary to drive the drill hole on a descending trajectory below the level of the reservoir and then climb upwards to the hydrocarbon trap. Some engineers doubt that this is feasible, but others, including the owners of Canuk, feel otherwise. Also, it will be necessary to find acceptable drilling sites for the production wells. For this purpose, farmland or, perhaps, industrial sites in environmentally nonsensitive areas are likely, but permission to drill must be negotiated with the individual owners. Given continuing rapid progress in developing horizontal drilling techniques during the past several years, it would appear probable that this technique will serve, provided there is enough oil to support the additional cost. Before any drilling for production can take place, however, a production plant must be prepared, submitted for approval, and granted. This, of course, will set off another round of debate and will require a favorable vote by the Berkshire County Council and the Queen's assent before the project receives a permit.

Canuk had planned to drill the exploratory well in August, 1995; but was unable to secure financing at that time. Their planning permit, however, was good for five years so they planned to attempt to drill in August, 1996. The UK government, however, refused to extend their license to drill the exploratory well, which expired in December, 1995. They were told that they would have to wait for the next onshore license offering, which has yet to be announced. Canuk, however, plans to continue pursuing the project.

David Knott, columnist for the *Oil and Gas Journal*, gently satirizes the uproar over drilling at Windsor by paraphrasing England's late Poet Laureate, John Betjeman's lament for industrial degradation of idyllic Slough, which begins with: "Come friendly bombs, and fall on Slough/It isn't fit for humans now…". Knott's parody follows:

> Come friendly oilmen, drill in Slough
> There isn't much employment now,
> Our industries moved east somehow,
> Where labor costs are cheap.
>
> Come oilmen, to our palace royal,
> Drill deep for lightest, sweetest oil,
> Suck up wealth from Berkshire soil
> And let us earn our keep."

(Oil and Gas Journal, Jan. 16, 1995, p. 24)

TAGGED OUT

NEW MARKERS FOR EXPLOSIVES MAY LAY OLD SAFETY QUESTIONS TO REST

BY CORINNA WU

Both deliberate and indiscriminate in its destruction, a bomb is the terrorist's favorite weapon. Within the past 3 years, several high-profile bombings on U.S. soil have made that fact all too apparent: the World Trade Center in New York, the Alfred P. Murrah building in Oklahoma City, and Centennial Olympic Park in Atlanta. Evidence now coming to light may add TWA flight 800's fiery crash to the list.

The violence of these events has cast a spotlight on an issue that has been debated for nearly 20 years. Marking explosives with tiny, color-coded plastic chips, or taggants, would enable investigators to trace explosives back to the point of sale. Information about that sale might provide a valuable clue to finding the perpetrators. Widespread tagging might also deter criminals from making and using bombs.

The Antiterrorism and Effective Death Penalty Act of 1996 signed by President Clinton last April authorizes $25 million for a 6-month study of taggants by the Treasury Department, which oversees the Bureau of Alcohol, Tobacco, and Firearms (ATF).

Consideration of taggants has been confounded by disagreement over gunpowder. Easy to obtain, it is a common ingredient of pipe bombs.

Gun users, however, are concerned that tagged gunpowder would be unstable and therefore unsafe for use in bullets. Pressure from lobbying groups such as the National Rifle Association (NRA) excluded gunpowder from the study that was included in the antiterrorism bill, although they say they wouldn't object to a study by an "independent agency." Another bill, passed by the House in July and ready for Senate consideration this month, provides for such a study. The last major government report on taggants, more than a decade ago, concluded that leaving out gunpowder would

take the teeth out of any tagging program.

Despite the controversies, a few companies have quietly proceeded with research into tagging. One new approach may make the old worries obsolete.

In the 1970s, Richard G. Livesay, a research chemist at 3M in St. Paul, Minn., invented the most widely used tagging technology. Dubbed Microtaggant, the marker consists of irregularly shaped particles, about a tenth of a millimeter in diameter. To the eye, a pinch of taggants looks like black pepper, but it's really made of up to 10 slabs of brightly colored melamine plastic, a material that's chemically inert and difficult to destroy.

The layers of color in the particles serve as a kind of bar code, identifying the manufacturer, the date of production, and the distributor of a batch of explosives, information that is stored in a database.

Marking explosives with tiny, color-coded chips, or taggants, would enable investigators to trace explosives back to the point of sale.

For easy detection and decoding, fluorescent and magnetic materials are added to the taggants. If a bomb contains tagged explosives, technicians can shine ultraviolet light to see whether there is any fluorescence among the debris. After scooping up debris samples, they collect the taggants with a magnet. Placing the taggants on a magnet orients them so that their colors are visible. The investigators can then read the colors with a simple light microscope.

Circumventing the technology would take a high level of sophistication. A particularly skilled criminal with the right equipment might be able to produce counterfeit tags, but tagging would eliminate "99 percent of the oafs out there," according to Gary Fuller, now director of research at Basic Technologies International Corp. in Annandale, Va., and a participant in a major study of taggants that began in 1977.

The largest U.S. producer of taggants today is Microtrace, based in Minneapolis. Livesay acquired the license for Microtaggant from 3M in 1985 and formed his own company to manufacture it. "We only make taggants [for use in explosives] for one customer: the Swiss government," says Charles W. Faulkner, general counsel for Microtrace.

The Swiss have used them to solve 559 bombing cases since 1984, he adds.

From 1977 to 1980, Aerospace Corp., now in El Segundo, Calif., conducted a study on Microtaggants for ATF. Working with three leading explosives manufacturers at the time, Atlas Powder Co., DuPont Co., and Hercules, Aerospace tagged about 7 million pounds of explosives, not including gunpowder, over a $1\frac{1}{2}$-year period. Fuller says, "We distributed them all around without a single problem."

For packaged explosives like sticks of dynamite, "the safety issues were put to bed back then," Fuller says. In 1979, a bombing case in Baltimore was actually solved using the taggants. But then the explosive manufacturers began to back out, he adds, mostly for fear of being held legally liable for the damage done by their products.

"Once they realized that [potential liability], the whole program died an ungraceful death."

A 1979 lawsuit filed by Goex, a gunpowder manufacturer, also undermined interest in taggants. Goex claimed that taggants produced by 3M were to blame for a blast at its plant in Camden Park, Ark. Ultimately, 3M was exonerated.

Fuller calls the lawsuit "a pure red herring," but he adds that "there are still some reasons to conduct more tests on smokeless powder and black powder [types of gunpowder]."

The NRA says early tests showed that the gunpowder interacts with some component of the taggants, promoting spontaneous combustion and accelerating degradation.

Those tests were conducted at a high temperature and used very high taggant concentrations, says Faulkner. Though Microtrace's recommended concentration is only 250 parts per million, equal parts of taggants and powder were mixed together in the tests. Under such extreme conditions, he says, "of course it's unstable."

An oft-cited 1980 report on taggants conducted by the Office of Technology Assessment (OTA), the now-defunct research arm of Congress, stated, "Until this presumed incompatibility is resolved, taggants cannot be safely added to these explosive materials." OTA did not independently verify the claims of instability but relied on interviews and the findings of previous studies.

Not much progress on resolving the gunpowder question has been made since. Passage of the pending bill would move the issue forward, Fuller and others predict. Faulkner notes that the Swiss haven't had any problems in their many

The layers of color in the particles serve as a kind of bar code, identifying the manufacturer, the date of production, and the distributor of a batch of explosives, information that is stored in a database.

years of experience with tagged gunpowder and other explosives.

Most attention has focused on packaged explosives and gunpowder, but the experience of Oklahoma City highlighted another kind of threat: the bomb made from ammonium nitrate fertilizer and fuel oil. The 1980 OTA report acknowledged the danger, saying an effective bomb could be made out of those materials "if the criminal has adequate time, skill, knowledge, and motivation."

A company in Houston claims to have a practical way to tag ammonium nitrate and perhaps other ingredients of explosives. By labeling explosives at the molecular level, Isotag says it can produce tags that are cheap, reliable, and chemically inert. "We believe that our technique makes the NRA's concerns regarding destabilization of black powder a moot point," says Isotag's chief financial officer, Desmonde Cowdery.

To the eye, a pinch of taggants looks like black pepper, but it's really made of up to 10 slabs of brightly colored melamine plastic, a material that's chemically inert and difficult to destroy.

Rather than using a foreign marker, Isotag modifies the molecules already present in the explosive. By replacing some of the atoms with nonstandard isotopes, which have more or fewer neutrons, the company creates molecules that are chemically identical to the standard version but have slightly different weights.

The isotopically labeled compounds are extremely uncommon in nature, so they can be detected readily. Adding several isotopic markers to an ingredient of explosives—ammonium nitrate is the only one they've tested so far—further increases the rarity of the isotopic bar code.

Unlike the plastic taggants, these markers can only be detected with fairly sophisticated laboratory equipment. If chemically tagged fertilizer were used in a bomb, technicians would need to collect residue at the site and send it to Isotag for analysis. To decode the marker, scientists would separate the constituent compounds with a gas chromatograph and then break each compound apart with a mass spectrometer to reveal the particular combinations of isotopes.

Thousands of search and rescue crews attend a memorial service in front of the Alfred P. Murrah Federal Building in Oklahoma City Friday, May 5, 1995. Rescue crews ended their search after 16 days for victims of the April 19 car bombing attack.

Officials examine the wreckage of a car in an underground parking garage at The World Trade Center in New York. The noontime explosion, which rocked the twin towers complex, killed at least five people and injured some 300 others.

Even though gas chromatographs and mass spectrometers are common fixtures in chemistry labs, a person trying to find the tags would have a hard time identifying the isotopically labeled compounds without knowing the code, says Isotag chemist Ken Laintz. "We take pride in our ability to hide the tags."

The labeled molecules would be used at concentrations of a few parts per billion, and they can be detected when present at concentrations of only parts per trillion.

Isotag completed a study in late 1995 with a major manufacturer of ammonium nitrate fertilizer. It showed that the markers are stable and can survive a blast. But fertilizer companies began to bow out of such marker investigations, as the explosives companies did earlier, preferring to spend their money on combating taggant legislation, says Laintz.

Now, they will have to pick up where they left off. Fertilizers, considered explosive precursor chemicals, are part of the Treasury Department study authorized by the April antiterrorism act. Isotopic marking will probably be included in the tagging study. "We've made information about our technology available to Congress," Cowdery says.

Whether these studies will actually lead to an explosives tagging program remains to be seen. The antiterrorism bill allows the Treasury Department to mandate the addition of markers to explosive materials if they're deemed safe and effective. The pending gunpowder bill, on the other hand, makes no such provision.

Tagging has turned out to be an explosive issue in more ways than one. ∎

3 | Astronomy and Space Exploration

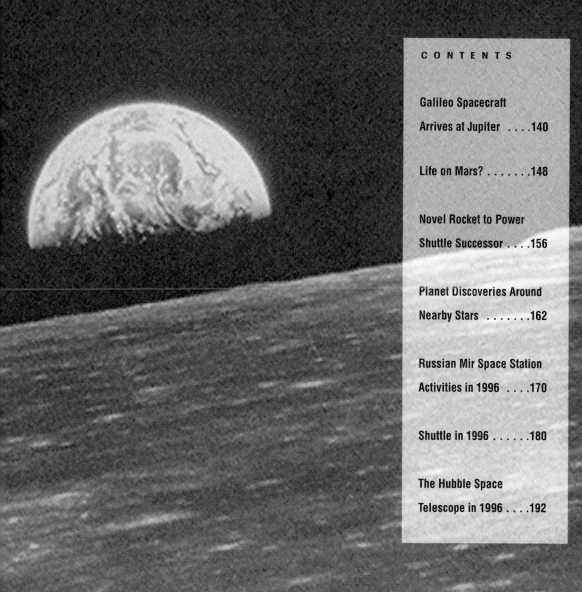

CONTENTS

Jupiter and its four planet-size moons, called the Galilean satellites, were photographed by Voyager 1 and assembled into this collage. They are not to scale, but are in their relative positions.

Galileo Spacecraft Arrives at Jupiter

BY GEORGE J. FLYNN

The Galileo spacecraft — named for the Italian astronomer Galileo Galilei, discoverer of the four largest moons of Jupiter shortly after the invention of the telescope — was launched by the space shuttle *Atlantis* on October 18, 1989. A thirty-eight-month flight took the Galileo spacecraft past Venus, Earth, and two asteroids before going into orbit around Jupiter on December 7, 1995.

Prior to Galileo, Jupiter and its moons were visited by the Pioneer 10 spacecraft in December 1973, the Pioneer 11 spacecraft in December 1974, Voyager 1 in March 1979, and Voyager 2 in July 1979. Each of these spacecraft flew quickly through the Jovian system, gathering data for only a few hours before continuing to Saturn. Galileo's mission was to perform the first long-term observations of Jupiter and its moons, and to send an instrument package deep into the atmosphere of Jupiter.

The Galileo spacecraft consists of two units, an orbiter and an atmospheric probe. The orbiter, weighing 4,896 pounds, carries ten scientific instruments designed to observe the atmosphere of Jupiter and the surfaces of its four largest moons over a two-year period from late 1995 through 1997. The atmospheric probe, weighing 747 pounds, carried ten instruments that returned data for 58.6 minutes as the probe descended through the atmosphere of Jupiter.

Galileo communicates to Earth using the National Aeronautics and Space Administration's (NASA's) Deep Space Network: large antennas located in California, Spain, and Australia. Soon after Galileo began its journey, engineers found that its high-gain antenna, which should have opened like an umbrella, would not open. This antenna was designed to allow high-speed transmission of scientific data to Earth. The project engineers developed techniques to allow the scientific measurements and photographs to be

Galileo Galilei

transmitted through a second antenna. If the high-gain antenna had deployed properly, Galileo would have sent data to Earth at a rate of 134,400 bits of information per second, but the other antenna can transmit only 160 bits per second. As a result, the scientific program had to be redesigned. Galileo will make fewer measurements and take fewer photographs than originally planned, but many of the original scientific objectives can still be accomplished.

The primary purpose of the Galileo orbiter is to investigate the processes that generate and sustain the major atmospheric features on Jupiter.

En route to Jupiter, Galileo passed through the asteroid belt, located between Mars and Jupiter. Its path was selected to allow close flybys of the asteroid Gaspera in October 1991 and the asteroid Ida in August 1993. Galileo returned the first close-up photographs of an asteroid and discovered that Ida has a small moon, which was named Dactyl, the first moon of an asteroid ever discovered. In late July 1994, Galileo was the only spacecraft in the right position to obtain photographs of the far side of Jupiter when fragments of Comet Shoemaker-Levy 9 crashed into the planet.

ARRIVAL AT JUPITER

The Galileo orbiter arrived at Jupiter on December 7, 1995, and fired its engine to reduce the speed of the spacecraft. The orbiter was placed in a highly elliptical orbit, coming within 300,000 miles of Jupiter at its low point, and going out to 12 million miles from the planet. Each orbit takes about two months to complete and includes a close approach to one of Jupiter's moons. The gravitational pull of the moon alters the orbital path of the spacecraft, retargeting the spacecraft to a close encounter with another moon a few months later, so each orbit is different from the previous one. This orbital path was designed to allow the Galileo orbiter to observe the motions of the Jovian atmosphere over time and to make close flybys of the four largest moons: Ganymede, Callisto, Io, and Europa.

The primary purpose of the Galileo orbiter is to investigate the processes that generate and sustain the major atmospheric features on Jupiter. When the spacecraft is closest to Jupiter it can photograph atmospheric features down to 20 miles in size. By comparing images taken an hour apart, scientists can observe the motion of these features, determining wind speeds, alteration of shape, and changes in color.

The Great Red Spot, the most prominent feature in Jupiter's clouds, was observed by Galileo. By comparing photographs taken 70 minutes apart, scientists were able to determine that winds within the Great Red Spot blow counterclockwise with a speed of about 250 miles per hour, substantially higher than the 75- to 130-mile-per-hour hurricane-force winds on Earth. Images at the highest resolution showed "convective features," regions of vertical motion of the atmosphere, near one edge of the Great Red Spot. These features are similar to clusters of thunderstorms on Earth.

FLYBYS OF GANYMEDE

On June 27, 1996, the Galileo orbiter made its first close flyby of Ganymede, the largest moon of Jupiter. The Galileo orbiter passed within about 530 miles of Ganymede, obtaining photographs with resolutions down to about 250 feet. Previously, the best photographs of Ganymede, taken by the Voyager 2 spacecraft in 1979, had a resolution of 4,500 feet. A second flyby of Ganymede, on September 6, 1996, came even closer, within 170 miles of the surface.

Based on the images taken by the Voyager spacecraft, scientists expected to find two distinct regions on Ganymede: flat, bright areas covered by recent eruptions of frozen water from beneath the surface and darker, older areas that were completely covered by craters. Because craters accumulate over time, the density of craters provides a rough measure of the age of a surface.

The Voyager photographs of the Uruk Sulcus region of Ganymede showed several bright groves, spaced a few miles apart. Scientists had speculated that this was a young, less heavily cratered region that was bright because it was covered with sheets of ice, erupted from below the surface by volcanoes of water. Instead of an ice sheet, the Galileo images of the Uruk Sulcus region showed a grooved terrain, with individual ridges spaced a several hundred feet apart, and many small circular features, believed to be impact craters. The grooves indicate that, rather than icy eruptions, tectonics—the movement of plates on the surface of the moon, which produces ridges where two plates push against each other or grooves where they move apart—shaped the surface of Ganymede. The presence of many small craters on the surface suggests it is older than previously suspected from the Voyager photographs.

The most surprising result was produced by the magnetometer, a device that can measure weak magnetic fields. Ganymede appears to have a relatively large magnetic field, about one-fortieth that of Earth. Such fields are believed to be produced on Earth and other planets by a molten metal core. However, models of the interior structure of Ganymede do not suggest the presence of a molten core. The detection of this magnetic field suggests that either Ganymede has a significantly different internal structure from that previously believed or other mechanisms can produce such fields. One model suggests that a briny ocean moving beneath the icy crust of Ganymede is producing this magnetic field; other scientists suggest that the rocks may preserve a weak remnant of a much stronger magnetic field earlier in Ganymede's history.

Additional flybys of Ganymede will occur on April 5, 1997, May 7, 1997, and June 26, 1997, but none will come as close as the September 6, 1996, flyby.

FLYBYS OF EUROPA

On June 27, 1996, only a few hours after the flyby of Ganymede, the Galileo spacecraft passed within 102,000 miles of Europa, the smallest of Jupiter's four large moons. Although the flyby distance was quite large, Galileo obtained photographs with a resolution of about 1 mile, somewhat better than the best resolution obtained by the Voyager spacecraft.

The surface of Europa shows numerous fractures, resembling the ice floes of the Arctic Ocean on Earth. These fractures, which are dark in color, are believed to occur by tidal stressing of the icy crust of Europa. Scientists speculate that the ice crust covering Europa is floating on a sea of slush or liquid water, allowing fluids from the ocean below to move upward through the cracks. Rocks and other contaminants in the water are believed to cause the dark color along the cracks.

The surface of Europa shows very few craters, suggesting that the surface is relatively young. New modeling suggests that the strong tidal forces produced by Jupiter, Io, and Ganymede may work together to warm the interior of Europa. These tides could maintain a liquid ocean beneath the frozen surface. This heat could trigger eruptions of ocean water over the surface, obliterating the evidence of past craters. This hint of liquid water on Europa, coupled with the suggested heating by tidal forces and previous evidence for the pres-

View of Europa, one of Jupiter's satellites.

ence of organic compounds, has prompted speculation that Europa might have conditions suitable for the development of primitive life-forms. The Galileo spacecraft does not carry instruments suited for a search for life in the Jovian system, so any such search will require a future mission.

During its tour of the Jovian system, Galileo will fly past Europa three more times: on December 19, 1996, when it will obtain photographs with a resolution of 60 feet for objects near the equator; on February 20, 1997, when it will examine objects down to 36 feet in size; and on December 6, 1997, when it will fly over the north pole of Europa, obtaining photographs of the polar region at a resolution of 30 feet.

FLYBY OF IO

The Voyager spacecraft observed active volcanoes on Io, the first time volcanic activity had been seen anywhere in the solar system other than on Earth. The Voyager observations raised many scientific questions: among them, do the same volcanoes remain active for a long period of time, and how rapidly are the surface features on Io altered by the accumulation of volcanic debris?

On June 28, 1996, the Galileo orbiter turned its camera on Io. One active volcano, Ra Patera, was seen ejecting an arc of fine particles that reached 65 miles above the surface of Io. The most violent terrestrial volcanoes eject particles only about 20 miles into the atmosphere. The volcanic plume from Ra Patera appears to be blue in the Voyager images, suggesting that the plume consists of sulfur dioxide gas that condenses into snow or ice as the gas expands.

Comparison of the Voyager and Galileo images of the area surrounding Ra Patera indicates that remarkable changes have occurred in the seventeen years between the two flybys. A 16,000-square-mile area surrounding Ra Patera, roughly the size of the state of New Jersey, is covered by new volcanic deposits not present in the Voyager images.

FLYBYS OF CALLISTO

Callisto, which of the four large moons orbits farthest from Jupiter, has the darkest surface of the four large moons. Because it orbits so far from Jupiter, the tidal heating of Callisto is expected to be smaller than for the other three moons, and it is expected to retain the largest amount of ice. Voyager images showed a dark surface pitted by bright, circular craters. Scientists believe the craters penetrate through a rocky covering, exposing an icy layer below.

Galileo will pass within 700 miles of Callisto on November 4, 1996. However, scientists will have to wait until June 25, 1997, for its closest surveillance, when the orbiter will fly within 270 miles of Callisto.

PROBE MEASUREMENTS

The Galileo probe, which was designed by Hughes Space and Communications Group under contract to the NASA Ames Research Center, separated from the orbiter in July 1995. The probe, containing ten scientific instruments, plunged into the atmosphere of Jupiter at a velocity of 110,000 miles per hour on December 7, 1995. Atmospheric friction heated the probe, which was protected by an "aeroshell," a heat shield that contributed half of the probe's total weight and slowed it down. Two minutes later the aeroshell was jettisoned, exposing the instruments to the atmosphere of Jupiter. A parachute was deployed and the probe sent a continual stream of information to the orbiter, where it was stored for later relay to Earth. The probe descended under the parachute for 58 minutes before data transmission ceased.

Astronomers on Earth used telescopes to observe the same region on Jupiter where the Galileo probe entered the atmosphere. Their observations indicate that the probe plunged into a "hot spot," an unusual region that is drier and has less cloud cover than 99 percent of the planet. This complicates how scientists interpret the probe's measurements, because they are unsure if the results are representative of the planet as a whole. Interpretation of the Galileo results is further complicated because the temperature in the interior of the probe reached extremes that were outside the anticipated range, and the instruments had not been calibrated at these temperatures.

Temperature and pressure sensors on the probe provided measurements during the descent. Comparison of these measurements with predictions for various atmospheric compositions suggests a very low water content and the absence of water clouds in the region sampled by the probe. A layer of ammonia clouds was detected, confirming what was expected from atmospheric models.

A mass spectrometer, a device that measures the masses of individual atoms and molecules, provided the first direct measurement of the composition of the atmosphere of Jupiter. The abundances of hydrogen, helium, methane, water, argon, neon, and hydrogen sulfide were determined.

By comparison of these abundances with those measured in the Sun and in the rocky planets, scientists hoped to determine if Jupiter formed mostly from the same gas as the Sun or instead incorporated a significant amount of rocky or icy bodies into its structure, as did Earth. The probe measured abundances of sulfur and carbon consistent with the preflight expectations; however, the abundances of oxygen and water were significantly less than scientists expected. If the probe results are representative of the atmospheric composition over the entire planet, then, the investigators believe, these measurements show that Jupiter cannot have incorporated even as much as several Earth masses of icy, water-rich bodies during its formation.

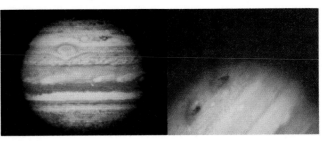

Left: This is the first true-color photograph of Jupiter from the Hubble Space Telescope. Right: Hubble image of large comet impact on Jupiter.

As the probe descended through the atmosphere it was blown around by the wind, and this motion caused very small, but measurable, changes in the frequency of the radio signal received by the orbiter, allowing scientists to determine the speed of the winds. The probe measured wind speeds of 360 to 480 miles per hour in the atmosphere. The winds remained strong as the probe descended well into the region where solar radiation deposits little energy. This observation supports models of Jupiter's atmosphere in which much of the energy for atmospheric motion comes from the interior of the planet, not from absorbed solar radiation.

The Voyager cameras had photographed lightning flashes in the atmosphere of Jupiter, so the Galileo probe carried a lightning detector to measure the radio wave emission from the lightning. However, the Galileo probe passed through a region of the atmosphere that did not produce lightning within 100 miles of the probe's descent path, though some lightning signals were detected at farther distances from the probe. On Jupiter the probe measurements indicate that lightning occurs less frequently than on Earth, but the typical electric current carried by a lightning flash on Jupiter appears to be larger than that on Earth.

Interpretation of the data obtained by the Galileo probe will continue for several years. first, scientists will recalibrate the instruments over the range of temperatures actually experienced on entry. Then they will develop models of the atmosphere of Jupiter that are consistent with the many new observations. ∎

Life on Mars?

BY CARL W. HOAGSTROM

Mars is the fourth planet from the Sun, just beyond Earth. Because of its proximity to Earth and some of the planet's characteristics observed (and imagined) from Earth, the question of whether life exists on Mars has entertained earthlings since its planetary nature was first understood. Telescopic observation has suggested to some astronomers the presence of elaborate canal systems. A rock formation that looked like a face suggested a Martian Mount Rushmore to some people. Both observations were, of course, suggestive of intelligent life on our neighboring planet. However, the canals proved to be optical illusions, and the face has never been taken seriously by scientists.

As scientists learned more about the development of the solar system and specific conditions on Mars, it became apparent that life could not exist on the surface of the planet, not now and probably not in Mars' recent past. The surface is too hot and dry, and has presumably been so for a very long time. The Mariner and Viking missions to Mars in the 1960s and 1970s sent back enormous amounts of information that tended to confirm these conclusions. Although chemical analysis from a Viking surface probe suggested that Martian surface material had organic compounds characteristic of living things on Earth, a closer look determined that not to be the case. The totality of the evidence suggested that Mars is now, and has always been, lifeless.

However, a more thorough understanding of the history of the solar system in general and of Mars in particular has suggested that at the time life was developing on Earth, Mars should have had very similar conditions. Viking and Mariner reported elaborate branching valleys, similar to those created by river systems on Earth. Landforms thought to be created by massive flooding and others apparently carved by glaciers also were discovered. All this evidence

suggested that Mars once had abundant surface water.

Continuing studies of primitive life-forms on Earth and the conditions under which they exist suggest that the one condition required for life is liquid water. Other requirements exist (including an energy source, proper temperatures, and nutrients), but given conditions at which water exists in its liquid state, the other requirements for life tend to be present as well. Therefore, the evidence for free water on Mars early in its history suggested that life may have evolved on Mars at the same time it was evolving on Earth. Some investigators think that primitive life may have developed on Mars before it lost its surface water, although conditions on Mars changed and complex life may not have had time to evolve further. A few of these investigators believe that simple, microscopic life may still exist in subsurface pockets supplied with water.

NEW DEVELOPMENTS IN AN OLD DEBATE

In the August 16, 1996, issue of *Science* magazine, David S. McKay of the Johnson Space Center and a group of collaborators declared that they had found signs of fossil life on Mars. The source of the evidence was not information from the Mariner or Viking missions, nor did it come from the Hubble or earthbound telescopes, but from a "free" sample of Martian rock, a meteorite derived from Mars.

In a letter in the September 20, 1996, issue of *Science*, Frank and Ted von Hippel suggested four ways that life could have come to be present on both Earth and Mars. (1) Life may have originated independently on each of the planets; (2) it may have originated on Mars and have been transported to Earth; (3) it may have originated on Earth and have been transported to Mars; or (4) it may have originated somewhere else in the universe and have been transported to Mars and Earth.

Any of the presumed transports would have occurred as the result of a meteorite colliding with the place of origin, hurling rocks from that planet into space, and those rocks falling to the surface of the place of introduction after some time in space. This scenario demands exceptionally hardy life-forms because they would have had to withstand bombardment by gamma rays and ultraviolet light during the trip through space, as well as the intense heat generated as the meteorite passed through the receiving planet's atmosphere. If the life-forms were buried inside the meteorite they might be protected from much of this abuse, though not from the intense cold of space. Spores or other inactive forms, which could be reactivated when they encountered favorable conditions on the receiving planet, might have been able to run this gauntlet. The growing knowledge of life-forms that occur in some of the most inhospitable places on Earth (boiling hot springs, hydrothermal vents, etc.) suggests that the possibility of such transport should not be dismissed lightly.

METEORITES FROM MARS

Meteorites are rocks traveling through space that are captured by Earth's gravitational field. They are not entirely vaporized as they pass through Earth's atmosphere, and thus fall to Earth's surface. Most are derived from the asteroid belt between Mars and Jupiter, but some are now believed to be de-rived from the Moon and from the planets.

The idea that the planets (and their moons) exchange material was considered implausible or impossible a few decades ago. Today such exchanges are accepted as fact: Meteorites produce meteorites. For a Mars rock to escape into space, Mars must be struck by a meteorite large enough to blast a large crater in the Martian surface and to give some of the rocks blown out of the crater sufficient energy to escape the pull of Martian gravity. Many geologists believe that such an event occurred 65 million years ago on Earth, in the Yucátan Peninsula of Mexico, and that it resulted in the extinction of dinosaurs and many other organisms. The large number of craters on the Moon, Mars, and even Earth, although defaced by erosion and weathering, attest the common occurrence of such collisions.

For a rock blown out of Mars in this way to become a meteorite on Earth, it must come under the influence of

Meteorites are rocks traveling through space that are captured by Earth's gravitational field. Most are derived from the asteroid belt between Mars and Jupiter, but some are now believed to bederived from the Moon and from the planets.

Earth's gravitational field and it must survive the trip through Earth's atmosphere to strike the planet's surface. Like most meteorites, the known meteorites derived from Mars are small and had a much smaller impact on Earth than either a meteorite that kicks rocks out of Mars' gravitational field or one that might have caused the extinction of the dinosaurs.

Twelve meteorites are believed to be derived from Mars. Aspects of the chemistry of these meteorites are different from meteorites derived from the Asteroid Belt or from comets, but similar to one another and to the chemistry of surface material found by the Viking lander on Mars. Some have been found to contain the same atmospheric gas mix that the Viking probe found in its tests of Mars' atmosphere.

One of the meteorites, ALH84001, was the first meteorite (001) found in the Alan Hills (ALH) region of Antarctica in 1984 (84). It was determined to be a Martian meteorite in 1994 and immediately became the target of a number of investigations because of its age. The other Martian meteorites are no more than 1.3 billion years old, but ALH84001 is thought to be 4.5 billion years old — implying that the rock from which it was blasted solidified from the molten state when Mars was first formed. ALH84001 is nearly as old as Mars.

The history of ALH84001, according to McKay and his coauthors, is as follows: Formed 4.5 billion years ago when Mars itself was consolidating out of asteroid-like planetesimals, it was fractured by the collision of another meteorite with Mars around 3.6 billion years ago. Shortly thereafter, microscopic organisms developed and lived on the fracture surfaces created by that impact. Another impact, about 16 million years ago, hurled the rock into space, where it traveled about the solar system until a few thousand years ago, when Earth's gravitational field captured it and it plunged into a glacier on Antarctica. Glaciers tend to concentrate meteorites at their leading edges and to preserve them, because minimal weathering occurs at the low temperatures that prevail there. ALH84001's discovery was made more likely by its deposition in Antarctica, and it was found in 1984, by a team of scientists searching for meteorites.

EVIDENCE OF PAST LIFE IN ALH84001

Four lines of evidence are central to the McKay group's conclusion that life probably existed on Mars 3.5

Surface of Mars showing a thin coating of water ice on the rocks and soil.

billion years ago. first, carbonate globules of the type found in the meteorite are formed by microorganisms on Earth. Second, organic molecules, called polycyclic aromatic hydrocarbons (PAHs), have been found in the meteorite; PAHs are produced during decomposition of living material on Earth. Third, iron oxides (compounds of iron and oxygen such as magnetite) and iron sulfides (compounds of iron and sulfur such as pyrrhotite) in the meteorite are arranged in thin layers of the sort produced by microorganisms under certain conditions on Earth. Fourth, tiny elliptical structures found in the meteorite are similar to structures interpreted as microscopic fossils on Earth.

Each line of evidence can be explained as a product of living microorganisms, but each can also be explained by strictly physical and chemical processes (abiotic processes, that is, processes not involving life). For example, carbonate globules similar to those in ALH84001 form under certain conditions, with no contribution from living things. In fact, some evidence suggests that the globules in the meteorite formed at temperatures too high for living things to tolerate. On the other hand, McKay and his group present evidence for the carbonate globules' formation at lower temperatures, temperatures that could support life. At any rate, the carbonate globules are explainable by mechanisms not requiring life.

The organic compounds (PAHs) found in the meteorite are formed when living cells die and decompose, but they can be formed by a number of other processes that do not involve life. In addition, it is possible that the meteorite became contaminated with organic compounds originating on Earth. McKay and his collaborators argue that they eliminated that possibility by demonstrating that the PAHs are in a higher concentration inside the meteorite. If they were present as contaminants, they would have had to enter from outside and thus should be at higher, or at least equal, concentrations in the outer layers of ALH84001. Critics argue that that viewpoint is oversimplified and that complex contamination processes could lead to the observed concentration gradients.

Critics also point out that a number of other organic compounds, amino acids for example, are much better indicators of life than are PAHs. None of these better indicators has been found in ALH84001. On the other hand, many have been found in meteorites from the asteroid belt (as have PAHs) without triggering a claim for life on the asteroids.

The magnetite and iron sulfide layers seem to be accepted as McKay's strongest evidence, but critics argue again that physical processes are capable of producing such layers. The McKay team argues that the series of changes in the environment required to generate the layers abiotically, repeatedly going from reducing to oxidizing conditions and back, is a less likely scenario than their production by past life. The other side agrees that it would take a complex sequence of physical changes to produce the layers, but that the physical sequence is probably no less likely to have occurred than the development of life, which is also a very complex process.

The tiny "fossil cells" are probably the weakest of the four lines of evidence. Many scientists are skeptical of the analogous "fossils" on Earth, arguing that even they may be of abiotic origin. Skeptics argue that a number of processes that do not involve living things at any stage can produce similar structures. According to some skeptics, the Martian "fossils" are at least one hundred times smaller than their earthbound counterparts, and some argue that if they are not too small to function as cells, they are at the very lower limit of size for functional cells.

The McKay group argues that, while physical and chemical processes could have produced any one of their lines of evidence, the combination is most easily explained as the result of life processes.

Interestingly, another group, led by Jim Papike from the University of New Mexico, conducted a search for evidence of life in meteorite ALH84001 by exploring the ratio of sulfur isotopes in the meteorite. On Earth, living things produce a characteristic sulfur isotope ratio, while nonliving processes produce distinctly different ratios. The New Mexico group found a sulfur isotope ratio characteristic of nonliving processes in ALH84001. They do not argue that their finding disproves the findings of the McKay group, but it is certainly not supportive.

This Hubble image of Mars shows a thick canopy of bluish clouds covering the icy north polar regions, where it was martian "winter" at the time of the observation.

IMPORTANCE OF LIFE ON MARS

If life were definitively shown to be present (or to have been present) on Mars, what would it mean? What are the implications?

It is perhaps more interesting to ponder the significance of life originating independently on each of the planets. That combination of events would suggest that life might be expected to develop in the normal course of plane-

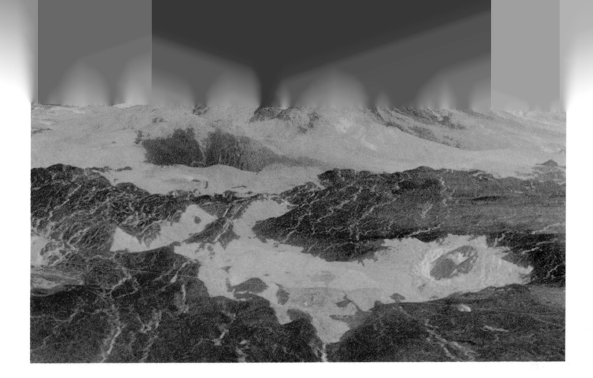

Mosaic of the Cerberus hemisphere of Mars projected into point perspective, a view similar to that which one would see from a spacecraft. The mosaic is composed of 104 Viking Orbiter images.

tary development, as long as the physical conditions were appropriate. The harsh places that life on Earth has colonized suggest that any environment with liquid water should be considered a possible site for the development of living systems at least somewhat similar to the primitive, single-celled life on Earth. Given these arguments, many scientists suggest that life should be expected to have developed on Mars, perhaps on some of Jupiter's moons, and, by extension, perhaps in many other places in the universe. However, most believe that the current, direct evidence for past life on Mars is circumstantial at best.

Nevertheless, even the strongest critics of the McKay group's conclusions are not arguing against the possibility of life on Mars, nor do they argue against the continued exploration of Mars for evidence of life. As more is learned about living things in the depths of Earth's crust, the ability of life to exist under exceptionally harsh conditions as long as liquid water is present has become abundantly evident. Most skeptical arguments are not against the possibility of life on Mars or the value of continuing the search for life on Mars and in other parts of the solar system and galaxy, but against the strength of the evidence presented by the McKay group. Most agree that the evidence is suggestive, but far from definitive — that the question is worthy of further exploration, but by no means strongly supported by the evidence presented by McKay and his coworkers. ▪

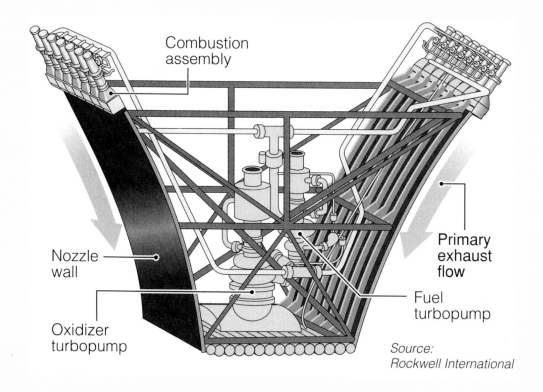

Combustion
assembly

Nozzle
wall

Oxidizer
turbopump

Primary
exhaust
flow

Fuel
turbopump

Source:
Rockwell International

Novel Rocket Chosen to Power Shuttle Successor

BY WARREN E. LEARY

WASHINGTON

Using an approach that in a sense turns rocketry inside out, engineers are building a new type of engine to power what could be the next generation of spacecraft to haul payloads into orbit.

Abandoning the familiar cone-shaped nozzles used by Goddard, von Braun and other pioneers to contain and direct the fiery exhausts propelling their rockets, the engineers are building a radically new type that shoots its flames along the outside rim of an inverted cone or another curved surface.

Engineers say this approach can make rocket engines simpler and more efficient. Because the combustion gases are only constrained on one side by an engine surface, they can adjust to atmospheric pressure at all altitudes and maintain better thrust throughout a rocket's flight, proponents say.

The innovation, which seems almost counterintuitive, is called the aerospike engine. It is the first major new rocket engine developed in the United States in more than 25 years.

The unusual engine, which has been tested extensively on the ground, is getting a chance to prove itself because it is part of the Lockheed Martin Corporation's winning proposal to build the X-33 experimental rocket. Earlier this month, the National Aeronautics and Space Administration picked the Lockheed Martin design over two others to test new technologies for a reusable rocket that could become the workhorse for carrying cargo into space after the turn of the century.

The X-33, which is to fly in 1999 using the power of two aerospike engines, is to be a half-scale prototype for a new generation of completely reusable rockets that can haul payloads into space far more cheaply and simply than current boosters. If the program is successful, it could lead to a large, remote-controlled rocket, termed a reusable launching vehicle, that could be operational within a decade for putting satellites and other payloads into orbit and would probably replace the space shuttle, NASA and industry officials said.

Lockheed Martin hopes that the X-33 proves the feasibility of building the bigger craft, which would be developed, built and owned by private industry, not the Government. The company estimates that it could build two or three of the ships, dubbed Venture Star, for a total of about $5 billion. Each Venture Star, a wingless, wedge-shaped ship that would take off and land in one piece, would be powered by seven large aerospike engines.

The aerospike engines to be used in the X-33, which will not fly high enough or fast enough to go into orbit, and the later Venture Star are being built by the Rocketdyne Division of Rockwell International.

The engine was conceived in the mid-1960's by Sam S. Iacobellis, an engineer who headed Rocketdyne's advanced programs division. In the early 1970's, Rocketdyne conducted more than 70 firing tests of large aerospike engines in hopes that they would be selected to power the space shuttle. The aerospike lost out to a more conventional engine for use in the shuttle, but the company and NASA continued research on the concept.

The most visible part of conventional rocket engines is the large, bell-shaped nozzle. This nozzle takes hot gases from the burning of fuel in a combustion chamber and allows them to expand to a high velocity so that when they come out the end, they produce thrust to propel the rocket.

In an aerospike engine, the large central combustion chamber is replaced by a series of smaller ones arranged along the outside rim of an inverted cone or another curved surface. These small chambers, called combustors, shoot their hot gases along these surfaces to produce thrust, but all but one side of the flames remain exposed to the surrounding air.

There are two basic types of aerospike nozzles: annular ones that are like upside-down cones, or spikes, with combustors arranged around a broad case and firing toward the tip, and linear types that are designed using two parallel lines of combustors thrusting against curved, rectangular plates or ramps. The X-33 and the Venture Star will be powered by linear aerospikes burning liquid oxygen and liquid hydrogen.

Each X-33 engine will have 20 combustors, or thrusters, aligned 10 to a side, that produce a total of 205,000 pounds of thrust. Two of these engines are to propel the experimental rocket as high as 50 miles at velocities of up to 15 times the speed of sound. As part of the same program, Rocketdyne is to build and fire on the ground a larger prototype engine for the Venture Star that will generate 431,000 pounds of thrust using 14 larger thrusters.

The aerospike engine is the first major new rocket engine developed in the United States in more than 25 years.

Rocket nozzles control the expansion of combustion gases and help optimize thrust to push a vehicle. But the ideal exhaust flow changes in response to atmospheric pressure and altitude, and bell nozzles, with their fixed dimensions, must be optimized for one specific ambient pressure or altitude, experts say.

Typically, a narrow nozzle would be best to produce an ideal straightedge column of rocket exhaust at sea level, while a longer, wider device is best at high altitudes. Designers usually pick a compromise nozzle size that works best during some crucial period of a rocket flight and are forced to accept less-than-ideal performance the rest of the time, experts say. For example, the space shuttle's main engines shake so violently during ignition and liftoff because the gas flow is pinched and pulled away from the nozzle wall because the nozzles are optimized for a higher altitude. With aerospike engines, proponents say, the combustion gases, constrained on only one side, can adjust to the atmospheric pressure at all altitudes and maintain a more optimum thrust.

Aerospike nozzles also offer a host of other advantages, the experts say. The X-33 and the proposed Venture Star are wedge-shaped, flat-bottomed craft with wide rectangular tail ends, ideal for lining up a row of linear aerospike engines that smoothly integrate into the shape of the vehicle, their designers say. Having engines spread across the base of the spacecraft means that the propulsion thrust is spread more evenly through the vehicle instead of at specific points, engineers say. Without those stress points, which would need to be reinforced, the craft can be lighter. Not having bell nozzles protruding from the rear means that designers do not need to include a heavy heat shield, like the one used on the space shuttle, to protect them during reentry from space.

Steven A. Bouley, manager of reusable launching vehicle programs for Lockheed Martin, said another advantage of the aerospike engines was their simple, but robust, design. On most rockets, bell nozzles are attached to mechanical gimbals, or swivels, that move them to help steer the vehicle. The aerospike nozzles do not have to move to control direction, eliminating the need for heavy gimbaling equipment, he said.

"The new engine will use differential throttling of the upper and lower banks of thrusters for directing the vehicle," Mr. Bouley said. "By applying more power to some thrusters than others, we will be able to steer the vehicle in different directions without moving the engines."

Steve A. Cook of NASA's Marshall Space Flight Center, the deputy manager for the X-33 program, said: "The aerospike engine, although it has never been flown, is fairly simple and the concepts are well understood. It's been extensively tested, and we have a lot of history with this kind of engine. We think it will work."

After years of tests on the ground, being fired from test stands and evaluated in wind tunnels, the aerospike engine will take to the air for the first time this fall.

An aerospike engine that generates 7,000 pounds of thrust will begin tests in October on the back of an SR-71

Blackbird spy plane that has been converted by NASA to do high-speed research. The project, called the Linear Aerospike SR-71 Experiment, was delayed from April because of development problems.

The engine is housed in half of a 10 percent scale model of the X-33 that looks as if it had been cut down the middle and mounted sideways on the SR-71. The Blackbird, flying from NASA's Dryden Flight Research Center in Edwards, Calif., is to test the engine on as many as 20 flights before the end of the year to see how it performs over a range of conditions, officials said. During the flights, the engine will be fired in three-second bursts to measure flame dynamics, thrust, the response to air flow and other parameters at altitudes and speeds as high as 80,000 feet and 2,000 miles per hour.

Mr. Cook said a crucial part of the experiment would be to see how the engine would react to the flow of air around the model spacecraft's body. "Because of the nature of the aerospike, it interacts more with the vehicle than a bell-nozzle engine," he said. "The shape of the vehicle becomes more important with this engine because the flow of air over the vehicle affects engine exhaust. This could result in some alterations in the craft's design."

Dr. Jerry Grey, a rocket expert and official with the American Institute of Aeronautics and Astronautics, said the aerospike was the first major new rocket engine developed in the United States in more than 25 years. "It's a good choice for a next-generation launcher," Dr. Grey said. "Of the choices available for a reusable launch vehicle, it is the most advanced engine. It's also the one with the highest risk but probably will have the best payoff in the long run."

Paul D. Castenholz, a Colorado Springs rocket consultant who served on a National Research Council panel that evaluated the reusable rocket program last year, said the aerospike represented new technology that needed more research and development. "You will have the problems you see on any engine, but I think it will be developable," he said. "There don't appear to be any show-stoppers."

Mr. Castenholz, who helped develop the space shuttle's main engines and motors for many of the nation's most important rockets during 45 years as an engineer, said the aerospike was significant for the industry and the nation. "It's exciting because it's a new engine, and we haven't had one in so long," he said. ∎

Planet Discoveries Around Nearby Stars

BY JOSEPH L. SPRADLEY

The discovery of the first extrasolar planets orbiting several Sun-like stars ranks among the most important of the year. At least seven candidates for planets around nearby stars have been announced in 1996, exciting the imagination of astronomers and the general public alike. If it can be demonstrated that planetary systems are a common occurrence among the billions of stars in our galaxy, then the possibility of extraterrestrial life in the universe takes on greater credibility. Indeed, the idea that intelligent civilizations may exist on other planets could become more compelling.

The January 1996 announcement of two new unseen planets orbiting nearby stars in Virgo and Ursa Major (70 Virginis and 47 Ursae Majoris) gave the first clear evidence that other Sun-like stars might have planets. This announcement was made by Geoffrey Marcy of San Francisco State University and Paul Butler of the University of California at Berkeley. In April, Marcy and Butler disclosed another candidate for a possible extrasolar planet around a Sun-like star in Cancer (Rho 1 Cancri); in May they announced another in Bootes (Tau); and in July they identified still another in Andromeda (Upsilon) and a possible second planet orbiting Rho 1 Cancri. In June, George Gatewood of the University of Pittsburgh announced evidence for a system of two planets orbiting the dim star Lalande 21185. It is important to emphasize that none of these planetary candidates can be seen directly, but are inferred from indirect evidence using new methods of analysis.

HISTORY OF THE SEARCH FOR PLANETARY SYSTEMS

The history of extrasolar planetary searches suggests that some caution is needed in assessing recent evidence. Early in the twentieth century, spectroscopic evidence from Barnard's star, a nearby red dwarf one-seventh the mass of the Sun, indicated a slight wobble that seemed to imply gravitational interaction by one or two Jupiter-mass planets in decade-long orbits. However, by 1980 further work showed that the wobble of Barnard's star was more likely the result of a companion star too small to observe.

Double-star systems like Barnard's tend to rotate around each other in larger orbits than the tiny wobble of a star with a planetary system. The mass of an unseen companion is estimated from the amount of wobble detected from a visible star. Masses between about 10 and 80 Jupiter masses usually qualify as brown-dwarf stars, defined as objects that formed like other stars by gravitational collapse of a dust cloud rather than from a stellar disk, but are too small to sustain the nuclear fusion processes that energize most stars.

The first confirmed extrasolar multiplanet system was discovered in 1992, but it was a far cry from a Sun-like system that could support life as we know it. This planetary system is bound to the pulsar PSR 1257+12 (sky coordinates) located about 1,600 light-years away in the constellation Virgo. Pulsars were discovered by Jocelyn Bell in 1969 at Cambridge University from their emission of rapid radio pulses. These pulses have such clocklike regularity that they were first thought to be signals from an alien civilization. It was soon determined, however, that a pulsar is a rapidly rotating neutron star, which is the core that remains after the supernova explosion of a massive star that has used up its nuclear fuel. This core compresses protons and electrons together to form neutrons with more mass than the Sun in a radius of only a few kilometers. Its rapid spin generates immense energy that is beamed out from its magnetic poles as intense radio waves.

After the discovery of the pulsar PSR 1257+12 with the 305-meter radio telescope at Arecibo, Puerto Rico, Alex Wolszczan noticed a slight variation in its 6.2-millisecond radio pulses (161 rotations per second). These variations fit a cyclical pattern with periods of 66.6 days and 98.2 days and appear to be caused by a wobble of the pulsar due to planetary orbits. Analysis initially revealed two planets, with masses about three times that of Earth, orbiting the pulsar at distances of 0.36 and 0.47 AU (one AU, or astronomical unit, equals the distance between Earth and the Sun). Later a third, Moon-sized planet was found at 0.19 AU. These pulsar planets were probably formed from the remnants of a companion star and are bathed with high-energy radiation that would make life impossible.

In October 1995, Swiss astronomers Michael Mayor and Didier Queloz (Geneva Observatory) announced evidence of a companion object orbiting a star in the constellation Pegasus (51 Pegasi) about 40 light-years away. Their method involves a new generation of computers and optical instruments, opening a new era for planet detection. The minimum mass of the companion object (51 Pegasi B) was set at 0.6 times the mass of Jupiter, but it could be as much as ten times larger. Its distance from 51 Pegasi was only 0.05 AU with a period of only 4.2 days, raising questions about its identity as a planet, brown dwarf, or new kind of celestial object altogether.

NEW PLANET DISCOVERIES

The methods of Mayor and Queloz were refined by Marcy and Butler to detect the first clear evidence of planets around Sun-like stars. The wobble of a star caused by its gravitational interaction with a planet-sized object is too small to observe directly. However, its radial velocity (back and forth along the line of sight) alternately increases and decreases the wavelength of light from the star, causing an alternating shift toward first the red and then the blue end of its spectrum. The variation in this Doppler shift reveals the period of a planet's motion. The amount of the Doppler shift can be analyzed to determine the minimum mass of the planet, but the unknown inclination of its orbit allows for a larger wobble than that suggested by the Doppler shift and thus a larger possible mass.

Marcy and Butler can detect radial motions as small as 3 meters per second compared to 13 meters per second for the Swiss group. Because Jupiter, which contains most of the mass of the solar system at 318 times the mass of Earth, causes the Sun to move at a speed up to 12.5 meters per second, Jupiter-sized planets can be readily detected. Marcy and Butler began collecting Doppler-shift data in 1987 for 120 Sun-like stars, using Lick Observatory's 3-meter telescope, but they only recently began to analyze their data with the computer methods used by the Swiss in their discovery of 51 Pegasi B. Their first discoveries resulted from running six computers day and night at the University of California at Berkeley to analyze data from sixty stars.

The first two planets announced by Marcy and Butler in January are still unusual compared to our solar system, but neither orbits as close to its star as 51 Pegasi B. Both of these new planets orbit stars that are similar to our Sun in size, mass, element composition, and surface temperature. However, each is more massive than Jupiter in orbits that are smaller than that of Jupiter. The star 47 Ursae Majoris is located 46 light-years away, while 70 Virginis is at a distance of about 80 light-years. The planet 47 Ursae Majoris B has a minimum mass of 2.3 Jupiter masses, which produces a stellar motion up to 45 meters per second. It has an orbital period of 3.0 years at a distance of 2.1 AU, less than half of Jupiter's distance of 5.2 AU from the Sun, and a surface temperature of $-80°$ C.

The planet 70 Virginis B is especially interesting to astronomers because its orbital period of 117 days at a distance of 0.43 AU gives it a surface temperature of about 85° C. Since this temperature is "just right" for liquid water, in which organic molecules might form, Marcy and Butler have called it the Goldilocks planet. However, its mass of at least 6.5 Jupiter masses (producing a stellar motion of 311 meters per second) suggests that it is a lifeless gas-giant planet like Jupiter, with stormy violent winds of 200 meters per second and surface gravity more than twenty times that on Earth. Its orbit appears to be highly eccentric, which would destabilize neighboring planets and raises questions about its true planetary status. Of course, one can speculate that these new planets might have systems of moons similar to Jupiter's that would be more hospitable to life. It is also possible that Earth-like planets might exist inside their orbits, but present methods cannot detect such small masses.

In April, Marcy and Butler disclosed another planet candidate around the Sun-like star Rho 1 Cancri, about 46 light-years away. It has an orbital period of only about 15 days at a distance of about 0.11 AU. Its small orbit and mass of at least 0.8 of Jupiter's mass put it in a class similar to that of 51 Pegasi B. Then in May, they announced a similar planet orbiting the star Tau Bootis, slightly larger and hotter than the Sun and about 60 light-years away. It has a minimum mass of 3.87 Jupiters, a period of only 3.3 days, and a near-circular orbit of only 0.046 AU, making it the closest of any of the new planets to its parent star. All three stars have similar high abundances of heavy elements, leading Butler to suggest, "There's a real hint of correlation, but what that correlation means is not known.... These 51 Peglike planets were completely unexpected" (see "A New

Planet in Bootes," *Astronomy*, September 1996, p. 25).

In July, Marcy and Butler announced a possible second planet orbiting Rho 1 Cancri with a minimum mass of about 5 Jupiters and an orbital period of about 20 years at a distance of 5 to 10 AU. This is only a preliminary result, however, since the 20-year period is based on only nine years of data. At the same time, they also announced a new planet orbiting the star Upsilon Andromedae, about 55 light-years away and slightly larger and hotter than the Sun. It is also similar to 51 Pegasi B, having a mass of at least 0.6 of Jupiter's mass and a period of only 4.61 days with a near-circular orbit at just 0.05 AU from the star. With this fourth Jupiter-mass planet close to its host star, Marcy noted, "People just a few months ago thought the 51 Pegasi planet was a freak, but you can't say that anymore" (see "Ho Hum, More New Planets," *Astronomy*, October 1996, p. 24).

Evidence for the nearest new planets yet were announced in June by George Gatewood of the University of Pittsburgh, who has been collecting photometric data on

This photograph was taken by the STS-31 crew aboard the Space Shuttle Discovery and shows the Hubble Space Telescope being deployed from the payload bay.

Jupiter, its Great Red Spot and three of its four largest satellites are visible in this photo taken Feb. 5, 1979, by Voyager 1.

many of the nearest stars with the 30-inch refractor at Allegheny Observatory. The dim red-dwarf star Lalande 21185, the sixth-nearest star to the Sun at 8.2 light-years, appears to have two Jupiter-mass planets in orbits similar to our solar system. Analyzing data from fifty years of photographic observations and eight years of photoelectric measurements has revealed tiny accelerations of the star that suggest one planet of about 1.1 Jupiter mass with a period of about thirty years in an orbit at about 11 AU (similar to Saturn), and a second planet of about 0.9 Jupiter mass, with a period of about 6 years in an orbit at about 2.2 AU (similar to the asteroid belt). The proximity of Lalande 21185 suggests the possibility of eventually capturing an image with the Hubble Space Telescope that would confirm its planetary system. Present evidence, however, indicates that the planets are too far away from a dim star to be warm enough to support any kind of life.

IMPLICATIONS FOR EXTRATERRESTRIAL LIFE

The rapid discovery of so many planets orbiting Sun-like stars may seem at first to offer new hope for the existence of extraterrestrial life. However, none of the newly discovered extrasolar planets gives any evidence to encourage the possibility that they might harbor life. On the contrary, the new planets seem to strengthen the idea that our kind of solar system is highly unusual if not completely unique.

Marcy and Butler have now completed their initial analysis of the 120 Sun-like stars in their survey, of which 5 percent had planets. Of these six planets, however, three (Tau Bootis B, Upsilon Andromedae B, Rho 1 Cancri B) are like 51 Pegasi B, having periods of 15 days or less and so close to their host stars (within about a tenth of the Earth-

Sun distance) that their surface temperatures would be near 1000° Celsius. Even their status as planets has been in question, although recent evidence from astronomers at the California Institute of Technology confirms that 51 Pegasi B is probably a planet, since it lacks the high X-ray emission of double-star systems with similar close separations. The other three planets in the survey (70 Virginis B, 47 Ursae Majoris B, Rho 1 Cancri C) are all more than double the mass of Jupiter and probably gas giants that are inhospitable to life.

ll the newly discovered planets have been very massive Jupiter-like planets, since these are the easiest to detect from the wobbles of their host stars. Refined methods of analysis might eventually detect extrasolar Earth-like planets with a better chance of supporting life. However, if the present survey results are statistically valid, they do not offer much hope for any kind of intelligent life. Planets orbiting Sun-like stars must be in a narrow range of distances from their host star, differing by less than 10 percent from the Earth-Sun distance to be able to retain liquid water. The new planet 70 Virginis B is at about 40 percent of the Earth-Sun distance from a dimmer star than the Sun, making it the only one that could have liquid water, but its huge mass of more than 6 Jupiters offers little hope for life.

I f Earth-like planets are eventually detected at the right distance from some of the stars in these surveys, there are indications that they might not be able to develop complex life-forms as readily as some might suggest. Earth is struck by asteroids and comets large enough to cause mass-extinctions of species (such as the dinosaurs) about every 100 million years. Without Jupiter in about its present orbit beyond Earth to sweep up many of these killer asteroids and comets, this rate would be about one every 100,000 years—too often to permit the development of higher forms of life. Either the 120 Sun-like stars observed by Marcy and Butler appear to have no Jupiter-sized planets to perform this function, or such giant planets as those that have been observed are much too close to their host stars to protect an Earth-like planet. With all the excitement over new extrasolar planets, it is perhaps most significant that they reveal how unique our solar system is, with its life-sustaining planetary arrangement. ▪

RUSSIAN MIR SPACE STATION ACTIVITIES
IN 1996

BY DAVID G. FISHER

Mir completed a full decade in orbit, receiving several long-duration teams, including international researchers and two shuttle dockings. The final science module attachment, Priroda, had completed construction five years behind schedule. Russian Space Agency (RSA) underfunding of Mir programs required commercial and international revenues to recover the deficit, a situation expected to continue through 1999.

European Space Agency (ESA) researcher Reiter performed his second spacewalk with Ghidzenko on February 8. Ghidzenko traversed the Strela arm, while Reiter attached equipment. Reiter retrieved space-exposed sample trays and installed a replacement unit.

RSA informed the National Aeronautics and Space Administration (NASA) that Priroda's shipment from the factory would be delayed. Without Priroda, supplies and equipment carried by *Atlantis* (STS-76) for Dr. Shannon Lucid's use would be temporarily stored inside *Spekter*.

Soyuz TM-23 launched on February 21, carrying Yuri Onufrienko, commander, and Yuri Usachev, flight engineer ("the two Yuris"). They expected another crew member when Lucid was delivered by *Atlantis*. The Russian freighter Progress M-30 undocked on February 22 and deorbited. Soyuz TM-23 docked to Kvant on February 23. One orbit later, the Mir 21 cosmonauts presented the Mir 20 crew with flowers. Earth observations using Kvant 2 instruments were made, biotechnology experiments were run, and samples were frozen for return to Earth. Ghidzenko, Avdeev, and Reiter entered Soyuz TM-22 on February 29 and undocked. Soyuz TM-22 landed, ending the Mir 20/EuroMir 95 flight after 179 days. Reiter became the single-time-in-space record holder for a non-Russian, surpassing Dr. Norman Thagard's 1995 accomplishment.

Atlantis (STS-76) launched on March 22, starting out

Astronaut Shannon Lucid shares a laugh with President Bill Clinton during a ceremony to welcome her home Friday, Sept. 27, 1996. Lucid spent a record-breaking six months in orbit aboard the Russian space station Mir.

13,000 miles behind Mir, closing at 694 miles per orbit. Commander Kevin Chilton slowed *Atlantis*' approach rate to 34 miles per orbit. The terminal initiation burn raised *Atlantis* to Mir's altitude. Chilton slowly moved *Atlantis* toward the docking module.

After docking, both crews verified the 250-ton complex's pressure integrity before opening the hatch. Following gift exchanges (the cosmonauts were presented shirts, chocolates, and two copies of *Lost Moon* autographed by Apollo 13 astronaut James Lovell), Lucid's transfer became official when she moved her Soyuz seat liner from *Atlantis* to Mir so she could land in a Soyuz spacecraft in an emergency. Lucid traded shuttle garments for a light blue cosmonaut jumpsuit. Lucid was not as isolated as Thagard had been. CNN International transmitted live news weekly to Mir, and she could regularly e-mail her family.

A farewell ceremony was held on March 28. Eight individuals hugged before separating and closing the hatch. Chilton moved back 600 feet and flew *Atlantis* around Mir, making a photographic survey before a final burn increased the separation. *Atlantis* returned to Earth on March 31.

During April's first week, experimentation centered on the Optizon Liquid Phase Sintering Experiment (OLiPSE). Seventy samples were processed in OLiPSE. Fundamental Biology Quail Eggs specimens were administered fixative on March 28 and April 1, 4, and 8. Others continued development until April 10, when they were fixed and the Inkubator was shut off.

For Anticipatory Postural Activity (POSA) work, a battery was recharged on April 10. Lucid began marking electrode placement sites during experimentation. She had not filled out back pain questionnaires for the MRI study, as she reported feeling none.

April 12 was a crew rest day in celebration of Cosmonautics Day and the fifteenth anniversary of the first space shuttle launch. The crew established audiovisual links with family, friends, and colleagues, including both Mir 22 and 24 crews.

An OLiPSE experiment was completed on April 20. On April 25, the Shuttle Acceleration Measurement System

(SAMS) was moved to Kvant for protein crystal growth work. Lucid inspected *Spekter*, taking inventory of NASA equipment and noting the locations and conditions of that equipment. Data were transmitted to Houston to update documentation.

Priroda launched on April 23. After a three-day rendezvous sequence, Priroda docked to Mir. Twelve meters long and 4.35 meters wide, Priroda weighed 19,700 kilograms and enclosed 66 cubic meters of habitable volume. Arriving minus solar arrays, Priroda had the potential to be so equipped via extravehicular activity (EVA). Priroda housed three Earth resources radiometers, two multispectral scanners, an imaging synthetic aperture radar, and a lidar system designed to vertically profile Earth's upper atmosphere. Total station mass now exceeded 110 metric tons and interior volume became 14,000 cubic feet.

Onufrienko and Usachev expected to depart in July after replacement by Gennadi Manakov, Pavel Vinogradov, and French researcher Claudie André-Deschays. However RSA delayed Soyuz TM-24's launch until August 30, so Mir 22's landing might avoid severe January weather.

SAMS collected microgravity data for the Protein Crystal Growth (PCG) Dewar. Lucid imaged the Altai Mountains, north Caspian Sea, and Danube delta regions. All three crew members participated in an April 30 POSA study.

To prepare Priroda for science operations, 168 storage batteries were disconnected and placed inside bags awaiting the next Progress freighter, into which they would be loaded for removal from Mir.

Lucid imaged fires raging in Mongolia, noting she had never before observed such widespread fires from space. Experimentation with the Ambient Diffusion Controlled PCG furnace continued.

Progress M-31 launched on May 5, docking to Mir on May 7. Over the next few days the crew unloaded supplies. Lucid completed Earth observations of the Great Plains, Gulf of Venezina, and Sea of Azov.

On May 9, her mother's eighty-first birthday, Lucid telephoned her parents in Oklahoma. On May 11 she viewed and talked to family in Houston using Mir's two-way video capability. Blood and saliva samples were collected after a new refrigerator was activated on May 12.

Mir's electrical power required supplementation. Outside the Docking Module were two stowed solar arrays, one cooperatively developed by RSA and NASA. On May 20, Onufrienko and Usachev exited Mir to move the solar array to Kvant. While outside, the cosmonauts participated in a commercial project for Pepsi-Cola: Both were filmed floating beside a large, inflated Pepsi can. The cosmonauts performed another spacewalk several days later to unfurl the solar array, which generated six additional kilowatts. On May 30, Onufrienko and Usachev exited Mir to attach the German Modular Optoelectronic Multispectral Scanner to Priroda.

Priroda's first activated apparatus up was the BioTechnology System (BTS). Although not activated, two Canadian experiments, Microgravity Isolation Mount (MIM) and Queens University Experiment in Liquid Diffusion (QUELD-II), were tested. MIM used dynamic sensors to monitor microgravity changes. As May ended, Lucid performed two QUELD-II runs. She initiated the Interface Configuration experiment, a capillary action study. A Mir Interface to Payload Systems computer card failed. Until a new card was delivered in the next Progress, Lucid recorded data on tapes for return to Earth.

On June 6, Onufrienko and Usachev exited Mir to replace NASA's dust detectors. Two replacement units, the Particle Impact Experiment (PIE) and the Mir Sample Return Experiment (MSRE), were delivered inside Priroda.

During June's second week, Lucid completed Humoral Immunity experiments, having injected herself with an immune system stimulant. Pre- and postflight blood and saliva samples would be compared to determine stimulant-induced immunity changes.

On June 12 Onufrienko and Usachev performed their final EVA, erecting a new payload transfer boom (Rapana) on Mir's core module and Kvant. Rapana replaced the Strela transporter.

On June 17 Lucid verified MIM function while monitoring vibrational accelerations. On June 18 she tested sensory-motor adaptation. The next day Lucid returned to microgravity studies and materials science furnace work. On June 24 and 25 the cosmonauts performed more Earth observations. Lucid monitored QUELD-II. Greenhouse investigations would be a significant part of John Blaha's STS-79/Mir 22 mission. Lucid performed an inventory of equipment and set up the Greenhouse. After concluding QUELD-II work and moving the Enhanced Dynamic Load Sensors (EDLS) from the Glovebox to MIM, Lucid ran the

Candle flame in Microgravity (CFM) experiment inside Priroda's Glovebox.

On July 3, the crew chatted with *Columbia*'s STS-78 astronauts. Billy Payne, president and chief executive officer of the Atlanta Committee for the Olympic Games, also spoke to them.

STS-78 solid rocket booster (SRB) refurbishment revealed hot gas impingement and soot contamination in field joint insulating materials, a concern requiring resolution before STS-79 could launch. Repairs required rollback of *Atlantis* and SRB segment demating, delaying retrieval of Lucid by at least six weeks.

Progress M-32 launch had been scheduled for July 22. However, pending investigation of two Soyuz booster failures (May 14 and June 20), the freighter's launch was postponed.

On July 15, Onufrienko, Usachev, and Lucid held a news conference. Lucid surpassed Thagard's 115-day record and recorded an address for the 1996 Olympic Games. Lucid returned to Candle flame in Microgravity runs, burning fifty-one candles by July 17. Meanwhile the EDLS and SAMS measured microgravity levels. During July's third week, the crew completed Greenhouse assembly and then planted wheat. Cosmonauts monitored biochemical and structural changes in plant tissues, key observations for understanding how photosynthesis, respiration, transpiration, and water use alter in microgravity.

Lucid requested personal items be transported in the next Progress freighter, including food selections (Twinkies, cheese pretzels, and enough M&Ms to last through September), books, and magazines. Progress M-32's July 24 launch attempt aborted when a propellant sensor failed. Launch was rescheduled after sensor replacement. Getting extra supplies to the crew was paramount.

Cosmonauts activated the Solid State Air Samples for the Volatile Organic Compounds experiment on July 29 and retrieved a sample the next day for toxicological analysis of Mir's atmosphere. Lucid changed Glovebox filters and set up the Forced flow flamespread Test on July 30 to study combustion processes in microgravity. Radiation data from the Tissue Equivalent Proportional Counter were sent to Kaliningrad.

The crew performed maintenance on *Spekter*'s Greenhouse, solving an electrical problem by running extension cords to the power distribution system. The Greenhouse root module was dried out to prevent fungal or microbial growth. Sample planting followed a watering procedure. The cosmonauts then began daily moisture measurements as seeds germinated. Reports to ground-based investigators described plant growth.

The cosmonauts performed European, Asian, and United States Earth observations as July ended. Lucid photographed crystals growing in the Ambient Diffusion-Controlled PCG experiment. She also transmitted data from the Tissue Equivalent Proportional Counter. Lucid performed her seventh POSA neuromuscular measurements on Onufrienko and Usachev.

Mir's backup oxygen generation system was activated on August 1, following four days of sporadic primary system operation. Additional oxygen reserves would arrive inside Progress M-32. If the backup system failed, oxygen generation candles were available.

Progress M-32 launched on August 1, carrying 880 pounds of fuel and two tons of food, water, and equipment. Progress M-31 undocked on August 2 and destructively reentered Earth's atmosphere. Progress M-32 docked on August 3. One nonstandard item in this freighter's hold was St. Andrew's flag, commemorating the Russian Navy's three hundredth anniversary. Mission Control delayed the Russian-French launch five days to provide Mir's residents time to unload Progress M-32.

RSA announced on August 12 that Mir 22's commander had been hospitalized, forcing flight assignment changes. Cosmonauts train as a unit, so if one member requires replacement usually the entire crew is substituted. Valeri Korzun and Alexander Kaleri replaced commander Manakov and flight engineer Vinogradov, respectively. This change affected neither France's André-Deschays or NASA's Blaha.

Soyuz TM-24 rolled out on August 15 and was raised onto its launch pedestal, lifting off on August 17. Progress M-32 undocked the next day and moved to a parking orbit from which it would return after Soyuz TM-23 deorbited. Soyuz TM-24 docked on August 19.

Mir's six occupants held a news conference on August 22, answering questions from French, American, and Russian reporters. Lucid described her experience as useful to International Space Station planning. A NASA news conference followed on August 26. Lucid stressed that her patience increased during prolonged station habitation.

By August's end, wheat plants had grown two inches. Growth would continue two additional months before termination for postflight analysis. The cosmonauts examined QUELD-II and verified furnace software. On August 23, four samples began processing, leaving only two more to be completed.

Lucid reported having difficulty locating everything she needed to pack. A total of 2,127 pounds of samples, equipment, and trash would be returned on *Atlantis* (STS-79).

On September 2, Onufrienko, Usachev, and André-Deschays departed Mir in Soyuz TM-23 and landed safely in Kazakhstan, concluding France's $13.7 million two-week research program and 193 days in space for the two Yuris.

Atlantis (STS-79) launched on September 16 after delays caused by three hurricanes and booster problems. Rendezvous was unaffected by an auxiliary power unit failure. *Atlantis* docked to Mir on September 18 while flying over the Carpathian Mountains.

Shannon Lucid was the first to greet the STS-79 astronauts. The astronauts and cosmonauts exchanged bread and salt, the traditional Russian greeting for guests. The crews then moved into the core module, running an air duct from *Atlantis* into Mir for official welcoming ceremonies. The crew exchange of Blaha for Lucid became official when his seat liner was put in Soyuz TM-24 in place of Lucid's. In an emergency Blaha could leave Mir inside the Russian spacecraft.

Blaha and Lucid held handover discussions during the early-morning hours of September 20. Lucid provided Blaha with an equipment inventory and showed him locations of various important tools and Mir systems.

During televised interviews, Lucid pointed out aspects of Earth-based life absent on Mir. She explained that dirty clothes were stowed away; there was no need to do laundry. She said she had not had a bath or shower in six months. Special wipes and a gel shampoo that is worked into the hair and then brushed out were used for hygienic purposes. Lucid began sleeping on *Atlantis*. Previously she had maintained a private sleeping area inside *Spekter*. John Blaha began sleeping on Mir.

Four thousand pounds of supplies and equipment were moved from *Atlantis* into Mir, and 2,000 pounds of samples, data, and logistics were loaded into *Atlantis* for return to Earth. Hatches between Mir and *Atlantis* were closed on

schedule. Lucid left chocolates shaped like space shuttles and wristwatches for her cosmonaut colleagues and Blaha.

Atlantis undocked, bringing to an end five days of joint activities between STS-79 and the Mir 22 crew, and effected NASA's first true crew exchange. Pilot Terence Wilcutt used controls at the aft flight deck, moving *Atlantis* 400 feet away, and flew one and a half times around Mir while recording images of the station. *Atlantis'* thrusters fired to increase the distance between the shuttle and station.

Atlantis landed on September 26, rousting marsh birds beside the runway. Like Thagard (STS-71), Lucid insisted on walking out of *Atlantis* under her own power rather than leaving on a stretcher.

Blaha's research included experiments covering six disciplines — microgravity sciences, human life sciences, fundamental biology, International Space Station risk mitigation, Earth sciences, and advanced technology. Blaha first started his BTS and Greenhouse work. Mammalian cartilage cells were placed in BTS growth chambers. Blaha observed dwarf wheat growing in the Greenhouse, noting by late September that plant heads had matured.

During early October Blaha started microgravity science studies. The first sample was processed in twenty-six hours. Later binary crystal samples required ninety days to grow. Blaha imaged the Panama Canal Zone, central Namibian coast, ocean currents off the south Falkland Islands, and South Africa. On October 7 Blaha tested the Metabolic Gas Analyzer System, designed to evaluate skeletal muscle performance during exercise. Korzun and Kaleri were given extensive medical tests on October 8. In mid-October, the Mir 22 crew performed X-ray astrophysical observations of galactic sources and solar flares using the Bouquet spectrometer.

Progress M-33's cargo delivery was scheduled to supplement materials delivered by STS-79. Continuing Russian economic difficulties forced a delay beyond the original October 15 launch date for lack of a booster. Sufficient consumable reserves on Mir permitted delaying Progress M-33 until early November.

Blaha's stay on Mir was set to last into January 1997, at which time space shuttle mission STS-81 would return *Atlantis* to Mir and deliver astronaut Jerry Linenger as Blaha's replacement, thereby continuing a NASA presence on the Russian space station. ∎

Russian space station Mir commander Yuri Onufrienko, left, and space shuttle Atlantis commander Kevin Chilton shake hands at the hatch that joins their two spacecraft following the thid docking operation between *Atlantis* and Mir March 23. 1996.

Shuttle Flies High
IN 1996

BY RUSSELL R. TOBIAS

A decade after the worst spaceflight accident took seven lives in the *Challenger* explosion, the National Aeronautics and Space Administration (NASA) continued its exploration of space with daring rendezvous missions and microgravity experiments. The highlight of the year was the six-month stay of astronaut Shannon Lucid on the Mir Complex, as America headed toward a permanent human presence in space.

The first shuttle mission of 1996 was an ambitious one, filled with a variety of goals. Its primary assignment was to rendezvous with and retrieve a Japanese scientific platform, which had been in orbit for nearly a year. The Space Flyer Unit (SFU), managed by Japan's Institute of Space and Astronautical Sciences, conducted a variety of microgravity experiments.

STS-72

Shuttle *Endeavour* departed from the Kennedy Space Center on its tenth flight at 4:41 a.m. eastern standard time (EST), January 11. The STS-72 crew of six included the commander, veteran Air Force colonel Brian Duffy. In the pilot's seat was Navy lieutenant commander Brent Jett, making his first spaceflight. Four mission specialists rounded out the crew: veteran astronaut Leroy Chiao, Ph.D., and three rookies, Captain Winston Scott, U.S. Navy; Koichi Wakata, from Japan's National Space Development Agency (NASDA); and Daniel Barry, M.D., Ph.D.

The nominal ascent to orbit was followed by four orbital maneuvering system engine burns to place the *Endeavour* in the proper chase orbit for its rendezvous with the SFU. The orbiter reached the satellite on the third day of flight. During the retrieval operations, several attempts were made to confirm that the satellite's two 9-meter-long solar panels had been properly retracted. When these attempts failed, the panels were jettisoned one at a time. The berthing of the SFU was delayed 93 minutes and was finally accomplished at 5:57 a.m. EST on January 13.

Later on the third mission day, the crew deployed the Office of Aeronautics and Space Technology (OAST)-Flyer, a Shuttle Pointed Autonomous Research Tool for Astronomy (SPARTAN)-carrier spacecraft. The seventh Spartan to fly held four experiments. The first experiment was designed to provide data for the determination of the accuracy of computer-generated models on contamination of equipment while on-orbit. A second experiment demonstrated the use of the Global Positioning System (GPS) in space. The GPS is a series of navigation satellites in low-Earth orbit that can be used to locate objects on the ground or in the air with a high degree of accuracy. The primary investigation of the third experiment was the testing of five different types of laser-triggered pyrotechnic devices in the environment of space, exposed to direct sunlight and temperature extremes. The fourth experiment was an amateur radio communications experiment to test satellite tracking using amateur packet radio and GPS. The OAST-Flyer was deployed by the Remote Manipulator System arm on day four and remained in orbit about 160 kilometers ahead of *Endeavour* for the next 46 hours.

A few minutes past midnight on January 15, astronauts Chiao and Barry, dressed in their extravehicular mobility units (spacesuits), floated out of the hatch near the front of the payload bay. Each of the two extravehicular activities (EVAs, or spacewalks) was designed to evaluate tools, techniques, and equipment for the construction of the International Space Station. Chiao and Barry conducted evaluations of a new portable work platform, which provides an aid for temporarily restraining replacement units and equipment a spacewalker might be using. It has a movable stanchion that provides stability for the astronaut and holders for tools, as well as a flexible foot

The $8 million solar-science Spartan satellite floats in free-flight several meters away from the *Endeavour*'s robot arm.

restraint. They also tested a rigid umbilical that may be used for electrical and fluid connections on the Space Station. The astronauts remained in the cargo bay for 6 hours and 9 minutes and completed all of the assigned tasks.

About an hour after midnight on January 16, Chaio was joined by Scott for the second EVA. During the 6-hour, 53-minute spacewalk, they evaluated a Space Station utility box, designed to hold avionics and fluid line connectors on the station. They also evaluated an on-orbit slidewire to which EVA tethers could be attached, and which is planned to be installed on the exterior of the Space Station.

The remaining days of the mission were spent conducting experiments involving the measurement of atmospheric ozone concentrations, laser altimeter measurements of the orbiter in flight, and the behavior of thermal energy storage fluoride salts that undergo repeated melting and freezing in microgravity. The growth of protein crystals in orbit has been studied for years in conjunction with space shuttle missions. These studies were continued on STS-72 with the use of an improved mixing apparatus to generate larger, higher-quality protein crystals.

Endeavour glided to a landing on concrete runway 15 at the Kennedy Space Center's Shuttle Landing Facility (SLF). It touched down at 2:42 A.M. on January 20 and rolled to a stop 65 seconds later. The flight had lasted 8 days, 22 hours, and 45 seconds.

STS-75

The most frustrating flight of 1996 was STS-75 and involved one of the most unusual and daring experiments conducted during the thirty-eight-year space program. In July 1992, during STS-46, the first Tethered Satellite System (TSS-1) was deployed from the cargo bay of the shuttle *Atlantis*. The 1.6-meter-diameter spherical satellite was to be reeled out on a 20.7-kilometer-long, 2.54-millimeter-diameter tether. Unfortunately, the deployer reel failed to fully deploy the satellite due to mechanical interference.

The reflight mission (TSS-1R) began with *Columbia*'s launch from the Kennedy Space Center at 3:18 P.M. EST on February 22. The early phases of the flight proceeded uneventfully for the crew of seven, led by Lieutenant Colonel Andrew Allen of the U.S. Marine Corps. Lieutenant Colonel Scott Horowitz, U.S. Air Force, was his pilot; Jeffrey Hoffman, Ph.D., Maurizio Cheli, Claude Nicollier, and

Franklin Chang-Diaz, Ph.D., were the mission specialists; and Umberto Guidoni of the Italian Space Agency (ASI) was the payload specialist. Cheli and Nicollier are astronauts from the European Space Agency (ESA).

At 3:45 P.M. of the third mission day (February 25), the tether began to unreel and scientists reading data from the satellite began to observe higher current in the tether than expected. One of the tests being conducted by the satellite was the determination of the amount of current that could be collected and voltage produced as the satellite and its tether interacted with Earth's ionospheric environment of charged particles. Earth produces a magnetic field that extends into space. By moving a long, electrically conducting line through this magnetic field, electricity can be produced in a manner similar to a generator.

The sphere suddenly broke free from the unreeling device at 8:30 P.M., with about 19.65 kilometers of tether deployed, and shot away from *Columbia* at a rate of approximately 22 meters per second. Most of the tether trailed behind the satellite. Plans to rescue the experiment were terminated when it was determined to be unfeasible with the limited amount of maneuvering fuel left on *Columbia*. The rescue would also have required an EVA and could have placed the astronauts in danger of electrocution from the charged satellite.

Experiments conducted with the third U.S. Microgravity Payload (USMP-3) hardware included crystal growth, the examination of the liquid-to-gas phase changes in xenon, and the environment immediately surrounding the orbiter in flight. The flight of STS-75 concluded with *Columbia*'s landing at the SLF on March 9 at 8:58 A.M. after 252 orbits. The 15-day, 17-hour, 40-minute, 21-second flight covered more than 10.5 million kilometers and was the twenty-ninth KSC landing of the shuttle program. The TSS-1 satellite and its tether burned up during reentry on March 19 at about 5:55 P.M. EST, over the Atlantic Ocean off West Africa.

STS-76

The primary mission of STS-76, launched on March 22, at 3:13:03 A.M. EST, was to transport astronaut Shannon Lucid, Ph.D., to the Russian Mir Complex. There the fifty-three-year-old veteran of four shuttle flights would join cosmonauts Yuri Onufrienko and Yuri Usachev for approximately 142 days of experimentation as part of the Mir 21 crew. The flight marked the third of nine planned space shuttle-Mir linkups between 1995 and 1998, which would pave the way for construction of the International Space Station beginning in November 1997. It would also feature the first spacewalk by American astronauts while the shuttle is attached to Mir.

In a slow, cat-and-mouse process, *Atlantis* chased the Mir Complex for more than a day, gradually closing the 24,000-kilometer distance between them. Commander Kevin Chilton (colonel, U.S. Air Force) successfully docked with Mir on March 24, at 9:34 P.M. EST. He was assisted by pilot Richard Searfoss (lieutenant colonel, U.S. Air Force). The docking mechanism aboard *Atlantis* was attached to a tunnel between the orbiter's crew compartment and the experiment-ladened Spacehab module. In addition to experiments to investigate life and microgravity sciences, Spacehab contained supplies for Mir, including food, water, batteries, navigation equipment, clothing, and U.S. supplies to support Dr. Lucid's stay aboard Mir.

At 1:36 A.M. EST, mission specialists Linda Godwin, Ph.D., and Lieutenant Colonel Richard Clifford, U.S. Army (retired) began a 6-hour, 2-minute spacewalk to install four experiments that would monitor the space environment on the exterior of Mir for a year and a half. Their activities were supported by mission specialist Ronald Sega, Ph.D., from inside *Atlantis*. The Mir Environmental Effects Payload, as the experiments are called, were clamped to outside rails on Mir's docking module, which had been brought to the Space Station by the crew of STS-74 in November 1995.

After four days of joint activities, the Shuttle and Mir crews bid an emotional farewell to each other, closed their respective hatches, and undocked at 8:08 P.M. EST on March 28. After several separation maneuvers to extend the distance between *Atlantis* and Mir, the shuttle crew resumed experiments and visual observations, while the Mir crew settled in for their extended mission. Bad weather at the Kennedy Space Center on March 30 caused a one-day delay in the return of the STS-76 crew, and at 8:28:57 A.M. the next day, *Atlantis* touched down on runway 22 at the SLF. The mission had lasted 9 days, 5 hours, 15 minutes, and 53 seconds and had covered 6.1 million kilometers.

STS-77

Endeavour and its six-person crew rocketed into orbit for the STS-77 mission at 6:30:00 A.M. eastern daylight time

(EDT) on May 19. The Air Force's Colonel John Casper and Lieutenant Colonel Curtis Brown, Jr., were in the commander and pilot seats, respectively. Mission specialists included Andrew Thomas, Ph.D., U.S. Navy commander Daniel Bursch, Mario Runco, Jr., Ph.D., and Canadian astronaut Marc Garneau, Ph.D.

The Spacehab-4 research facility was in *Endeavour*'s cargo bay, loaded with ten commercial space product development payloads in the areas of biotechnology, electronic materials, polymers, and agriculture as well as several experiments for other NASA payload organizations. The payload bay also contained the Spartan-207 carrier spacecraft. Aboard Spartan was the Inflatable Antenna Experiment (IAE). The IAE was designed to lay the groundwork for future technology development with inflatable space structures. The Spartan satellite was released at 7:29 A.M. on Monday, May 20. At 9:38 A.M., the antenna structure inflated with nitrogen gas to its full 28-meter length supporting a 15-meter-diameter dish. Cameras and sensors on the Spartan spacecraft took precise measurements of the smoothness of the antenna dish surface. IAE was jettisoned about 90 minutes later according to plan. The Spartan carrier was retrieved on May 21 at about 10:53 A.M. EDT with *Endeavour* 176 statute miles above New Guinea. Before berthing Spartan back in *Endeavour*'s payload bay, the astronauts conducted a video and photographic survey of the satellite attached to the robot arm.

Experiments were conducted in an orbital aquarium called the Aquatic Research Facility. This joint project of NASA and the Canadian Space Agency was used to study the early development in weightlessness of sea urchins, mussels, and starfish. The studies may provide clues to how humans may develop in weightlessness.

Inside the payload bay, the Hitchhiker experiment carrier managed by the Goddard Space Flight Center carried four experiments called Technology Experiments for Advancing Missions in Space (TEAMS). These experiments included the Global Positioning System (GPS) Attitude and Navigation Experiment (GANE), the Vented Tank Resupply Experiment (VTRE), the Liquid Metal Thermal Experiment (LMTE), and the Passive Aerodynamically Stabilized Magnetically Damped Satellite (PAMS). The experiments were flown together at reduced cost and with the Hitchhiker carrier providing the needed resources (power, data, etc.) to each experiment. GANE was flown to determine the accuracy with which GPS-derived attitude can be measured in an orbital environment. VTRE tested improved methods for in-space refueling. The purpose of LMTE was to evaluate the performance of liquid-metal heat pipes in microgravity conditions. PAMS consisted of a small deployed satellite, which was weighted in such a manner that the heavy end would face forward, and a measuring system to observe the satellite during the mission. After Mario Runco deployed the satellite from a canister in the rear of *Endeavour*'s payload bay on time at 5:18 A.M. EDT, it drifted away from the orbiter in a rotating, unstable attitude by design to evaluate how quickly and effectively the spacecraft could stabilize itself using the aerodynamic stabilization method rather than with thrusters. Three rendezvouses were conducted with the satellite on separate days. Data indicated that the satellite had indeed stabilized as planned.

Endeavour completed its 10-day mission at 7:09:18 A.M. EDT on May 29, with a landing on runway 22 at the Kennedy Space Center's Shuttle Landing Facility. During its 160 orbits of Earth, *Endeavour* had traveled 6.5 million kilometers and had completed a record four rendezvouses and four station-keeping activities.

STS-78

The fifth shuttle flight of 1996 would be a record breaker, too. The oldest shuttle in the fleet, *Columbia*, was launched from the Kennedy Space Center at 10:49:00 A.M. EDT on June 20. The crew of seven included Air Force colonel Terence "Tom" Henricks as mission commander and Kevin Kregel as pilot. Three mission specialists — Richard Linnehan, DVM, Lieutenant Colonel Susan Helms, U.S. Air Force, and Commander Charles Brady, Jr., U.S. Navy — and two payload specialists — Jean-Jacques Favier, Ph.D., of the French Space Agency (CNES), and Robert (Bob) Thirsk, M.D., P.Eng., from the Canadian Space Agency (CSA) — rounded out the crew.

STS-78 Astronauts, front row from left, Payload Commander Susan Helms, Mission Commander Tom Henricks, second row, Mission Specialist Charles Brady, and Canadian Payload Specialist Robert Thirsk, third row, Pilot Kevin Kregel, French Payload Specialist Jean-Jacques Favier, and Mission Specialitst Rick Linnehan, head for Launch Pad 39-B and a planned liftoff on the Space Shuttle *Columbia*.

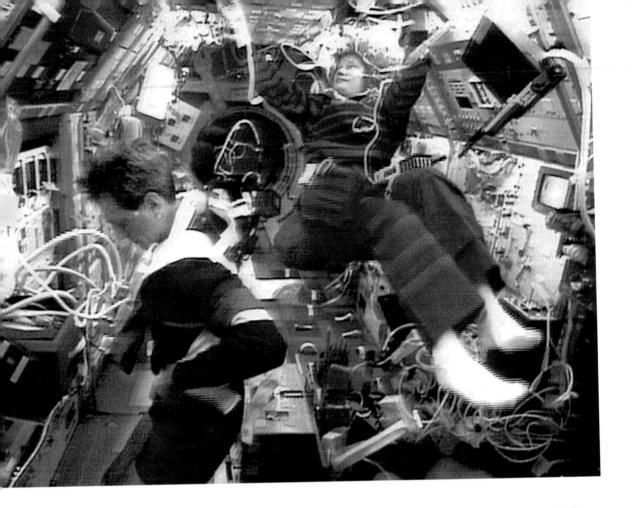

Astronauts Richard Linneham, left, and Susan Helms set up an experiment that studies voluntary head movements in microgravity in the Spacelab module of the Space Shuttle *Columbia*.

The STS-78 mission included the Life and Microgravity Sciences (LMS) payload, carried in the pressurized Spacelab module in *Columbia*'s cargo bay, and focused on two main areas. The LMS life science studies probed the responses of living organisms to the low-gravity environment and highlighted musculoskeletal physiology. LMS microgravity experiments focused on understanding the subtle influences at work during processing of various samples, such as alloy materials, when gravity's effect is greatly reduced.

The STS-78 crew also took on the role of teachers as they educated students in the United States and other countries about their mission objectives. Using the Shuttle Amateur Radio Experiment-II, which is carried aboard the shuttle on a regular basis, crew members spoke with students around the world about what it is like to live and work in space.

Columbia glided to a landing at the Kennedy Space Center at 8:37 A.M. EDT on July 7, setting the new record for a shuttle flight by lasting 16 days, 21 hours, and 48 minutes. *Columbia* had traveled 11.4 million kilometers during its record-setting mission and had completed 272 orbits of Earth. *Columbia*'s astronauts returned to Ellington Field that evening after Henricks and Kregel participated in an Olympic Torch Relay ceremony at KSC.

STS-79

STS-79, the flight to bring Shannon Lucid home from Mir, was scheduled to be launched in late July. Shortly after *Columbia* was launched on the STS-78 mission, the two crayon-shaped solid rocket booster casings underwent routine postflight inspection in preparation for reflight. It was discovered that hot gases generated inside the motors during the launch had penetrated into new areas of all six field joints and had deposited soot. (The field joints are the sites where each of the two-section segments are joined to the next segment during stacking of the boosters.) An analysis showed that the most probable cause for the sooting was a new adhesive used in the field joints for the first time on STS-78. Managers decided to take a conservative approach and replace the STS-79 motors with a new set using the old adhesive material. Launch was set for September 14.

On August 17, Soyuz TM-24 rocketed into space from the Baikonur Cosmodrome in Kazakhstan carrying the Mir 22 crew, including Russians Alexander Kaleri and Valery Korzon and French astronaut Claudie André-Deschays. They joined the Mir 21 crew on August 19 for two weeks of international cooperation. Deschays, who conducted experiments on space motion sickness, also provided Lucid with some female companionship. On September 2, Deschays and Mir 21 crew members Onufrienko and Usachev returned to Earth, leaving Lucid with her two new station mates.

Tropical storm activity delayed the launch of *Atlantis* until the early-morning hours of September 16. At 4:54:09 A.M. EDT, *Atlantis* lit up the night sky with a spectacular on-time launch. Captain William Readdy of the U.S. Naval Reserve commanded the STS-79 mission with Lieutenant Colonel Terrence Wilcutt, U.S. Marine Corps, serving as pilot. Four mission specialists joined them, Jay Apt, Ph.D., and three Air Force officers: Lieutenant Colonel Tom Akers, Lieutenant Colonel Carl Walz, and Colonel John Blaha (retired). Blaha would replace Lucid as the third of seven Americans to live and work on Mir, beginning a four-and-a-half-month research mission on the Russian complex. He will be replaced by Astronaut Jerry Linenger, scheduled to arrive on *Atlantis*' next visit in early January 1997 on mission STS-81.

Following a nominal launch, *Atlantis* began the two-day chase of Mir. During the flight the crew would perform experiments in the Spacehab module attached to the cargo bay. The first flight of a double module, Spacehab, would permit the storage of food, clothing, experiment supplies, and spare equipment for Mir. The STS-79 mission included several experiments in the fields of advanced technology, Earth sciences, fundamental biology, human life sciences, microgravity, and space sciences. Data were expected to supply insight for the planning and development of the International Space Station, Earth-based sciences of human and biological processes, and the advancement of commercial technology.

Atlantis docked with the Mir Complex at 11:13 P.M. EDT on September 19. The rendezvous and docking went flawlessly as Readdy flew the orbiter manually through the final 600 meters. Docking occurred within seconds of the planned time, and flight controllers reported that only slight oscillations were felt through the Orbiter Docking System as the two spacecraft locked together. Within hours of the hatch's opening, crew members John Blaha and Shannon Lucid formally swapped places, with Blaha becoming a member of the Mir 22 crew and Lucid joining the STS-79 crew to wrap up 179 days as a member of the Mir station.

During five days of joint activities, the two crews performed several fundamental biology experiments to determine the role gravity plays in molecular mechanisms at a cellular level and in regulatory and sensory mechanisms, and how this affects development and fundamental biological growth. The STS-79 crew transferred more than 2,100 kilograms of food, water, clothing, personal hygiene supplies, Mir hardware replacement components, and U.S. science experiments and supplies to Mir, including five powered experiments (experiments requiring electrical power on the shuttle and immediately on Mir). The *Atlantis* crew simultaneously received more than 950 kilograms of Russian hardware, empty food and water containers, ESA return science items, and U.S. science hardware, data, and specimens from Lucid's data-gathering activities during her stay on Mir.

After an emotional farewell, the hatches between the two spacecraft were sealed in preparation for undocking. On September 23, at 9:33 P.M. EDT, the two spacecraft separated. *Atlantis* then initiated a tail-forward flyaround of Mir and observed it for one and a half revolutions before backing away for its return to Earth. *Atlantis* landed at the Kennedy Space Center Shuttle Landing Facility runway 15 at 8:13 A.M. EDT, September 26, ending a 6.4-million-kilometer, 10-day flight. Shannon Lucid marked the completion of 188 days in space, setting the endurance record for an American astronaut. Like Dr. Norman Thagard, who had set the previous record in 1995, she exited the shuttle under her own power rather than on a stretcher.

During routine STS-79 postflight inspections of the solid rocket motors, contractor and NASA engineers observed erosion in the right-hand nozzle of a different nature from that typically observed in the nozzles. Typically, about half of the carbon phenolic material that lines the nozzle erodes during the flight of the motors. On STS-79, the right-hand nozzle had the typical erosion, but also had several troughs eroded into the insulation that sloughed off an additional three-eighths of an inch of insulation. There was no indication that this would impact the launch of STS-80 in November.

STS-80

STS-80 will mark the third flight of the Wake Shield Facility (WSF) that flew on STS-60 and STS-69 and the second flight of the Orbiting Retrievable Far and Extreme Ultraviolet Spectrometer (ORFEUS) satellite that flew on STS-51. Both satellites will be deployed and retrieved during the mission. The saucer-shaped WSF is designed to fly free of the shuttle, creating a super vacuum in its wake in which to grow thin film wafers for use in semiconductors. The ORFEUS instruments are mounted on the reusable Shuttle Pallet Satellite (SPAS) and will study the origin and makeup of stars. The combination is known as ORFEUS-SPAS.

Columbia is set for launch on November 8, at 2:47 P.M. EST. The commander for the mission is Kenneth Cockrell, with Commander Kent Rominger, U.S. Navy, serving as pilot. The three mission specialists are Tamara Jernigan, Ph.D., Thomas Jones, Ph.D., and F. Story Musgrave, M.D. ∎

THE HUBBLE SPACE TELESCOPE IN 1996

BY RUSSELL R. TOBIAS

L ife is full of little hills and valleys. Sometimes the hills are bigger than the valleys; sometimes they are not. And sometimes the valleys get so deep, you think you will never see level ground again, let alone a hill. That is how the engineers and scientists involved with the Hubble Space Telescope felt in 1990 when they discovered their precious telescope was partially blind.

The National Aeronautics and Space Administration's (NASA's) Hubble Space Telescope (HST) was designed to be the most powerful astronomical observatory ever built. flying above Earth's atmosphere, Hubble would have a clear view of the cosmos, capable of seeing farther back in time than could ever be accomplished from the ground. The largest on-orbit observatory ever built, HST is capable of imaging objects up to 14 billion light-years away. Unhampered by Earth's atmospheric distortion, resolution of HST images was expected to be seven to ten times greater than the resolution of images from Earth-based telescopes.

HST measures 13 meters long and 12.5 meters in diameter and weighs approximately 11,000 kilograms. Roughly the size of a railroad tank car, it looks more like two huge cylinders joined together and wrapped in aluminum foil. Winglike solar arrays extend horizontally from each side of these cylinders, and dish-shaped antennas stretch out on rods above and below the body of the telescope. Hubble's original scientific instruments included the Wide field/Planetary Camera, the Faint Object Camera, the Goddard High Resolution Spectrograph, the Faint Object Spectrograph, and the High Speed Photometer. Although each of the instruments was capable of producing data of great importance to the scientific community, only the Wide field/Planetary Camera was capable of producing images that could capture the imagination of the general public.

Opposite: This color photograph is a composite of separate images taken at the wave lengths of the two abundant elements in the nebula — hydrogen and oxygen. The images were taken with the Hubble Telescope Wide Field and Planetary Camera.

INITIAL FLAWS

The launch of HST on the space shuttle *Discovery* on April 24, 1990, was flawless; Hubble was not. Two months after HST was deployed into orbit 595.5 kilometers high, Hubble produced a disquieting discovery—not about space, but about itself. The curvature of its primary mirror was slightly, but significantly, incorrect. Near the edge, the mirror is too flat by an amount equal to one-fiftieth the width of a human hair. It was later determined that the flaw was caused by the incorrect adjustment of a testing device, a "null corrector," used to check the mirror curvature during manufacture.

The result was a focusing defect, or spherical aberration. Instead of being focused into a sharp point, light collected by the mirror was spread over a larger area in a fuzzy halo. Images of extended objects, such as stars, planets, and galaxies, were blurred. NASA began steps to cope with Hubble's fuzzy vision using computer processing to sharpen the images. For bright objects, this technique yielded breathtaking detail never seen from the ground. NASA also began concentrating on the analysis of ultraviolet light, which ground-based telescopes cannot see because of Earth's intervening atmosphere.

The continued capability of Hubble to provide data pleased NASA but disappointed the news media and the public. While a few newspapers reported the true nature of the problems, many others suggested that the telescope was a useless pile of expensive junk. NASA, however, was busy refining the already planned servicing mission scheduled for late 1993. Hubble had been designed with replaceable components for on-orbit servicing and replacement. NASA knew that, during its fifteen-year lifetime, improved components would be developed and some parts of the telescope might need repair after long exposure to the harsh conditions of space.

In December 1993, the space shuttle *Endeavour* and its crew of seven spent eleven days in orbit with the primary goal of repairing or replacing Hubble's optics, electronics, and solar arrays. The repairs required a total of five spacewalks during five consecutive days, each spacewalk lasting an average of more than six and a half hours. All phases of the repair work went according to plan, and the Space Telescope Team was confident that Hubble would be capable of returning focused images within a few days of being redeployed by *Endeavour*'s crew.

BREATHTAKING IMAGES

Early in the morning of December 18, 1993, the first image began being received at the Space Telescope Institute in Baltimore, Maryland. The room, filled with project engineers and scientists, was tense with an air of excitement. Did the corrective mirrors work? Were the instruments properly calibrated before flight? A picture came up on the computer screen, and there was a moment of silence. Slowly people moved closer to the screen and saw a tiny, bright dot: the main target star. It was sharp and clear, with no halos or spikes of light. The repairs had been successful.

Since then, Hubble has returned myriad images, both in visible light and in other regions of the spectrum. HST was no longer a joke. It was now a triumph of American ingenuity and determination. Numerous newly discovered galaxies, planets, and stars have added to our knowledge of the universe and have generated as many questions as answers.

Hubble discovered several ancient galaxies in December 1995 and January 1996. A mosaic image assembled from more than 250 images taken in a tiny region of the sky has revealed at least 1,500 galaxies, most of which are 4 billion times dimmer than anything that can be seen by the naked eye. Astronomers are still not sure if they have now glimpsed the earliest epoch of galaxy formation in these images. Also seen for the first time was the image of a star in its death throes. The image revealed outer spherical layers of material ejected during the early stages and a bright, explosive-looking inner cloud.

In March, the first photographs of the only unexplored planet in the solar system were unveiled. Photographs of Pluto taken in the summer of 1994 reveal sharp contrasts between the light and dark regions of the planet, but geological features are not evident. These patches of varying brightness might be the result of Pluto's surface of methane ice and nitrogen snow. It appears that Pluto has darker equatorial regions and lighter polar regions. It took nearly two years for scientists to decipher the fuzzy images. The twenty-four images of the planet each had only about eight picture elements (pixels) across the whole disk of Pluto. Each pixel represented more than 275 kilometers and presented a problem of determining what was actually seen. It took months of intensive study before Alan Stern, planetary scientist with the Southwest Research Institute office in

Boulder, Colorado, and astronomer Marc Buie of the Lowell Observatory in flagstaff, Arizona, released the images and discussed their significance at a news conference.

There are still many questions about Pluto, which even Hubble cannot answer. As 1996 came to a close, Pluto was nearly 4.5 billion kilometers from Earth (inside the orbit of Neptune) and smaller than Earth's moon. As it approaches its perihelion, Pluto grows a halo of reflective gases caused by frozen methane and nitrogen escaping. As Pluto heads back out from the Sun, this temporary atmosphere freezes

Hubble views of the "string of pearls" comet, P/Shoemaker-Levy 9.

and falls back to the planet's surface. To get a closer look at Pluto and its moon Charon, NASA plans to send a couple of probes, dubbed the Pluto Express, in the year 2001.

Hubble probed the inner regions of the comet Hyakutake as it passed by Earth in late March. It focused on the small, icy nucleus at the comet's center as Hyakutake passed 15 million kilometers from Earth.

Gigantic, tadpole-shaped objects, called "cometary knots," were found in abundance by HST and appear to be the result of the final gaseous outbursts of a dying star. Details given in April by Rice University astronomer C. Robert O'Dell and graduate student Kerry P. Handron indicate that these cometlike objects are several billion kilometers across. They were found in the Helix nebula, 450 light-years away in the constellation Aquarius.

In June, HST images revealed that a tiny pulsar that powers the Crab Nebula is far more dynamic than astronomers had previously thought. The Crab Nebula is the remnant of a supernova explosion that occurred more than 900 years ago and stretches 10 light-years across. It is powered by the Crab Pulsar, which is the collapsed core of the exploded star. The pulsar has a mass greater than that of the Sun but is only 10 kilometers across.

On June 22, after being in orbit for only six years, Hubble snapped its one hundred thousandth exposure. The orbiting observatory has taken an average of 1,389 exposures per month, exceeding preflight estimates by 20 percent. Better management of telescope observing time has been credited for the accomplishment, without which the 100,000 exposure mark would have taken ten years to reach. Data are being processed within forty-eight hours of receipt. Data processing involves data calibration, evaluation, and subsequent archiving. The data are then sent to specific astronomers who have been awarded observing time, and eventually are made available to researchers worldwide in a data archive. This archive presently contains more than 2.5 trillion bytes of Hubble science data stored on 375 optical disks. About 2 gigabytes of data are processed and archived daily.

New HST images analyzed in the fall of 1996 revealed what may be galaxies under construction in the early universe, out of a long-sought ancient population of "galactic building blocks." These detailed images, taken with the Wide field/Planetary Camera 2, reveal a grouping of eighteen gigantic star clusters that appear to be the same distance from Earth and close enough to one another that they will eventually merge into a few galaxy-sized objects. They are so far away—11 billion light-years—that they existed during the epoch when it is commonly believed galaxies started to form. The building blocks consist of only about a billion young stars each. Star formation is demonstrated by the presence of many blue stars and glowing gases. Astronomers have seen stars forming before; star formation is an ongoing process. However, they have never before seen galaxies form, because galaxy formation took place such a long time ago.

On October 24, the Space Telescope Science Institute released a film of the rotation of Neptune about its axis and of its weather patterns. The film, made from a series of Hubble's observations over nine consecutive orbits, shows a full sixteen-hour rotation of the planet. The clear images show Neptune's powerful equatorial jet stream, immense storms, and dark spot in Neptune's northern hemisphere, first identified in 1995 by a Massachusetts Institute of Technology team using Hubble. Using a combination of images from Hubble and NASA's Infrared Telescope Facility

(IRTF) on Mauna Kea, Hawaii, researchers gathered information about Neptune's clouds, their structure, and how they circulate. Scientists can now make more precise calculations of Neptune's wind speeds and directions, yielding refined information about the planet's dynamic weather system.

FUTURE MISSIONS

Space shuttle mission 82 is set for launch on February 13, 1997, at 1:35 A.M. eastern standard time from the Kennedy Space Center. The primary objective of *Discovery*'s ten-day flight will be the second servicing of the Hubble Space Telescope. The crew of seven will be commanded by Kenneth Bowersox with Scott Horowitz as pilot. five mission specialists will be on board: Mark Lee, Steven Hawley, Gregory Harbaugh, Steven Smith, and Joseph Tanner.

The astronauts will capture HST and berth it on its special servicing structure before beginning a series of spacewalks to remove and replace several instruments. Two second-generation scientific instruments scheduled for installation will give astronomers their deepest look into space yet. Data provided by these new instruments will span the spectrum from infrared to ultraviolet wavelengths and answer basic questions about the formation of galaxies, black holes, and stars.

The Goddard High Resolution Spectrograph (GHRS) and Faint Object Spectrometer (FOS) are still functional, but they are to be replaced by instruments incorporating newer technology. The GHRS and FOS will be removed for return to Earth for possible refurbishment and installation on a future mission. In place of the GHRS will be the new Space Telescope Imaging Spectrograph (STIS), a wideband, multipurpose imaging system that enables observations in four spectral bands. The FOS will be replaced by the Near-Infrared Camera and Multi-Object Spectrometer (NICMOS). It will provide high-resolution infrared imaging and limited spectroscopic observations in wavelengths between 0.8 and 2.5 microns, a region not currently explored by other HST instruments.

Science observations using STIS will be made in thirteen different spectroscopic modes—four low-, six medium-, and two high-resolution modes, as well as one objective mode — across spectral bands spanning 115 to 1,000 nanometers. These extend from ultraviolet to near-infrared wavelengths.

NICMOS is the first infrared instrument flown on Hubble and is capable of observing objects at much farther distances than is currently possible. Because NICMOS is dealing with light in the infrared region of the spectrum, it is very sensitive to heat. Its temperature must be kept as close to absolute zero as possible. Absolute zero on the Kelvin scale (0 Kelvins) is equivalent to 273 degrees Celsius. To maintain the cold, the cameras and associated equipment are buried in a block of solid nitrogen and enclosed in the shell of a unique cryogenic Dewar assembly (a heat-management system that is a hybrid of a passive ice-filled cooler and a refrigerator). The nitrogen tank is surrounded by a vacuum, much like a thermos bottle. The temperature inside the Dewar is to be maintained at 58 Kelvins and the nitrogen ice is expected to last more than four years in orbit.

Lagoon Nebula–M8.

In November 1999, a third servicing mission is scheduled. This flight will bring another new instrument to Hubble. The Advanced Camera for Surveys is composed of three instruments: the Wide field Camera (WFC), the High Resolution Channel (HRC), and the Solar Blind Camera (SBC). The WFC will be optimized for surveys in the near-infrared to search for galaxies and clusters of galaxies in the early universe. The HRC will be used for diffraction-limited studies of the light in the centers of galaxies with massive black holes, as well as ordinary galaxies, star clusters, and gaseous nebulae. The SBC will be used to find hot stars and quasars and to study auroras on Jupiter. Any instruments already in place on HST that might need repair or replacement could be added to the manifest for the flight. Plans to refill the nitrogen on the NICMOS instrument have not been developed because of the extremely complicated nature of such an undertaking.

The Hubble Space Telescope should be capable of fulfilling its original science plan during its fifteen-year life in space. After that, the orbiting observatory will be returned to Earth and could be refurbished and returned to orbit or given a place of honor in the National Air and Space Museum in Washington, D.C. ∎

4 | Communications and Computer Science

CONTENTS

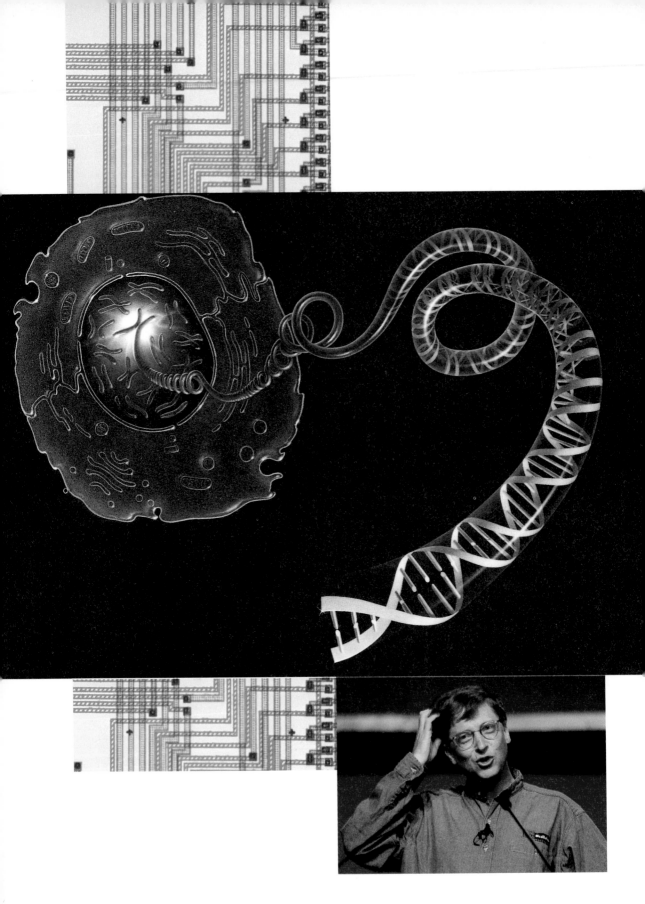

Biology's Big Project Turns Into Challenge For Computer Experts

BY GINA KOLATA

The University of Washington has jumped into the DNA sequencing business in a big way, building a world-class center to study the exact order of the chemicals that make up human DNA. And the seed money, the $12 million that has allowed the university to lure the stars of science to its campus? It came from Bill Gates, chairman of the Microsoft Corporation.

Experts on sequencing, the term for determining the order of a gene's building blocks, say that the connection is not surprising. In the last few years, it has become increasingly clear that the Human Genome Project, the plan to sequence human DNA and map the position of human genes, would have to turn into a project in computer science and in engineering such things as robots to do laboratory work. So computer scientists who used to spend their days devising clever methods for speeding up solutions to classic mathematical problems are now figuring out how to speed up the processing of data on DNA sequences.

"We've always known that the day would come when engineering would play a critical role" in the human genome project, said Dr. David Botstein, referring to the invasion of computer engineers and programmers into biology laboratories. "That day has arrived," he added.

The influx has not come without some resistance from biologists dismayed at the prospect of having their own subject wrested away from them, Dr. Botstein said. At first, he said, "biologists viewed it with considerable alarm and, on the part of some people, quite vocal distaste about the necessity of making it that way." But most have become resigned to the situation, he said. These biologists hope, some would say in vain, that once the computer experts have processed all the information in the genome, they will go back where they came from and let biologists resume the study of life.

One of the computer scientists is in fact a biologist who spent years learning the computer side of the business. Dr. Eric Green, chief of the Genome Technology Branch at the National Center for Human Genome research in Bethesda, Md., said, "I was drawn in for the engineering challenge." Since he is, in fact, a biologist, albeit one with a strong computer science bent, some of his colleagues have looked askance at his current technical focus. Dr. Green said, "Some academics would say, 'You're not doing real science. You're not doing real biology.'"

There's a revolution occurring in biology…
it's turning biology into an information science…

Seemingly overnight, the technology became so sophisticated that the major academic players, selected a few months ago for what Dr. Botstein calls the "heavy duty sequencing," are at just six centers in the United States and four outside the country. The work has become so specialized that "it's getting very late for new start-ups," said Dr. Maynard V. Olson, a biologist on the team at the University of Washington in Seattle.

Computer scientists say that it takes a full-time commitment to remain a player in this field. Dr. James Orlin, a professor of operations research at the Massachusetts Institute of Technology, said that he had recently dropped out of the project after three years of work because he could not devote all his efforts to it. "To succeed in this area," Dr. Orlin said, "you have to devote yourself to it more or less full time."

Although biologists are still calling the shots, some see an entirely new field of science emerging as the processing of biological data becomes the domain of computer experts.

"We still do frame the problems and define the areas," said Dr. Leroy Hood, a biologist who heads the molecular biotechnology department at the University of Washington and who personally interested Mr. Gates in the project. But Dr. Hood added, "As computer scientists come in knowing more and more about biology, they will chart their own course. Once they get into it, we don't tell them what to do or where to go. They just take off."

Dr. Hood said that it had been hard for some computer scientists to appreciate the complex nature of biological problems and the creative effort it takes to solve them. When he first approached computer scientists for help, he said, they were arrogant and somewhat dismissive.

"Computer scientists would say, 'I can solve your problem—just tell me what it is,'" Dr. Hood said. But then, he said, they would come back with a solution to an idealized problem with all the wrinkles removed, which had little to do with reality. Computer scientists, Dr. Hood said, "aren't worth anything unless they really learn the biology."

But now, Dr. Hood said, "several of them see this as an unbelievable opportunity" to solve new types of problems as they help decipher the ancient codes that evolution has embedded in the genome. Computer scientists are now starting to change the way biologists think, Dr. Hood said. They can help biologists move from the level of a single gene to the level of complex systems of genes working together, he explained.

"The future of molecular biology is studying complexity," Dr. Hood said. "The past has been studying one gene or one protein. The brain is a nice example. If we were to take one nerve cell and study it for 30 years, it wouldn't tell us one iota of how the system works."

The immediate goal of figuring out the human genome is so formidable that the old ways of the molecular biologists who work at the single-gene level are inappropriate to the task.

"We want to take the human out of the loop as much as possible," said Dr. Richard M. Karp, a leading computer scientist who joined the University of Washington team in August.

"The act of running sequencing experiments is deadly boring," Dr. Karp said. "If it is done by humans, it requires a meticulous attention to detail that few people can summon eight hours a day. The keys to making it effective are to automate the process—to design robotic systems to do most of the work, to automate the process of scanning the data into the computer and then to use algorithms" so computers can analyze the data, he added.

One reason for the reliance on computers is the sheer scale of what is being attempted, scientists said.

"This project is huge," said Dr. Robert Waterson, a former mathematician who directs the sequencing effort at Washington University in St. Louis. The human genome consists of three billion nucleotides, the basic building blocks of DNA, arranged like beads on a string. The project aims to find out their correct order.

Dr. Waterson's group has been cutting its teeth on a project to determine the complete DNA sequence of the roundworm, *Caenorhabditis elegans.* The group has been working for six years with a group headed by Dr. John Sulston, director of the Sanger Center in Cambridge, England, the world's largest DNA sequencing center, and it is about halfway through, while starting on human DNA at the same time.

To give an idea of the magnitude of the task, Dr. Waterson said that if each nucleotide were one millimeter, or four-hundredths or an inch, wide, the nucleotides that make up the worm's DNA would stretch about 120 miles, the distance from St. Louis to Columbia, Mo. Those making up the human genome would stretch from St. Louis to Los Angeles, about 1,600 miles.

"In the last six years, with all this sequencing, we are not even halfway to Columbia yet," Dr. Waterson said. "And now we have the temerity to suggest that it is time to set out for L.A."

Because the human genome is so enormous, scientists had to find some way to orient themselves along its long stretches. A first step in the sequencing was to find landmarks, making it possible to have maps of the DNA with particular sequences flagged. Recently, scientists completed the first such map. Now Dr. Karp and his colleagues are trying to make it more detailed.

The information in each human chromosome—each cell has 23 chromosome pairs—is roughly equivalent to the information in 50 thick telephone books, Dr. Karp said. A map like the one that was recently generated gives the equivalent of 20 telephone numbers from each book. "We're trying to give a phone number on every page," Dr. Karp said, devising computer algorithms that can create the maps from DNA sequencing data.

But scientists still face the thorny computational problem of actually determining the sequences of DNA within the landmarks.

DNA sequencing machines, which can automatically determine the sequence of a piece of DNA, can handle only small segments, no longer than about 500 nucleotides each. So the trick is to feed small chunks of DNA to a sequencer to get the linear order of the nucleotides in those chunks, then to assemble the pieces in order.

Because of the way the DNA segments must be obtained, the sequences overlap; because of the nature of the DNA itself, many segments contain sections in which a particular sequence is repeated over and over. The scientists must figure out clever ways to take those sequences and cut out the overlaps, then put the nucleotides in order.

Dr. Waterson said that every week, his group generated the sequences of 27,000 DNA segments, each made up of 500 nucleotides. The problem is to reassemble them, a process akin to putting together a giant jigsaw puzzle.

Even though finding the sequences of 27,000 DNA fragments each week is a tenfold improvement on the rate at which the group found sequences three years ago, it is still too slow. Dr. Waterson said that his goal was to be getting the sequences of 40,000 DNA segments a week by the end of the year. "We figure that for us to do one-third of the human genome in five to six years," he said, "we have to get reads of 80,000 to 90,000 a week."

One measure of the importance of the invasion of computer scientists into the human genome project is the fame of the people who have joined in.

For example, Dr. Karp is founder of the field of theoretical computer science who yesterday was awarded the National Medal of Science, the nation's highest science award. His decision to move from the University of California at Berkeley, where he studied classic problems in computer science, to the University of Washington, where he works on the sequencing projects, made a strong impression on computer scientists.

Dr. Karp, said Dr. Tandy Warnow, a computer scientist at the University of Pennsylvania, "is one of the most important forces in the field," adding, "He's helping to change the ways we think about what we are doing as computer scientists."

Dr. Karp said he saw the genome project as a large part of the future for his field.

"There's a revolution occurring in biology, particularly at the molecular level," Dr. Karp said. "It's turning biology into an information science. Many biologists consider the acquisition of sequences to be boring. But from a computer science point of view, these are first-rate and challenging algorithmic questions."

Dr. Karp added that at this point, the work "is far removed from biology.

"There are these basic experimental techniques that people worked very hard to refine," Dr. Karp said. "But we think of them as black boxes that pour out all of these data." ■

Kasparov vs. "Deep Blue"

HANS G. GRAETZER

arry Kasparov, a native of Azerbaijan now living in Moscow, is the world's best chess player. He won the world championship in 1985 at age twenty-two and has held the title for more than ten years by defeating all challengers.

In February of 1996, a chess match pitting Kasparov against a sophisticated IBM computer program called Deep Blue was held at the Philadelphia Convention Center. The match was organized by the Association for Computing Machinery (ACM). Prize money was $500,000, with 80 percent going to the winner and 20 percent to the loser. A total of six games was played, with each side alternately having the opening move. According to standard chess tournament rules, each player was allowed two hours for the first forty moves, giving an average of three minutes' thinking time per move. If a game went beyond forty moves, it would be continued on the following day.

Deep Blue has a built-in library of standard chess opening games as played by Grandmasters during the last one hundred years. Also, an endgame database is activated when fewer than six pieces are left on the board. For the midgame, Deep Blue can search more than 50 billion positions in three minutes to analyze the consequences of a given move for ten to fifteen steps ahead. A sequence of moves that leads to the gain of a piece, such as capturing the opponent's bishop while losing only a pawn, is clearly advantageous. Subtler positional advantage can be obtained by gaining control of the center squares or by sacrificing a piece to weaken the opponent king's defenses.

Interest by the general public in the Kasparov vs. Deep Blue matchup was high, with press coverage by *Time* magazine, *Sports Illustrated*, *The New York Times*, *USA Today*, and the major television networks. Two International Chess Masters provided live commentary to a large audience at the Philadelphia Convention Center. Chess enthusiasts with a home computer could follow the match on the World Wide Web.

D eep Blue has a built-in library of standard chess opening games as played by Grandmasters during the last one hundred years.

In the first game, Deep Blue (having the first move) played the white pieces. After thirty-seven moves, Kasparov was two pawns behind and the position had become hopeless, so he resigned. For the first time, a computer chess program had beaten a world champion in a regulation time match. It was a stunning victory for the computer. In the second game, Kasparov, playing white, defeated Deep Blue in seventy-three moves. Games three and four were draws, meaning that both players agreed to discontinue the games because neither one could checkmate the opponent. Games five and six were won by Kasparov. According to tournament chess scoring, a victory counts one point for the winner while a draw gives one-half point to each player. In this tournament, Kasparov had three victories and two draws, so he won by a score of 4 to 2 and collected the winner's share of $400,000.

How did Kasparov feel after losing game one to Deep Blue? His coach, Frederick Friedel, says that he was devastated: "It was a shattering experience. There was the theoretical possibility that the computer would be invincible, and that he [Kasparov] would lose all six games." After coming back from his first-round loss to Deep Blue, Kasparov later stated, "I'm quite happy that I escaped so narrowly at the end."

PLAYER RATINGS BY THE U.S. CHESS FEDERATION

The United States Chess Federation (USCF) has about 35,000 members who have a numerical rating. A novice starts with a rating of 1000. The rating goes up when she or he wins, especially when competing against someone with a higher ranking. Conversely, a player's rating goes down when losing to a lower-ranked opponent. An average local tournament player is rated about 1500. For stronger players, the Chess Federation has established the following categories: Class B, 1600 to 1800; Class A, 1800 to 2000;

Expert, 2000 to 2200; Master, 2200 to 2400; Senior Master, 2400 or more. Those players who win international titles are called International Masters (2400+) and Grandmasters (2500+). Kasparov had a rating of 2775 in the year 1996, the highest rating ever attained.

Computer programs can receive USCF ratings depending on their performance against human players. In 1967, a program called MacHack was able to play club-level chess with a 1200 rating. In March of 1977, a program called Chess 4.5, developed at Northwestern University, won the Minnesota Open Championship against Class A and Expert players, giving it a rating over 2000.

In 1968, the chess champion of Scotland and later International Master, David Levy, had made a two-thousand-dollar bet with four computer scientists that no computer would beat him in a chess match within the next ten years. In 1978, Levy made good his boast by defeating the U.S. computer chess champion, Chess 4.7, an improved version of Chess 4.5.

In 1983, a program developed at Bell Telephone Laboratories, called Belle, for the first time achieved a USCF rating over 2200. It was designed to look ahead four moves by each player, which is called eight "half-moves" among chess players. five years later, a program called Hitech was developed at Carnegie-Mellon University in Pittsburgh to look ahead nine half-moves. It achieved a USCF rating of 2400. Powerful programs such as Chess 4.7, Belle, and Hitech all need to run on large, mainframe computers, accessible only at major universities or industrial computer laboratories.

Chess computers for home use were developed in the 1980s. Some programs were designed to run on personal computers with a CD-ROM disk drive. Alternatively, battery-operated portable chess sets with a single-purpose chip became available for less than one hundred dollars. A wide choice of challenging chess machines is advertised monthly in Chess Life, a magazine published by the USCF.

Commercial chess machines are designed to operate at various levels, from beginner to expert. An amateur player generally finds the most enjoyment by setting the machine level near his or her ability. If a player makes a blunder, the machine allows the move to be taken back. In some commercial machines, other features let players change which color they are playing in the middle of a game or have the machine suggest a good next move.

Chess computers for home use were developed in the 1980s. Some programs were designed to run on personal computers with a CD-ROM disk drive.

For advanced players, the first commercial program rated above 2200 and running on a microcomputer was developed in 1987. Tony Marsland, a computer chess pioneer at the University of Alberta, Canada, and president of the International Computer Chess Association, claims that today's desktop computers equipped with chess programs can defeat most of the world's chess players. "It is only the world's twenty or so most gifted players who can still compete against computers."

"DEEP THOUGHT" AND "DEEP BLUE"

In 1988, five graduate students at Carnegie-Mellon University designed a powerful chess program that they named Deep Thought. It could search ten half-moves ahead (five each by the machine and its opponent). It ran on four parallel processors, capable of searching more than 100 million positions in three minutes. It won the World Computer Chess Championship (playing against other computer programs) in 1989.

David Levy, the International Master who had won his famous bet that no computer could beat him by the year 1978, played a four-game match against Deep Thought in December 1989. This time the computer won 4-0. The program received an official USCF rating of 2551, which is in the Grandmaster range. In 1993, Deep Thought defeated Judit Polgar, the best female player and youngest Grandmaster in the world. Deep Thought also won the International Computer Chess Championship for 1993. The designers of Deep Thought have written an informative article about their project, published in *Scientific American* (October 1990).

It is interesting to note that the strongest chess player of the Deep Thought design team had a rating under 2200, while Deep Thought rated nearly 400 points higher. When human thinking can create a machine to outthink its creators, memories of the Frankenstein story are revived. Science-fiction writers have always been fascinated with the possibility of scientists creating a monster that eventually becomes more powerful than its creators. Perhaps the great public interest in human-vs.-machine chess tournaments can be attributed to such an origin.

The chess program Deep Blue is an improved version of Deep Thought. Three of the students who had created Deep Thought took jobs at the International Business Machines (IBM) Corporation's Thomas J. Watson Research

Above: Garry Kasparov
Below: Judit Polgar

Center after their graduation. IBM supported their effort to build a more powerful chess machine in order to investigate parallel processing for other large-scale, complex situations. Some potential applications would be for air-traffic control at a busy airport or improved prediction of weather patterns.

Named for IBM's dark blue logo, Deep Blue runs on a supercomputer that is more than one hundred times faster than its predecessor, Deep Thought. It utilizes 256 processors working in parallel. It can search fourteen or fifteen half-moves ahead, whereas Deep Thought was limited to ten. With continuing improvements in software and hardware technology, most chess experts and computer scientists concede that a machine probably will become the undisputed world champion in the near future.

THE HARVARD CUP

The Harvard Cup, inaugurated in 1989, is an annual chess tournament in which Grandmaster players (2500+) compete against the world's best computer programs. The 1994 competition was held at the Computer Museum in Boston, Massachusetts. Six Grandmasters competed against eight computers, all of which were commercial programs running on Intel Pentium processor-based personal computers. Every Grandmaster played one game against each of the eight programs; if the Grandmaster won all the games, his or her score would be eight points. Every computer played one game against each of the six Grandmasters; if a computer won all of its games, its score would be six points.

Each game in this tournament was played with a time limit of twenty-five minutes per side. In a typical game lasting for forty moves, each player would have to average only about thirty-eight seconds per move, much less than in a regulation tournament. With less thinking time per move, the possibility of developing a long-range strategy is decreased, which probably gives an advantage to the computer.

4th Harvard Cup Chess Challenge. 1994.

The winning computer program was WChess, giving a remarkable performance against six of the best American players. It defeated three former U.S. 2E chess champions and a two-time Harvard Cup winner, and had draws against the 1994 U.S. champion Patrick Wolff and the defending Harvard Cup champion Joel Benjamin. With one point per win and one-half point per draw, WChess attained a score of five points out of six, or 83 percent. The winning human player was Benjamin, who had five wins and three draws against the eight computers. His total score was 6.5 points out of eight, or 81 percent. The top-scoring computer program and human both get their names engraved on the Harvard Cup as co-winners.

The audience at the Harvard Cup had an opportunity to challenge commercial computer programs in the competition. The world's best-selling chess program, Chessmaster 4000 Turbo (more than 100,000 units sold), was a popular feature. Portions of the Harvard Cup were filmed by the Public Broadcasting Service and the Discovery Channel. Extensive coverage by newspapers and magazines is helping to make chess a growing spectator sport.

DESIGNING A COMPUTER CHESS PROGRAM

Suppose a list of names is to be put into alphabetical order. There is only one correct answer to this assignment and a computer can easily do such sorting. By contrast, in a game of chess a player has to choose among twenty-five or more allowable moves at each turn, all of which may have advantages and/or weaknesses. Chess programs must have an evaluation function to select the best option.

One essential criterion in the evaluation function is the capture and loss of pieces on the board. A typical numerical scale gives a value of one point for pawns, three for knights and bishops, five for rooks, and nine points for the queen. Capturing an opponent's bishop plus pawn in exchange for losing only a bishop is clearly a gain. Capturing a bishop plus pawn while losing a rook would be a net loss.

A second feature in the evaluation function is the possibility of obtaining a positional advantage. For example, exchanging a bishop for a bishop would be a gain if a pawn that is guarding the opponent's king gets pulled out of position. Other positional goals would be to move bishops and knights off the back rank early in the game, to gain control of the center of the board, and to advance one's pawns.

One of the gambits used by skilled chess players is to offer a sacrifice, such as the loss of a knight in exchange for a pawn. The opponent's defensive capability may become so weakened by a gap in the pawn structure that the king becomes vulnerable to a frontal attack a few moves later. Early chess programs had difficulty refusing a sacrifice whose positional advantage was not immediately evident.

To understand how a machine "thinks" about its next move during a game, consider the following example. Out of perhaps twenty-five possible moves, some are rejected immediately as blunders, such as failing to defend a threatened piece. Suppose the machine selects ten possible moves for further study. For each of these ten moves, it considers ten possible replies by its opponent, or a total of one hundred moves. For each of the opponent's one hundred moves, it analyzes ten possible replies or a total of one thousand moves. Looking ahead in this manner for five more steps leads to 100 million different positions for the pieces on the board. The evaluation function calculates a numerical score for each of the 100 million different sequences. The highest score favoring the machine then is selected for its next move.

Deep Blue can search more than 50 billion positions in three minutes to analyze the consequences of a given move for ten to fifteen steps ahead.

The most difficult part in designing a computer chess program is how to weigh the various factors in the evaluation function. For example, is it better to pull back an exposed bishop or to mount a counterattack? One procedure used by program designers is to set up championship games played by human Grandmasters in the past. The machine is allowed to calculate a next move and compare it to the move actually made in the game. Then the evaluation function is adjusted until it selects the same move made by the winning Grandmaster. By playing through hundreds of games from past tournaments, the machine can be tuned to improve its performance.

When Garry Kasparov played against Deep Blue, in the first game the computer offered a pawn sacrifice. Deep Blue had calculated that six moves later it could win back a pawn and gain an advantage in position that eventually would allow it to win the game. Kasparov said afterward that he learned something from his first-game loss: "I was able to exploit the traditional shortcomings of computers throughout the rest of the match. If it can't find a way to win material, attack the king, or fulfill one of its other programmed priorities, the computer drifts planlessly and gets into trouble. In the end that may have been my biggest advantage: I could figure out its priorities and adjust my play. It couldn't do the same to me." ■

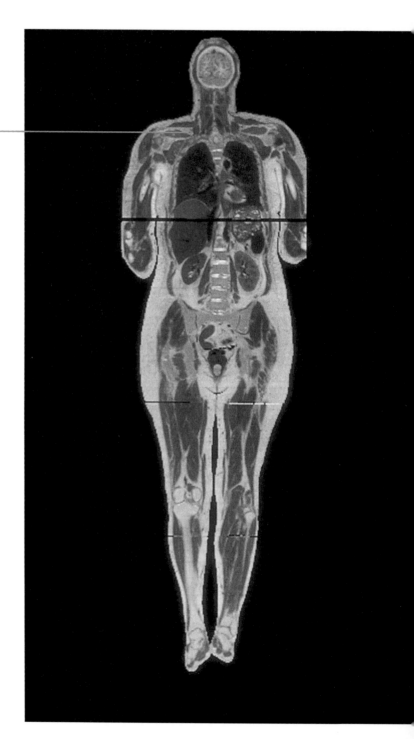

One view of the visible woman
from the Visible Human Project.

RESEARCH USES GROW FOR
VIRTUAL CADAVERS

BY DENISE GRADY

He was a 39-year-old convicted murderer, executed in Texas by lethal injection. She was a 59-year-old woman from Maryland who died of a heart attack. In life, they never knew one another. But in death they have been united by a common wish, a parting gesture of good will that has earned them a status they probably could not have begun to anticipate: immortality, in cyberspace.

Both donated their bodies to science and were chosen to be the subjects of the Visible Human Project, the world's first computerized library of human anatomy. Images of their bodies—1,800 thin cross sections of the man and 5,000 of the woman along with CT and MRI scans—were created and stored in a computer at the National Library of Medicine in Bethesda, Md., accessible over the Internet.

In the two years since the library made the Visible Man's images available on the Internet, more than 500 medical researchers, educators, law firms, computer-imaging companies, high-school teachers and artists have developed uses for the images.

Yesterday and today, medical researchers from this country and abroad have gathered at the National Library of Medicine to show each other and the public some of the more amazing things they have been doing with the data from the Visible Humans. Practically all the applications involve the use of computer programs that reconstruct the scans and tissue sections into three-dimensional images that can be rotated and flipped, and taken apart and put back together on a computer screen.

"Quite a few people are suggesting that the Visible Human might eventually replace cadavers," said Dr. Donald Lindberg, the library director. "With cadavers, you destroy the specimen as you dissect it, and sometimes you wonder if there were things you didn't see right at the beginning. With

The Visible Human Project is the world's first computerized library of human anatomy images, accessible over the Internet.

these computer images, you can reverse the dissection. You can go back and repeat your study."

Anatomy students are already using compact disks containing three-dimensional renderings of Visible Human images. Designed for use on personal computers, the CD's, which sell for $20 to $50, are meant to supplement traditional anatomy classes, not replace them, said a spokesman for the company that produced them, Engineering Animation Inc., of Ames, Iowa.

Researchers are using the visible human data to develop a virtual reality system that hopefully will help some patients to avoid invasive diagnostic procedures, or at least make those procedures safer by helping doctors plan and rehearse them.

Researchers are also finding ways to use the images to help surgeons plan difficult operations and to develop simulators that will work for doctors and nurses as flight simulators do for pilots, letting them practice their techniques and test their reflexes, with realistic feedback provided by robotics, before they take a needle or scalpel to the patient. The images are also being used to help plan invasive diagnostic procedures, and, in the future, techniques developed using the Visible Human images might even eliminate the need for some of those procedures.

Two dentists at the University of Maryland in Baltimore, Dr. Gary Hack and Dr. Gwendolyn Dunn, have also used the images to confirm their discovery of a facial muscle that had never been identified before.

The $1.4 million Visible Human Project was conceived in the 1980's, when advisers to the National Library of Medicine recommended that the library develop medical images that could be transmitted over computer networks. By 1989, planners decided the images they needed were scans and frozen sections of the bodies of "a complete, normal adult male and female."

Six research teams, representing about 100 American medical schools, competed for the job of preparing the images. In 1991, the contract went to a team at the University of Colorado at Denver, led by Dr. Victor Spitzer and Dr. David Wheelock. The team's first challenge was to find suitable cadavers, which turned out to be harder than expected. "We were looking for a normal cadaver," said Dr. Michael Ackerman, head of the library's Visible Human Project. "Think about that. It's an oxymoron. Cadavers are not normal, or they'd still be alive."

A committee of radiologists and anatomists took two years to find the male specimen, and two and a half to find the female. "The man is excellent," Dr. Ackerman said. "Medically, he died for no reason. In fact, the experts were very puzzled when they first looked at his scans, because they couldn't find a cause of death."

But the woman showed signs of heart disease, and some researchers were disappointed because she was post-menopausal and medically less relevant to younger women. "But I think the committee reasoned that she was as good as we were going to get," Dr. Ackerman said.

In 1993, Dr. Spitzer and Dr. Wheelock set to work on the male cadaver. They had actually been making frozen cross sections of parts of human cadavers for several years before the Visible Human Project came along, and they had developed a way of doing it that was highly successful, and equally unconventional. In fact, some of their techniques were derived from Dr. Spitzer's hobby, blacksmithing. "Nobody told us how to do it," said Dr. Spitzer, who is an associate professor of cellular and structural biology. "Three or four years after we did our first specimen I read in the literature that you can't do it this way."

In their procedure, the bodies were first frozen and sawed crosswise into four segments. Then, each segment was fastened into a mold, which was filled with gelatin and frozen to 94 degrees below zero. The resulting frozen blocks were then positioned on a platform with the body parts standing upright. To make the sections, the scientists moved the platform horizontally through a rotary blade, which was also horizontal.

Unlike most tissue specimens, the sections were not cut or sliced, even though the images of cross sections are often referred to as slices. In fact, no slices ever existed. Millimeter slices through an entire human torso would have been too hard to handle. "There are a lot of places in your body where things would not stick together in a slice," Dr. Spitzer said. "If you cut through the belly, everything falls apart."

So instead, the cadavers were milled, from head to foot: with each pass, the blade actually ground away a millimeter—less than one twenty-fifth of an inch—or a third of a millimeter, of the frozen tissue. Anything the blade left,

Practically all the applications involve the use of computer programs that reconstruct the scans and tissue sections into three-dimensional images that can be rotated and flipped, and taken apart and put back together on a computer screen.

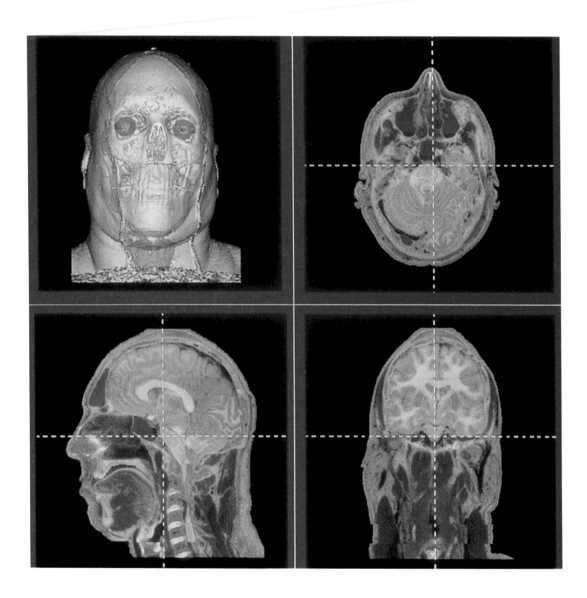

Views of the visible man's head from the Visible Human Project, the world's first computerized library of human anatomy.

like tendon fragments, was cut away by hand with a scalpel. Then, the newly exposed surface was photographed. Each section was therefore an image of what remained after the previous one had been ground away, and each section was destroyed in the process of exposing the next layer.

By the autumn of 1994, the three sets of Visible Man images—the CT and MRI scans, and the tissue sections—were complete. The Denver team began working on the female cadaver, cutting thinner sections in order to create even higher-resolution images.

One of the first researchers to receive a set of Visible Man images was Dr. Richard Robb, of the Biomedical

Imaging Resource at the Mayo Clinic in Rochester, Minn. A great advantage of the raw images, Dr. Robb said, is that they let doctors compare the CT and MRI scans of the cadavers with the real anatomy, reconstructed from the cross sections, something that was not possible before. "We can use that to validate the imaging methods," he said, "to find out how much information they really contain."

Dr. Robb's greatest interest lies in using computer techniques to generate three-dimensional images, known as volume renderings, from the Visible Human data. His goal is to help surgeons plan and ultimately even practice operations. Among the first procedures that he has tackled is prostate surgery.

Troubled by the high incidence of impotence and incontinence among men who undergo radical surgery for prostate cancer, Dr. Robb hopes to create images that will help surgeons to identify the hard-to-see nerves and muscles that should not be cut. "Every patient is a little bit different anatomically," he said, "and the surgeon is working with a very limited field of view. Can we help the surgeon to know the relationships of the structures in the pelvic region?"

Dr. Robb and his colleagues hope eventually to generate three dimensional images from a patient's own scans to give doctors more specific information about that patient's anatomy. They are also developing a system that will let the surgeon put on a virtual reality helmet and practice the operation on three-dimensional images of a patient, perhaps just minutes before actually taking up a scalpel.

Dr. Robb is also one of several researchers using the Visible Human data to develop a virtual reality system that he hopes will help some patients to avoid invasive diagnostic procedures, or at least make those procedures safer by helping doctors plan and rehearse them.

"One of doctors' favorite things to do is to stick tubes inside us," Dr. Robb said, referring to endoscopic procedures that are used to examine the colon, esophagus, stomach and lungs. "I like my clinical colleagues, but I am trying to put those kinds out of business."

Using the Visible Human data, he has generated "fly-throughs" of the colon, esophagus, trachea and female reproductive system. Dr. Robb compared the fly-throughs, in which viewers feel as if they are actually zipping through the lungs or gut, to the film "Fantastic Voyage," in which members of a medical team shrunk themselves and cruised a patient's circulatory system. ∎

In the two years since the library made the Visible Man's images available on the Internet, more than 500 medical researchers, educators, law firms, computer-imaging companies, high-school teachers and artists have developed uses for the images.

5 | Earth and the Environment

CONTENTS

Even though they are considered sanctuaries, the park units have always
been places of controversy, from their beginning to the present.
THEIR VERY PURPOSE SEEMS TO BE CONTRADICTORY:
HOW CAN A PARK BE PRESERVED AND USED AT THE SAME TIME?

CHALLENGES FOR THE
National Parks

MARGARET F. BOORSTEIN

T he United States Congress has recognized that certain places in the United States are so special that they must be preserved unchanged for future generations. Yet, at the same time, their wonders are so amazing that people should also be able to enjoy them. These areas, now numbering more than 350, have been designated part of the national park system. They have various names, including national monuments, national historic sites, and national parks. Since they are all managed by the National Park Service, they are all part of the national park system and are sometimes called park units. Even though they are considered sanctuaries, the park units have always been places of controversy, from their beginning to the present. Their very purpose seems to be contradictory: How can a park be preserved and used at the same time? This question, in turn, raises others: What is preservation, and what kind of use of a national park is appropriate?

DEBATES ABOUT NATIONAL PARK MANAGEMENT

In 1996, debate continued about the management of the national parks, about the areas bordering them, and about the establishment of the newest national monument. Several specific issues arose in the most famous national parks, and each issue was indicative of the problems and successes of national park use, preservation, and management.

First was the issue of where airplanes should be allowed to fly over the Grand Canyon. This debate has involved not only evaluating the relative value of quiet compared to the value of scenic views from the air, but also millions of dollars of revenues for private enterprises. The second issue concerned the reestablishment of the gray wolf in Yellowstone National Park. The concerns of livestock owners on nearby lands had to be balanced with the alteration of natural ecosystems within the park. Yellowstone was also the site of the third issue, involving the use of land outside the park. A proposed gold mine north of Yellowstone threatened to pollute the lands inside the park. The fourth issue involved a new national monument, Grand Staircase Escalante National Monument, which has been established in southern Utah, starting the process of protecting thousands of acres of beautiful scenery at the cost of preventing potential exploitation of resources.

The National Park Service must decide how best to balance the preservation of the lands for future generations with the desire to use and enjoy the land now.

AIRPLANE FLIGHTS AND THE GRAND CANYON

In the Grand Canyon, the Federal Aviation Administration (FAA) and the National Park Service were trying to balance safety, the importance of quiet and solitude, access to scenic views, and revenues for private enterprises. Until 1986, scenic flights were permitted below the rim; these were prohibited after twenty-six people were killed when a helicopter collided in the air with a commercial sightseeing airplane. After the collision, flights below the rim were prohibited; private air tour companies, rather than the National Park Service, now manage the air space above the park.

Currently, airplane flights are allowed in only 45 percent of the park, in more remote parts of the Grand Canyon. A proposal would expand the ban to 87 percent of the park and would limit the number of flights to 70,000 per year, which is the number flown from August 1, 1995, to July 30, 1996, according to the FAA. It would also limit the hours of the day when the flights would be allowed.

The National Park Service has defended the flight-free corridors, advancing the position that quiet is a resource. However, the number of visitors who value airplane-free quiet is not clear. According to *The New York Times*, in 1994 the Park Service reported to Congress that 95 percent of the visitors to the Grand Canyon said air tours did not detract from their visit. Whether one believes the FAA's figure of 682,500 passengers on 70,000 flights or the United States Air Tour Association's figure of 800,000 passengers on 117,000, the number of flights and passengers is significant. On Earth Day, 1996, President Bill Clinton said that low-flying aircraft could "mar the natural beauty of the parks and create significant noise problems as well." The flight association says that the loudest protesters against the flights are only a few of the 53,000 people who hike and take river trips through the Grand Canyon, compared with more than 4.5 million visitors each year. The airplane companies also claim that the airplane flights will greatly enhance a visit to the Canyon, while doing little damage to those who remain on the ground. The flights leave no footprints. Moreover, flights are often the only way that disabled visitors can see the Canyon.

Like many issues involving the national parks, this decision is being handled through public hearings. The potential costs are great. The air tour industry could lose as much as $6.6 million per year over the next ten years; total annual revenues are around $116 million. However, the value of quiet is more difficult to quantify. One of the greatest assets of the Grand Canyon and all the national parks is the opportunity for people to experience the absolute wonders of nature, including immense quiet. The FAA was expected to make a decision by the end of the year.

NATURAL ECOSYSTEM RESTORATION

In Yellowstone National Park, the reestablishment of the natural ecosystem through the reintroduction of wolves has been controversial. The gray wolf is an endangered species. Once thousands of gray wolves lived in North America, but now only around 2,100 remain in the contiguous forty-eight states and around 7,000 in Alaska. Over the years, the gray wolves were hunted and poisoned, as they were often seen as a threat to livestock and people. However, no healthy wolf is known ever to have attacked or killed a human being in North America.

After many years of debate, the National Park Service was given permission and funds (around $6.7 million) to reintroduce wolves to the Yellowstone ecosystem, which includes the park and neighboring parts of Montana and Idaho. Many park visitors had responded to surveys by indicating that they wanted the wolf brought back. Local livestock owners, however, were concerned about the safety of their animals. To balance the desires of park visitors, the need to restore the natural ecology of the park, and the economic concerns of landowners, and to remove the wolf from the list of endangered species, the Park Service introduced wolves carefully and with plans to protect neighboring livestock.

Calf Creek Falls, Utah.

In January 1995, fourteen gray wolves from Hinton, Alberta, in Canada, were brought to Yellowstone National Park. To inhibit their natural tendency to return to their original homes, they were kept in isolated pens before being released. Those wolves produced two litters. The next year, seventeen wolves from Pink Mountain in British Columbia were delivered to the Yellowstone area. As a result, in October 1996, after two breeding seasons, eight wolf packs, including forty-three wolves, had established territories in the Yellowstone ecosystem, reported Doug Smith, Wolf Biologist at Yellowstone.

The ecology of the park has returned to a more natural state much more rapidly than expected. Without wolves, the elk and deer population had grown tremendously, and coyotes were the most significant predator. According to Robert Crabtree, a field biologist, as reported in the *Bergen Record*, the wolves have led to "elk huddling in larger groups, grizzly bears fighting wolves, wolves killing coyotes and coyote pups, wolves forcing coyotes to den in places where they are running into black bears." The wolves can be expected to kill around 1,200 elk, deer, and moose per year, which, although a large number of animals, is a relatively small proportion of the total wildlife in the park.

The major goal of the Wolf Restoration Project is to have the gray wolf removed from the list of endangered species.

The wolf restoration project has been very successful, running ahead of schedule. Not all wolves have survived. Causes of death include being hit by a truck, falling into a hot spring, being killed by other wolves, being killed by wildlife authorities (as required to prevent livestock predation), or being killed illegally by humans. However, the number of deaths is smaller and the number of births of wolf pups is higher than anticipated. Therefore, the Park Service decided not to import any wolves in the third year of the project, as originally planned. The major goal of the project is to have the gray wolf removed from the list of endangered species. The wolf will no longer be considered endangered if ten breeding wolf pairs in Yellowstone, northwestern Montana, and central Idaho produce pups for three consecutive years. According to Doug Smith, that goal of full restoration (around one hundred wolves total) may be reached in the year 2002, earlier than originally expected.

Many local livestock owners remain concerned that wolves will eat their animals. No livestock were killed by wolves in 1995, but in 1996 at least twelve animals were killed. The number is much lower than the hundreds of sheep and cattle once predicted by livestock owners and their supporters in Congress, as well as the estimates in the original environmental impact statement. All ranchers were compensated for their losses. Even so, some ranching organizations want the wolf restoration program stopped and the wolves taken to Canada.

No healthy wolf is known ever to have attacked or killed a human being in North America.

MINING DEVELOPMENT NEAR YELLOWSTONE

Outside the borders of Yellowstone, the development of a gold mine was stopped, at least temporarily. Crown Butte Mines, a subsidiary of the Canadian mining conglomerate Noranda, Inc., owns the New World Mine northeast of Yellowstone in Montana. The mineral deposits were estimated to be worth more than $600 million. However, the potential for damage from mining and storage of wastes was considered potentially catastrophic to the park. Mining operations might have led to underground flows of toxic materials into Yellowstone Park. Mining wastes created another problem. Although Crown Butte would have built a state-of-the-art reservoir to store the wastes, geologists were concerned that the reservoir would crack someday because of the potential for earthquakes and the severe weather in the Yellowstone area. There was a very real concern that tons of toxic wastes would then flow into the Clarks Fork of the Yellowstone River, thereby causing inestimable damage to wildlife and scenery.

President Clinton in August announced a plan to stop the development of the gold mine and to exchange other federal lands for the site northeast of Yellowstone. The actual federal lands were not specified, but they were to be worth more than $60 million—the cash investment by the company and the costs of site cleanup. Noranda agreed to place $22.5 million in an escrow account to pay to clean up mining wastes produced by the company that controlled the mine earlier.

Once thousands of gray wolves lived in North America, but now only around 2,100 remain in the contiguous forty-eight states and around 7,000 in Alaska.

If the federal government had instead used administrative action to stop the mining, it would have faced years of litigation because of the General Mining Law of 1872, under which Crown Butte had gained title to the land. The General

Mining Law of 1872 gave anyone who discovered a hard-rock mineral on federal land the right to stake a claim to that land, an unpatented or exclusive right to extract the mineral. Once the claimer proved the ground held profitable hard-rock minerals, he could pay $2.50 per acre and acquire a patent and use that land in any manner, even for nonmining purposes. The law was passed largely to encourage settlement and economic exploitation of the public domain.

The problem of mining on federal lands and the accompanying environmental damage are not limited to the area around Yellowstone. However, because of the importance of Yellowstone as a national park, special action was taken. Political motivation likely contributed to the timing of the action. Clinton made the announcement on the first day of the Republican National Convention, thus removing some attention from his opponent in the presidential race, Robert Dole. No guarantee exists that the swap will actually take place. The Greater Yellowstone Coalition, including various environmental groups, was generally pleased with the announcement, but it was concerned about which land would be exchanged; transferring an environmental problem to a different location would not be desirable. An alternative might be for the government to give Noranda mineral reserves instead of land.

BEGINNINGS OF A NEW NATIONAL PARK?

Grand Staircase Escalante National Monument, established in September 1996, contains 1.7 million acres of some of the most beautiful scenery in the United States. The Navajo sandstone, described by a national park ranger as white rock on which pink paint was splashed, has been carved into amazing canyons by the Escalante River. The lands contain rock paintings by the Anasazi Indians who once inhabited the area. Private companies had planned to mine the area for coal and to prospect for oil and gas. The debate over use or preservation of the wilderness of southern Utah has continued since at least 1936. The designation of this new national monument will not stop the debate.

A Dutch company, Andalex Resources, had had plans to open an underground coal mine. Some Utahans were upset by the apparent loss of nine hundred potential jobs. Another company, Pacific Corporation, which also held a federal coal lease in the area, agreed to exchange its lease for land in an undisclosed place as well as an undisclosed amount of money. Conoco Oil apparently will not prospect

There are more than 350 areas designated as part of the national park system, including national monuments, national historic sites, and national parks.

for oil and gas in the area.

President Clinton used the Antiquities Act of 1906 to establish the monument. The act allows the president to set aside and protect lands of historical, scientific, or cultural interest without the approval of Congress. The act has a history of being used to protect lands that later became national parks, including Grand Canyon and Mesa Verde National Parks. The Escalante area has some additional complications. Approximately 200,000 acres of state lands are intertwined with the federal lands; the federal and state governments must work out some sort of compensation satisfactory to the state. Because mining on the state lands would have generated revenues to support state functions, including schools, the federal government could substitute federal lands that would provide similar revenues.

The debate over the wilderness of southern Utah involves power struggles among several factions. Some people think that the state should manage its lands without interference from the federal government. Some Utahans were annoyed that logging, ranching, mining, and oil and gas interests were not consulted before the reserve was established. Although many people think that the scenery is spectacular, Dale Clarkson, a longtime resident and real estate developer of Kane County (which is part of the designated area) disagrees. According to *The New York Times*, he said, "It's not even second-class scenery — its third or fourth class...part of it was used in the motion picture 'Planet of the Apes.'" Others in Utah disagree, recognizing also that tourism is the most important industry in Utah. Lodging revenues, tourist spending, and jobs have been growing in the 1990s. The new monument will join other national parks in southern Utah, including Zion, Bryce Canyon, Canyonlands, Capital Reefs and Arches, which have greatly contributed to the income of the state.

Escalante Canyon, Utah.

Although the president was able to establish the monument without congressional approval, Congress must appropriate funds for any development and operation. The Grand Staircase Escalante National Monument is illustrative of the challenges of national park management. Congress must now decide how much money should be allocated to the new monument, as well as how much development should be permitted. The National Park Service must decide how best to balance the preservation of the lands for future generations with the desire to use and enjoy the land now. ∎

A Sea of Dunes Lies in Wait

BY WILLIAM K. STEVENS

As devastating as the present drought in the southern Great Plains has been, scientists who study ancient climates are finding that droughts, floods and severe cold far surpassing anything in the modern era have punctuated the 10,000 years since the last ice age.

The discovery has surprised experts because the climate of this most recent period in earth history, called the Holocene, has long been considered relatively stable and serene, and its comparative tranquility has long been thought essential to the development of civilization.

Now, paleoclimatologists are finding in case after case that the Holocene climate has been more volatile than had been believed. The disturbing implication is that these natural catastrophes could come again at any time, quite apart from any change in climate that might result from emissions of waste industrial gases that can trap heat.

"We like to think of whatever climate we're in as normal," said Dr. Daniel Muhs, a geologist with the United States Geological Survey in Denver, "And our natural assumption is that it will keep on that way—that's a very tenuous assumption."

It turns out that the climate of the last century and a half, the brief period in which people have been measuring temperature and precipitation, has indeed been relatively placid. These comparatively calm recent decades have nevertheless had their own ups and downs, like the drought that struck the southern Great Plains in the 1930's, creating the Dust Bowl.

That drought, modern America's worst, stripped farms of their topsoil after farming had exposed the soil to wind erosion, touching off the mass migration of the Okies to California. The relentless wind "cried and whimpered over the fallen corn" while people huddled inside, tying handker-

California experienced two droughts beginning about 1,100 years ago, the first lasting 220 years and the second 140 years.

chiefs over their noses and donning goggles to go out, John Steinbeck wrote in "The Grapes of Wrath."

But according to new evidence presented by Dr. Muhs last week at a meeting of the American Quaternary Association in Flagstaff, Ariz., there have been several times during the Holocene when even more severe droughts have converted other, larger stretches of the Great Plains to seas of windblown sand dunes like those of the Sahara. These conditions were seen most recently in the 18th and 19th centuries, before the region was heavily settled.

Evidence is mounting that severe droughts and floods devastated a number of early civilizations. An analysis of Andean ice cores dating back to the fifth century A.D. has revealed that the region endured alternating droughts and wet periods lasting up to 400 years each.

In 1810, in one of a number of historical accounts collected by Dr. Muhs and his colleagues, the explorer Zebulon Pike wrote this about parts of Kansas and Colorado: "These vast plains of the western hemisphere may become in time equally celebrated as the sandy deserts of Africa; for I saw in my route, in various places, tracts of many leagues, where the wind had thrown up the sand, in all the fanciful forms of the ocean's rolling wave, and on which not a speck of vegetable matter existed."

The dunes are still there, mostly grazed by cattle, and only a thin, fragile cover of vegetation holds them in check. In the 1930's, the dunes were on the verge of becoming active when the drought ended; that is, the vegetation was just beginning to succumb and unleash the blowing sands. Should the sands be unleashed today, Mr. Muhs said, some highways and railroads would probably be buried. Lots of grazing range would cease to exist, and much habitat, including extensive wetlands, would disappear. Stifling sand would rain onto productive agricultural fields downwind, and some dunes could migrate onto adjacent farms.

"It would be pretty catastrophic, I think," Dr. Muhs said.

The Sahara-like conditions could be touched off if predicted climatic changes resulting from atmospheric accumulations of heat-trapping greenhouse gases like carbon dioxide come to pass, according to a study by Dr. Muhs and his colleagues. Experts predict that a greenhouse world would make the Great Plains both drier and warmer, perhaps enough to reactivate the dunes. But natural forces could also do the trick: "With or without the greenhouse, potentially we could have this kind of effect," Dr. Muhs said.

The litany of Holocene climatic extremes has been growing of late. About 8,000 years ago, for instance, much of Earth was in the grip of a cold spell more severe than the so-called Little Ice Age of the 15th to the 19th centuries, according to analyses of ice cores from Greenland. "This is a big event," said Dr. Richard Alley, a paleoclimatologist at Pennsylvania State University, "clearly something that affected a huge chunk of the world, and it's a lot bigger than modern humans have ever experienced." Even though the Little Ice Age was less severe, it caused great hardship, bringing crop failures and starvation to much of Europe.

During some periods in the Holocene, some places have been characterized not by drought, heat or cold, but by outsized floods. Starting about 3,300 years ago, according to an analysis of ancient sediments by Dr. James Knox, a geographer at the University of Wisconsin, the upper Mississippi Valley suddenly began experiencing a series of what would today be called 500-year floods. The 1993 floods in that region were of that magnitude, but paleoclimatologists are uncertain whether they presage another outbreak of severe floods. One remarkable feature of the great floods 3,300 years ago is that they were touched off by relatively modest changes in the global patterns of atmospheric circulation, Dr. Knox said.

Evidence is also mounting that severe droughts and floods devastated a number of early civilizations. The Peruvian coast of South America is a case in point. An analysis of Andean ice cores dating back to the fifth century A.D. has revealed that the region endured alternating droughts and wet periods lasting up to 400 years each. Dr. Lonnie G. Thompson, a paleoclimate expert at Ohio State University, said that archeological evidence indicated that the rise and fall of a number of pre-Inca cultures "are in sync with these precipitation changes."

The wet-dry variations might have been caused by long-term oscillations in the ocean-atmosphere climate system, analogous to the short-term changes typical of El Niño —the vast pool of warm water in the tropical Pacific that appears from time to time, altering regional climates around the world. That theory is bolstered, Dr. Thompson said, by

Ten years of drought could recreate a Sahara.

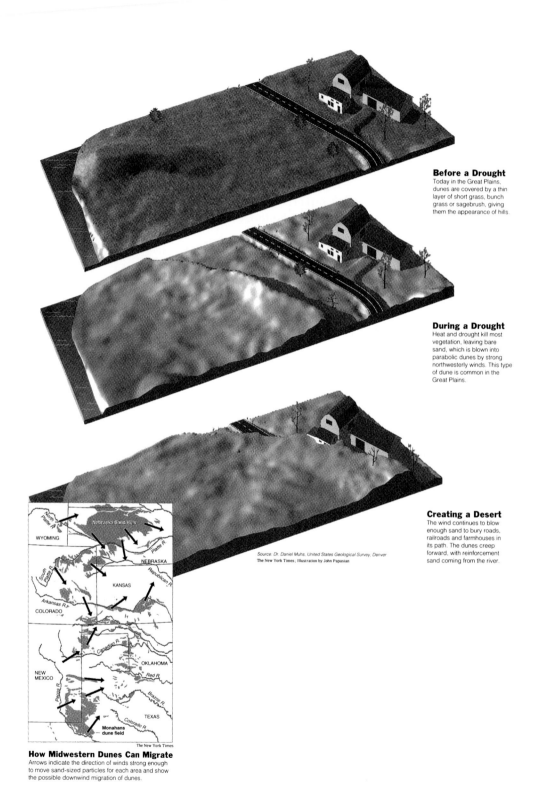

Before a Drought
Today in the Great Plains, dunes are covered by a thin layer of short grass, bunch grass or sagebrush, giving them the appearance of hills.

During a Drought
Heat and drought kill most vegetation, leaving bare sand, which is blown into parabolic dunes by strong northwesterly winds. This type of dune is common in the Great Plains.

Creating a Desert
The wind continues to blow enough sand to bury roads, railroads and farmhouses in its path. The dunes creep forward, with reinforcement sand coming from the river.

Source: Dr. Daniel Muhs, United States Geological Survey, Denver
The New York Times; Illustration by John Papasian

How Midwestern Dunes Can Migrate
Arrows indicate the direction of winds strong enough to move sand-sized particles for each area and show the possible downwind migration of dunes.

core samples from Tibet that show wet-dry cycles matching those in Peru.

Other evidence of global or at least hemisphere-wide climatic changes affecting earlier civilizations has previously emerged. Two years ago, Dr. Scott Stine of California State University at Hayward reported that what is now California had experienced two droughts beginning about 1,100 years ago, the first lasting 220 years and the second 140 years. Both droughts were much more intense than the six-year dry spells that afflict modern California from time to time. They also coincided roughly with similar droughts in South America that caused the collapse of that continent's most advanced pre-Inca empire, a state called Tiwanaku—and they coincided with a warm period in Europe that allowed the Vikings to colonize Greenland and vineyards to flourish in England.

Last year, a University of Florida team led by Dr. David A. Hodell reported that an unusually severe drought about 1,200 years ago might have contributed to the abrupt decline of the classic Maya civilization in Yucátan.

And in 1993, an American-French archeological team headed by Dr. Harvey Weiss of Yale University reported that the sudden onset of a 300-year drought had brought about the collapse, 4,200 years ago, of the Akkadians, the Middle East's earliest known empire.

Until recently, paleoclimatologists have focused more on the climatic record of the ice ages because those temperature swings were much larger, and therefore more interesting to scientists, than those of the Holocene. By comparison, "people figured that the Holocene is truly boring," Dr. Alley said. Then, in 1993, attention shifted to the last warm interglacial period before this one, which lasted from about 130,000 to 120,000 years ago. Reports in that year on studies of Greenland ice cores suggested that the last interglacial period had experienced abrupt and previously unexpected swings of global temperature. But that finding turned out to be ambiguous.

Now, as the results of studies under way for some time are beginning to come in from around the world, the spotlight is shifting to the current era, and a broad pattern of abrupt and severe climatic change in the Holocene is being seen for the first time. The studies show clearly that the Holocene has abounded in climatic swings "large enough to

The Nebraska Sand Hills are the biggest dune field in the Western Hemisphere.

dwarf changes seen in the instrumentally based climate record of the last 150 years," Dr. Jonathan T. Overpeck wrote recently in the journal Science. Dr. Overpeck directs the paleoclimatology program of the National Geophysical Data Center in Boulder, Colo.

Some of the most arresting findings are those having to do with the Great Plains. Vast stretches of the plains, from Texas and New Mexico to Nebraska and South Dakota, consist of classic sand dunes covered thinly by vegetation. One area, the Nebraska Sand Hills, is the biggest dune field in the Western Hemisphere. When atmospheric circulation settled into a characteristic pattern of no rain and high heat over the region, the vegetation dies. The dunes, naked to the wind, go into their Sahara mode.

Through radiocarbon dating of strata in the dunes and historical accounts from the 1700's and 1800's, Dr. Muhs and colleagues have found that the stripping of vegetation caused by droughts has several times activated the dunes over large areas in the last 3,000 years.

The historical accounts make it clear that when 19th-century textbooks referred to the Great American Desert, the allusion was not just born of some effete Eastern bias. The Nebraska Sand Hills, for instance, were described by an explorer in 1796 as a "great desert of drifting sand, without trees, soil, rock, water or animals of any kind, excepting some little varicolored turtles, of which there were vast numbers." In 1855, a sketch by another explorer depicted bare, peaked dunes in the Sand Hills stretching to the horizon.

In the 1860's, a drought much more severe than the one that caused the Dust Bowl apparently brought the desertification of the West to its most recent peak; after that, the dunes stabilized again. Dr. Muhs said that it might take less than a decade of drought to kill enough vegetation to create desert conditions again.

Aerial photographs show that in much of the plains in the mid-1930's, including the Dust Bowl region, some dunes were already "going active." Had the drought not ended when it did, Dr. Muhs said, a repeat of the 1860's could have resulted.

The mega-droughts have come so often, he said, that it is impossible to judge whether the "normal" condition of the plains is to have controlled or active dunes.

The present drought in the southern Great Plains, which threatens cattle ranchers and wheat growers with

The Nebraska Sand Hills are the biggest dune field in the Western Hemisphere.

bankruptcy, is a little more than six months old. It would probably take at least two or three more years of drought, Dr. Muhs said, for the desert to begin to be unleashed again. He and his colleagues have concluded that the predicted greenhouse effect would probably mobilize the dunes once again. "If you superimpose that on one of the warm, dry periods we know has recurred repeatedly in the last 1,000 years or more," Dr. Muhs said, "you're looking at an enormous impact on the landscape."

Either way, Dr. Overpeck wrote in Science, future climatic changes of the kind produced earlier in the Holocene "may be our biggest worry in the years to come." ∎

Drought created the Dust Bowl in the years 1934-38, with dust and debris burying cars and farm vehicles.

Healing Waters

FLOODING RIVERS TO REPENT FOR THE DAMAGE DONE BY DAMS

BY TINA ADLER

If Noah had been hanging around the Grand Canyon at the end of March, he'd probably have thought he was having one distorted flashback.

He would have seen Department of the Interior Secretary Bruce Babbitt push a button controlling the Glen Canyon Dam and let loose a huge flood of the Colorado River below. As in the Bible story, much preparation preceded the deluge. More than a hundred investigators who had received word of the coming torrent moved some endangered animals to higher ground and set up about 30 projects to study the effects of the flooding.

Babbitt and his crew didn't plan this flood to punish anyone. Instead, they wanted to restore the river to at least a shadow of its former self, before the dam was constructed in 1963. They hoped to improve certain features of the river, such as sandbars, that benefit both native fish species and human campers.

This marked the first time that dam managers have used a large flood to renew the health of a river ecosystem, they say.

The flood began gradually, then flowed at 45,000 cubic feet per second (cfs) for a week. A flood that big hadn't hit the Grand Canyon since a natural deluge in the mid-1980s. Before the dam was built, floods averaging 125,000 cfs occurred annually. In recent years, 12,000 cfs of water would normally travel over the dam during late March.

Huge water flows alter a river's ecology by scouring out backwater lagoons, washing away the banks' vegetation, and moving sand from the bottom toward the shore to create sandbars. New lagoons form behind these sandbars. Ecologists liken the services that floods provide rivers to the benefits that fires offer forests.

Today, most big rivers in the United States are controlled by dams, which floods rarely overpower. As part of its

EARTH AND THE ENVIRONMENT | **241**

recent efforts to make up for ecosystem changes that have resulted from the lack of flooding, the Interior Department's Bureau of Reclamation decided to go along with scientists' requests to run a trial flood in the Grand Canyon.

Final reports from the researchers who monitored the effects of this $1.5 million flood are due out at the end of the year. A couple of weeks after the event, Interior Department staff were describing it as a resounding success, but scientists who collected data on the river this summer are providing mixed reviews.

High on the project organizers' list of goals for this torrent was creating better conditions for the beleaguered native fish. Only five native species remain of the eight that graced this stretch of the Colorado River before the dam began operation, explains ecologist Richard A. Valdez of Bio/West, an environmental consulting firm in Logan, Utah. Of those five, the humpback chub and razorback sucker are endangered.

Before construction of the dam, the Colorado River ran hot and cold through the Grand Canyon, reaching highs of almost 90° F in the summer and dropping to almost freezing in the winter. Now, 45° F water from the bottom of Lake Powell gets pumped into the river at the dam, so the temperature rarely exceeds 60° F.

The native fish, however, need a warmer environment for spawning and for their young to develop. They still reproduce in tributaries, which are warmer than the river, but there they must endure cramped quarters and an occasional flash flood, Valdez explains. Moreover, the young often die of cold when they leave the tributaries to enter the Colorado.

Since the dam began operation, the fish have had fewer nurseries—the warm lagoons where the young mature before competing with the adults in the river. Without flooding, few new lagoons had developed, and established ones had become overgrown with vegetation.

This year's artificial flood created at least 55 new sandbars, the Interior Department announced at the end of May. More than half of the existing sandbars grew bigger, and

Department of the Interior Secretary Bruce Babbit at the Glen Canyon Dam.

only 10 percent lost sediment. It's difficult, however, to predict how long any of them will last.

"Sandbars are relatively ephemeral," explains Edmund D. Andrews of the U.S. Geological Survey in Boulder, Colo. They can erode in a few days to a few years.

Some nurseries will form behind the new and the improved sandbars as the river gradually scours out the channel between the shore and the sandbar, predicts Lawrence E. Stevens, a river ecologist with Applied Technology Associates who works as a consultant to the Bureau of Reclamation's Glen Canyon Environmental Studies program in Flagstaff, Ariz.

Because of its modest size, the flood proved less successful at carving out lagoons than at creating sandbars, at least in the near term. "With this flow, it doesn't look like backwater habitats did all that great," asserts geologist Matt Kaplinski of Northern Arizona University in Flagstaff.

"Rejuvenation of backwaters? Some happened, but not as much as we would have liked to have seen," agrees Stevens. Only four of the several hundred along the flooded stretch improved dramatically. Others filled in with sediment or remained unchanged. Overall, he says, "we may have gained a little bit in backwater."

Besides water temperature and lack of nurseries, the native fish have another big problem: their nonnative neighbors, which eat them, their food, and their eggs; carry parasites and diseases; and compete with them for the river's prime habitat. The greatest threats include the channel catfish, fathead minnow, common carp, mosquito fish, brown trout, and rainbow trout, says Valdez. Most of the trout come from tributaries, where they were stocked in the 1940s, says David L. Wegner, a fisheries biologist and program manager of the Glen Canyon program.

Researchers had hoped that the flood might flush some of the nonnative fish into Lake Mead, about 300 miles below the dam, Valdez says. Most of the nonnatives had evolved in slow-moving waterways, so researchers expected them to be unprepared for huge rushes of water.

During the flooding, the natives either took to the tributaries or to eddies in the river. The centers of these swirling waters remain fairly quiet and trap an abundance of insects and plant matter on which the fish dine.

Unexpectedly, most of the nonnatives also survived the March torrent—by hiding in the shoreline vegetation, which a bigger flood would have destroyed, he notes.

Larger, naturally occurring floods, including one in 1984 in the Colorado River above Lake Powell, have knocked down the nonnative populations, Valdez says. The 1984 Colorado flow carried twice the water of this year's event.

Staging a flood that big "would be politically difficult to do and maybe structurally too," Valdez warns. The flood might damage the dam walls. Also, it would probably prove unpopular with people who benefit from the water and the electricity the dam generates; the upper basin states would have to agree to give the lower basin states the water.

Ecologists liken the services that floods provide rivers to the benefits that fires offer forests.

"Out here [people say], 'You can have my beer and my wife, but not my water,'" Valdez jokes.

The artificial flood ripped out or buried much of the shoreline vegetation that had grown up since the last big flow. Such destruction provided campgrounds for tourists and returned the shore closer to its pre-dam state. The loss of vegetation, however, worried some scientists, including Stevens.

Two of the waterway's endangered terrestrial natives, a snail and a bird, live near the river's edge. They have both come to rely on vegetation that spread down to the river after the end of the regular floods, explains Stevens.

The kenab ambersnail traditionally lived higher up on the banks and consumed both bacteria living on the crimson monkeyflower and decayed parts of its leaves, flowers, and stems. The dam's control of flooding allowed that native plant, and thus the snails, to move closer to the river's edge. The snails have also developed a taste for watercress, a nonnative plant flourishing along the banks, thanks to the dam, Stevens says.

To protect the snail population, he and his coworkers moved 1,300 of the approximately 3,100 creatures to a higher elevation. The flood, as expected, washed away those left behind, as well as the plants. However, the fecund survivors are doing a good job of boosting the depleted population. Much of the monkeyflower and watercress has also returned, and the snails are beginning to move back towards shore, Stevens finds.

In the course of their flood-related research, he and his colleagues unraveled a mystery. By observing the snails, they discovered the perpetrator of mass ambersnail murders that have occurred twice in the past few years. Mice, they learned, enjoy an occasional feast of escargot. "They hammer the [population of] snails pretty hard," Stevens says.

The endangered bird, a type of flycatcher, has also come to rely on a nonnative species — salt cedar trees — that thrives along the river. The few flycatchers that remain in the Grand Canyon nest in these trees, feeding on the insects that live among their branches and in the marshes. These birds survived the flood without human intervention. Their nesting sites remain intact, and enough vegetation persists that they have plenty to eat, Stevens reports.

Because of the successes of this large Colorado River flood, scientists hope to repeat it in 5 to 10 years.

Owners and managers of power systems are discussing plans for restoration floods in the Columbia River basin in the Pacific Northwest and in the Missouri River basin, says Wegner. Government officials and others in Japan and Turkey have talked to him about organizing such floods in their countries, he reports.

Initiating any large torrent inevitably involves many people and a lot of land, water, electricity, and money, say participants in the Grand Canyon project. Moreover, each river has different needs and obstacles. Designing the studies for this recent flood and getting the approval of all the groups took about 10 years, says Wegner.

Restoration floods may not become a trend, Valdez suspects. However, river managers are experimenting with other techniques to make the dams more environmentally friendly. For example, at Glen Canyon they are considering pumping warmer water from Lake Mead into the river to help the native fish. They must first determine whether such a move benefits the natives more than the nonnatives, he adds.

Mark Schaefer, deputy assistant secretary for water and science with the Department of Interior, says, "In general, most people [at the Bureau of Reclamation] feel that we can do more to try to run some of our river systems more naturally. ■"

Out of Arid Africa

Debate heats up on whether climate change sparks evolutionary outbursts

BY RICHARD MONASTERSKY

Something strange started happening to the world around 2.5 million years ago. In the far north, the once balmy climate turned bitter as glacial sheets advanced over the landscape and icebergs started bobbing in the Atlantic. In the Andes of South America, forests disappeared and grasslands took over as the weather turned cooler and drier. In northwest Africa, an infant desert started gobbling up acreage en route to becoming the vast Sahara. In southern and eastern Africa, increasing aridity withered woodlands and helped savannas spread.

Amid all this ecological change, a group of erect apes underwent a burst of evolution that led eventually to the appearance of the genus *Homo*.

Coincidence or not? That is the question raised by a provocative idea called the turnover pulse hypothesis, proposed in 1985 by paleontologist Elisabeth Vrba of Yale University. The theory holds that species tend to remain stable until the environment changes, triggering rapid spells of extinctions and originations.

The hypothesis reaches far beyond the origin of human ancestors and addresses the broad sweep of biological upheavals throughout time. Darwin saw competition between individuals as the primary engine driving evolution. While not denying the role of competition, Vrba looks to an external agent, broadly defined as climate change, as the instigator of major evolutionary spasms.

Shifting rainfall, fluctuating sea levels, erupting volcanoes, and the wanderings of the continents all combine, through their effects on the environment, to set the pace at which species appear and disappear. Vrba says that climate sparks these evolutionary changes by breaking up habitats, causing populations of animals to become separated from other members of their own species.

Although intriguing and controversial, the turnover

pulse hypothesis went largely untested for many years. Now, paleontologists are challenging the hypothesis using rigorous statistical examinations of the fossil record. If theories live and die like species, then the current scrutiny may determine whether Vrba's hypothesis thrives, goes extinct, or evolves into a new form.

Vrba lays out the case for the idea in two chapters in *Paleoclimate and Evolution, with Emphasis on Human Origins* (Yale University Press), which came out this spring. Because the fossil record of humans and their direct kin includes fewer than a dozen species, it is a poor choice to use in testing the turnover pulse hypothesis. So Vrba has turned to the African bovids, a family of ruminants whose best-known living members include the antelopes.

Shifting rainfall, fluctuating sea levels, erupting volcanoes, and the wanderings of the continents all combine, through their effects on the environment, to set the pace at which species appear and disappear.

Bovids, she argues, make a good testing ground for the turnover pulse hypothesis because they are usually the most plentiful large mammal at African fossil sites — a fact readily understood by anyone who has watched film footage of the great wildebeest migration across the Serengeti. Vrba has compiled a database of 147 African bovid species reaching back over the last 14 million years.

Africa, as some biologists have noted, is antelope heaven, with 72 different species currently bounding around the continent. To trace the ascendancy of the antelopes and other bovids, Vrba tallied the first appearance of each species at 41 sites in 10 nations.

During the Pliocene epoch, from 5.3 million to 1.6 million years ago, one period stood out as a time of exceptional expansion in this family. Within the interval 2.7 million to 2.5 million years ago, the number of species surged by 44, far more than for any other period. Among the newcomers during this interval were several that survive today, including the greater kudu, roan antelope, blue duiker, and the oryx.

Even accounting for gaps in the fossil record, which can make appearances seem to cluster in time, Vrba finds that the pulse remains strong. Of the 44 species that debuted as fossils during this key interval, she estimates that only 12 may actually have evolved during previous gaps.

The acceleration in evolution at this time also bred a different type of antelope, notes Vrba. Before 3 million years ago, the majority of new bovids appearing in Africa were adapted to warmer, moister, and more wooded environments. But between 2.7 and 2.5 million years ago, the number of new species adapted to colder or arid conditions increased relative to previous times.

"The late Pliocene bovid evidence taken together is consistent with a turnover pulse that started 2.8 million years ago and is seen in the record by 2.7-2.5 million years and that was initiated by a major cooling trend," she states in *Paleoclimate and Evolution*.

From the firm ground of the bovid data, Vrba leaps into the spindly branches of the human family tree and asks whether hominids — *Homo sapiens* and our nearest extinct relatives — experienced a similar pulse.

Although the fossil record of hominids is sketchy and anthropologists agree on few details, the available evidence does support the idea of a pulse in speciation at this time, asserts Vrba. Sometime around 2.8 million years ago, *Australopithecus afarensis*, which includes the fossil widely known as Lucy, split into at least two lineages, *Australopithecus africanus* and *Australopithecus aethiopicus*.

A third group may have appeared then as well. Anthropologists have found remnants of stone tools — considered the handiwork of *Homo* — in deposits 2.5 million years old (SN: 4/15/95, p. 237). Although they have yet to find clearly identifiable *Homo* fossils in rocks of that age, researchers suspect that our genus may have first appeared more than 2.5 million years ago.

Speciation among hominids at this time also bears the stamp of a changing environment. *A. aethiopicus* had enlarged molars and premolars and beefed-up chewing muscles, mouth specializations that are often viewed as adaptations for eating tough grasses rather than the softer fruits of the woodlands. The newer hominids also sported larger bodies than their predecessors, and biologists find that body size tends to increase as the climate grows colder.

These and other observations, says Vrba, support her contention that climatic change between 2.8 million and 2.5

million years ago triggered pulses of evolution among hominids, bovids, and other African mammals.

Other paleontologists, however, discern a strikingly different picture of evolution when they look at that period.

Anna K. Behrensmeyer and her colleagues at the Smithsonian Institution in Washington, D.C., have tested Vrba's idea by examining fossil records for the Lake Turkana basin in Kenya and Ethiopia. This region has the advantage of containing the best-dated rock formations for the critical time period in Vrba's work.

Africa, as some biologists have noted, is antelope heaven, with 72 different species currently bounding around the continent.

As part of the Smithsonian's Evolution of Terrestrial Ecosystems Program, Behrensmeyer and her coworkers used statistical tests to analyze the extinctions and originations of mammals at 342 sites in the Turkana basin. Whether they assigned questionable fossils to separate species or lumped them into known species, they found no statistically significant pulse of extinctions or originations between 2.8 and 2.5 million years ago. Neither bovids nor mammals as a whole underwent massive changes during this 300,000-year span, they report.

These mammals did experience significant turnover, but it dragged out over the entire interval between 3 million and 2 million years ago, Behrensmeyer reported in June at the Sixth North American Paleontological Convention in Washington, D.C.

"We wouldn't contest that there's something important going on ecologically and evolutionarily and that it is probably related to global climate change. The sticking point is that it's a revolutionary pulse at 2.8 to 2.5," she says.

"The image that has gotten out there is that there was suddenly this demise of the forests and the woodlands, the opening of the savannas, and the hominids striding out into this brand-new, open country—with all this happening in a fairly short geological period of 300,000 years. There just doesn't seem to have been this kind of urgency to the transition."

Water buck at the Arusha Game Park,
Tanzania.

J ohn Harris, a bovid specialist at the Natural History Museum of Los Angeles County, could not find a short turnover pulse during Vrba's critical period either. Harris, the former head of paleontology at the National Museums of Kenya, examined records of bovids and other ungulates in the Turkana Basin for the period 2 million to 4 million years ago as part of a broad study, published in 1991. "We came to the conclusion that there was no support in the Turkana Basin for a major turnover in the fauna at about 2.5 million years ago," he says.

Both Behrensmeyer and Harris restricted their studies to the rocks of the Turkana Basin, whereas Vrba looked at fossils from all over Africa. This may explain the divergent results, because species from southern Africa might have been more susceptible to the climatic cooling, admits Behrensmeyer.

Differences in approach also appear important, however, particularly in the choosing of fossil ages. Some of the fossils in Vrba's analysis, especially those in South Africa, are not well dated, making it difficult to relate the ages of these fossils to those found elsewhere, says Harris.

The turnover pulse hypothesis fares no better in studies reaching further back in time. John Alroy, a paleontologist at the University of Arizona, tested the idea in his analysis of 3,900 mammal fossil sites in North America over the last 55 million years. Alroy broke the time span into 1-million-year intervals and computed how species extinctions and originations varied throughout this period.

"What I found was there was no support for the major predictions of the hypothesis on this timescale," he says.

Vrba's theory predicts that climate change should affect disparate groups of animals by triggering a round of extinctions and then speciations within a limited time. Alroy's analysis suggests no relationship in North America between surges in extinction rates and bursts in evolution. What's more, he finds that different animals experienced evolutionary pulses at very different times.

Alroy calls the turnover pulse idea "very, very reasonable. It's a very intuitive hypothesis." But his analyses, "taken together, make it pretty hard to argue for turnover pulses in the North American mammal record at the timescale of a million years."

Donald R. Prothero of Occidental College in Los Angeles took a different tack but nevertheless reached similar conclusions. He looked through the North American mammal record to see how species responded to three periods of extreme climate change during the last 40 million years: a global cooling during the Eocene epoch, 37 million years ago; a severe cooling in the early Oligocene, at 33 million years ago; and a drying in the Miocene at 7.5 million to 7 million years ago.

Although many marine and some land creatures apparently suffered during these climatic crises, North America's mammals weathered them with little change, Prothero reported at the Washington meeting. "In the three big cases, there was no real turnover pulse," he says.

Prothero's study, like most of the other tests, has yet to go through the peer-review process and appear in published form. If these studies hold up to further scrutiny, however, they will undermine Vrba's hypothesis, at least in its present incarnation, says Behrensmeyer.

Even if the turnover pulse hypothesis falters, it need not bring down the idea that climatic upheavals have shaped human evolution. This broader concept, popular among paleontologists, has spawned several recent books, including *Humanity's Descent* (William Morrow, 1996) by Smithsonian paleontologist Richard Potts and *Children of the Ice Age* (Harmony Books, 1996) by Steven M. Stanley of The Johns Hopkins University.

Yet faced with the lack of firm evidence, many paleontologists prefer to duck the debate and retreat to the rocks, where they know the answer lies. "My first thought," says Behrensmeyer, "is let's keep looking for fossils." ∎

Impala at Kariba Lake, Zimbabwe.

The River Ganges' Long Decline

IN THE BASIN OF A HALF-BILLION SOULS,
PURIFICATION AND POLLUTION SWIM TOGETHER IN UNHOLY WEDLOCK.

BY PAYAL SAMPAT

According to Hindu mythology, the Ganges river of India—the goddess Ganga—came down to the earth from the skies. The descent was precipitated when Vishnu, the preserver of worlds, took three giant strides across the Underworld, the Earth, and the Heavens, and his last step tore a crack in the heavens. As the river rushed through the crack, Shiva, the god of destruction, stood waiting on the peaks of the Himalayas to catch it in his matted locks. From his hair, it began its journey across the Indian subcontinent.

Whatever one makes of this myth, the Ganges does, in fact, carry extraordinary powers of both creation and destruction in its long descent from the Himalayas. At its source, it springs as melted ice from an immense glacial cave lined with icicles that do look like long strands of hair. From an altitude of nearly 14,000 feet, it falls south and east through the Himalayan foothills, across the plains of northern India, and down to the storm-lashed Indo-Bangladesh delta, where it empties out into the Indian Ocean.

Another version of the myth tells us that Ganga descended to earth to purify the souls of the 60,000 sons of an ancient ruler, King Sagara, who had been burnt to ashes by an enraged ascetic. Today, the river symbolizes purification to millions of Hindus the world over, who believe that drinking or bathing in its waters will lead to *moksha*, or salvation. It has been esteemed by other religions and cultures, as well: the ancient Greeks, the first century Jewish scholar Josephus, and the medieval Christians all believed the Ganges to be Phison, the first river of Eden. And the 16th century Moghul ruler Akbar revered Ganges water as the water of immortality, refusing to drink from any other source.

Curiously, some evidence suggests that there may be a scientific as well as religious basis for the beliefs that this river can bring purification. Rivers continually purge themselves. Fresh infusions from rain or groundwater dilute their streams. The flow of water flushes solid materials downstream rather than letting them settle to the bottom. (Damming a river reduces its flow, and hence obstructs its flushing capacity, but free-flowing rivers keep washing out the garbage put into them.) The cleansing process is further aided by aquatic microorganisms that break down waste materials. These microbe-collaborators require dissolved oxygen (DO) in the water to do their job, and a high level of DO is normally a sign of a healthy river.

The more organic waste there is in the water, the more oxygen is needed by the microorganisms that break it down. The measure of this need is biological oxygen demand, or BOD. The organic wastes that drive up a river's BOD include sewage, dead aquatic life, agricultural wastes, and plant-based industries like food-processing, alcohol distilling, and paper production.

According to studies reported by environmental engineer D. S. Bhargava of the University of Roorkee, the Ganges decomposes organic waste 15 to 25 times faster than other rivers. Bhargava conducted his studies in collaboration with the Indian Institute of Technology in Kanpur. He monitored water at various locations along the river at different seasons over a five-year period. Bhargava's findings tally closely with those of the government's Central Board for the Prevention and Control of Water Pollution in New Delhi. This finding has never been fully explained.

Both sets of findings indicate that the Ganges has an extraordinarily high rate of recreation, the process by which it absorbs atmospheric oxygen. When organic waste is dropped into it, as much as 60 percent of the BOD is processed within an hour. The water quality samples also suggest that the Ganges retains DO much longer than does water from other rivers. If this is true, it could explain why bottled water from the Ganges reportedly does not putrefy even after many years of storage. Many Hindus keep water from the Ganges in glass bottles as a sacred relic, or for use in religious ceremonies.

The most life-giving qualities of the Ganges, however, are not unique, but universal: they are characteristic of rivers everywhere on the planet. Great rivers have always been the fountainheads of civilization. The Nile, the Huang He, the Indus, the Tigris, and the Euphrates were all centers of ancient societies. All were ascribed mythical qualities by the peoples they supported. These rivers, like hundreds of others around the world, brought life where they flowed, feeding agriculture, fisheries, trade, and culture, and taking away what civilizations discarded. The Ganges is venerated in India as a mother, *Ganga Ma*, for her capacities to create, preserve, and destroy life—reflecting the same powers as those of the Hindu trinity of Brahma, Vishnu, and Shiva.

If Ganga originally came to bring salvation to Sagara's 60,000 sons, as the legend has it, the poor goddess has now ended up with a burden ten thousand times greater than she bargained for. India's fertility rate has declined since the days of that prolific procreator, but its population has nonetheless grown vastly. The river supports a staggering 400 million people along its 2,510 kilometer (1,560 mile) course. If the delta it shares with the mouth of the Brahmaputra River is included, the number of people it supports rises to half a billion, or nearly one-tenth of all humanity, making it the most populous river basin in the world. To put that in perspective, note that the Amazon basin, where the incursions of human activity have galvanized the concern of environmentalists, is still one of the most thinly populated parts of the world. The Ganges, by contrast, is one of

Pollution of the Ganges River, Varanasi, India.

the most densely populated, at about a thousand people per square mile. Its total population is projected to rise to 750 million by the year 2020, and to almost a billion ten years later.

The Ganges plains were settled by invading Aryan tribes around 1200 B.C. In the 3,200 years since then, the landscape of the region has been completely transformed. The fertile alluvial soils that first attracted those settlers have supported a hundred generations of agriculturalists. More recently, industrial and mining activity has burgeoned in the region. Today, over 29 cities, 70 towns, and thousands of villages extend along the Ganges' banks. Nearly all of their sewage — over 1.3 billion liters per day — goes directly into the river, along with thousands of animal carcasses, mainly cattle. Another 260 million liters of industrial waste are added to this by hundreds of factories along the river's banks. A map of South Asia reveals an intricate web of tributaries that flow into and branch out the Ganges. Through this web, four of the world's most densely populated nations — China, Nepal, Bangladesh, and India — empty their waters and wastes into the Ganges each day, adding to the load that comes directly from the region's residents.

Municipal sewage constitutes 80 percent by volume of the total waste dumped into the Ganges, and industries contribute about 15 percent. While the industrial wastes are smaller in volume, they can have far more insidious impacts than the sewage. Both, however, enter the river largely untreated; only a handful of towns process their waste at all. To the raw sewage and factory effluents are added the runoff from more than 6 million tons of chemical fertilizers and some 9,000 tons of pesticides. And finally, the Ganges becomes the last resting place for thousands of dead Hindus, whose cremated ashes or half-burnt corpses are put into the river for spiritual rebirth.

The result is deeply ironic: this ancient symbol of purity and cleansing has become, over much of its length, a great open sewer. The transformation began centuries ago, when the basin's rich cropland and abundant wildlife made it a perfect place for human settlement. For a long time, the river seemed impervious to damage; its enormous volume of water diluted or decomposed waste very rapidly, and the annual monsoons regularly flushed it out. When the 15th-century poet Kabir wrote of the Ganges, "Hell flows along that river, with rotten men and beasts," few would have believed that his impious lament would one day prove to be prophetic. But with 20th century pressures of burgeoning population and industrial growth, the Ganges is teetering under the burden placed on its cleansing capacities.

THE SOURCE

The Ganges begins its long trek to the sea as a stream of pure, glacial water flowing from a cave at Gaumukh, in the Indian state of Uttar Pradesh in the Himalayas. Here it is known as the Bhagirathi, the smaller of two headstreams that come together to form the Ganges. The other is the Alaknanda, which originates near the border between India and Tibet, and meets up with the Bhagirathi 214 kilometers from its source. Gaumukh has been described as a desolate place; no real roads lead to it, and besides the occasional pilgrim, the only human visitors are hardy shepherds who graze their herds on mountainsides below the cave, at an altitude of about 4,000 meters (13,000 feet).

Twenty-three kilometers from Gaumukh, the river reaches Gangotri, the first town on its path. Thousands of visitors come to Gangotri each year, arriving by road from every part of the world. Some of them are religious pilgrims, but many are trekkers on their way to the mountains. The Himalayas are still growing—rising at a rate of one to nine centimeters a year—and the upward movement causes incessant erosion, pouring an unusually heavy load of soil into the streams. It also makes the region seismically vulnerable. For this reason, local communities and activists have long protested the construction of the Tehri Dam (projected to be the world's fifth highest) now taking place on the Ganges, in the Garhwal Himalayas. If the dam is completed, say critics, the weight of the water backed up behind it would put heavy pressure on the unstable geological structure below, forcing water into fissures and increasing the risk of triggering seismic activity that could break the dam and cause a catastrophic flooding of the entire Ganges valley and New Delhi region.

In southern Nepal and the Garhwal hills of India, developers clearing forests and building roads to meet the

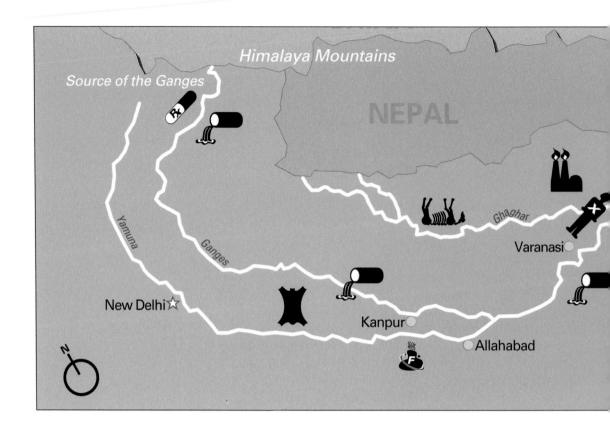

needs of tourists add to the already heavy natural erosion. By the time the Ganges reaches its mouth, it will have picked up 340 million tons of sediment each year. This comes to around 27 tons per hectare per year, as compared to 13 tons per hectare for the Amazon and 8 for the Nile. In English measure, that is about 20 pickup-truck loads of soil per acre every year.

This enormous load of silt continuously alters the river's course over time—sometimes creating new land where there was once only water, and sometimes disintegrating existing land. The largest deposits are laid down toward the end of the river's course, mainly in the eastern state of West Bengal, where the Sundarbans mangroves, for example, were created from land the river brought from the mountains. In some places, the sites of whole communities —such as the ancient cities of Gaur and Satgaon—have disappeared as the river has shifted its banks farther and farther to the west, shearing off pieces of the western shore as it moves downstream.

This process of continuous remolding is facilitated by the same dramatic phenomenon that gives the river much of

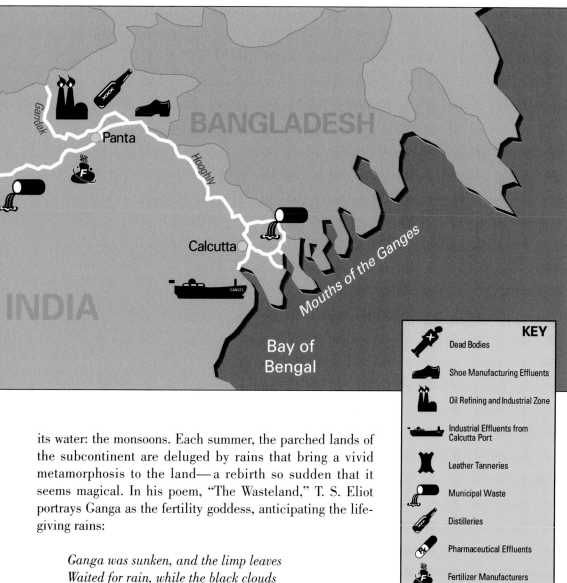

KEY

	Dead Bodies
	Shoe Manufacturing Effluents
	Oil Refining and Industrial Zone
	Industrial Effluents from Calcutta Port
	Leather Tanneries
	Municipal Waste
	Distilleries
	Pharmaceutical Effluents
	Fertilizer Manufacturers
	Carcasses

its water: the monsoons. Each summer, the parched lands of the subcontinent are deluged by rains that bring a vivid metamorphosis to the land—a rebirth so sudden that it seems magical. In his poem, "The Wasteland," T. S. Eliot portrays Ganga as the fertility goddess, anticipating the life-giving rains:

> *Ganga was sunken, and the limp leaves*
> *Waited for rain, while the black clouds*
> *Gathered far distant, over Himavant.*

Watered by the monsoons, this silt-enriched land produces a significant portion of the rice, wheat, millet, sugar, and barley needed to feed the world's second most populous nation. The rain feeds the land, dilutes the river's muddy stream, flushes out excess sediment and suspended matter, and revitalizes the river where its flow was sluggish. The Ganges can swell a thousand-fold during the monsoons. This force brings destruction further downstream in the Indo-Bangladesh delta, where increasing development has shorn the coast of its flood-buffering mangrove forests.

But little of this volatility is apparent in the relatively small river that flows down from the mountains toward the pilgrimage town of Rishikesh, the last point it traverses in the Himalayas before descending to the plains. Until this point, the Ganges is fairly unspoiled. It is at Rishikesh that the defilement begins, as raw sewage is dumped into the river along with hydrochloric acid, acetone, and other effluents from large pharmaceutical companies, and heavy metals and chlorinated solvents from electronics plants. The electronics industry, like any other that uses heavy machinery, consumes large amounts of hydraulic fluid and heat transfer fluids that contain polychlorinated biphenyls (PCBs). PCBs are highly toxic compounds that concentrate in the higher links of the food-chain and are resistant to breakdown, and accumulate in the environment and body tissues.

I n the basin of a half-billion souls purification and pollution swim together in unholy wedlock.

DOWN TO THE PLAINS

The Ganges, with its apparent abilities to retain DO for long periods of time and to continuously reduce the BOD it carries, along with its huge annual flushing out at the monsoon, has an unusually high capacity to rid its basin of waste. But the sheer enormity of the waste that is now dumped, poured, or washed into the Ganges once it enters the plains has overwhelmed even this high regenerative capacity. From Rishikesh on, the river is never able to regain its balance before the next onslaught of unsought offerings comes its way. Perhaps the worst assaults occur at the city of Kanpur, where the hides of horses, goats, and cattle are brought to factories for tanning. Some 80 tanneries operate here, consuming and discharging large quantities of water as skins go through an extensive chemical treatment from the time they are scoured with lime to when they are treated with chromium salts. The chromium lends a greenish hue to the drinking water the city draws from the river. Organic wastes—hair, flesh, and other animal remains—are thrown into the river, giving it a fetid stench. As they sink into the water, they mingle with the effluents of some 70 other industrial plants—mainly sugar factories that disgorge a thick molasses-like substance, and textile companies that throw in various bleaches, dyes, and acids. Kanpur also contributes to the river about 400 million liters of sewage each day.

These great plains of the north were originally covered with dense, deciduous monsoon forest, inhabited by large mammals like the Asian elephant, lion, rhinoceros, and Bengal tiger. Over the past three millennia, the plains have been vastly altered—stripped of their trees and converted to agricultural and urban development, interspersed with occasional patches of open grassland. What plant and animal life remains in the region is threatened by continuing habitat destruction, and only 14 percent of the region's original forest cover remains. One result is that the original riverbank ecology has largely disappeared. Root systems that once slowed runoff are gone.

Runoff that carries soil back into the river also carries farm chemicals. Organochlorine pesticides, such as aldrin, benzene hexachloride, and DDT (banned in the United States for its dangers to human and environmental health) are used extensively in the basin. These chemical compounds have toxic and carcinogenic effects on people and wildlife, and bio-magnify up the food chain. Like PCBs, organochlorines are highly resistant to breakdown, and accumulate both in the environment and in body fat.

Farms in these plains consume 35 percent of the fertilizer used in India, and the large quantities that wash off into the Ganges promote the growth of algal blooms and phytoplankton—green slimy masses that suck up large amounts of dissolved oxygen. In addition to impinging on the river's capacity to decompose waste, this chokes off the oxygen supply to fish. Another dose of nitrates and phosphorus comes straight from the Indian Farmers Fertilizer Cooperative, a group of fertilizer factories just before the city of Allahabad. Thus laden—with mud, raw sewage, heavy metals, fertilizers, and pesticides—the river heads east toward its junction with another great river, the Yamuna.

Unfortunately, what might have been a fresh infusion of water here is not to be. The Yamuna, it turns out, has a sorry saga of its own. Flowing parallel to the Ganges just a little to the west, the Yamuna passes through New Delhi, picking up another massive quantity of sewage and other pollutants. At Allahabad, the now voluminous Ganges receives an additional load of 150 million liters of sewage each day.

Evidence suggests that there may be a scientific as well as religious basis for the ancient belief that the Ganges River can bring purification.

Through these middle stages of the journey, it becomes apparent that the river's native flora and fauna have suffered sorely. Freshwater animals like the gharial crocodile, the smooth Indian otter, the Asian small-clawed otter and various species of turtles are in decline. The freshwater Ganges dolphin—a blind, putty-colored mammal with a long, narrow snout—has an estimated population of just 4,000 to 5,000 animals worldwide, but most of that population now lives in exile in more hospitable rivers like the Brahmaputra in India and Bangladesh, and the Karnali in Nepal. In the Ganges itself, only a few hundred dolphins remain.

About 150 kilometers east of Allahabad, the Ganges reaches Varanasi, the place most associated with the river by its devotees. Varanasi is one of India's oldest cities, and is considered to be its holiest. Its sewer system was built by the British in 1917, designed to serve one-tenth the population of the city today. This antiquated system does little more than pipe raw sewage into the river. Varanasi is also where large quantities of crematory ash, along with thousands of dead bodies, are immersed in the river by the devout.

At the same time, multitudes of pilgrims come to Varanasi to bathe in the Ganges and drink its water, convinced of its purifying qualities—and undissuaded by the fact that coliform bacteria levels here far exceed the limits considered safe. The World Health Organization standards for drinking water stipulate coliform levels of no more than 10 per 100 milliliters of water. In Varanasi, coliform counts are as high as 100,000 per 100 ml. Elsewhere in the river, they range from 4,500 upstream to 120,000 downstream. Not surprisingly, water-related ailments like amoebic dysentery, gastro-enteritis, tape-worm infestations, typhoid, cholera, and viral hepatitis are extremely common in the Gangetic region. One person in the region dies of diarrhea every minute, and eight of every 10 people in Calcutta suffer from amoebic dysentery each year.

Varanasi is the last major city the river passes in Uttar Pradesh before moving on to the state of Bihar. Though eight Indian states discharge their wastes into the river, Uttar Pradesh contributes half of the river's total pollution. Its final inputs downstream from Varanasi are the by-products of a diesel works, coal yards, and a number of distilleries and sugar factories. The last two are among the worst degraders of dissolved oxygen, as they discharge huge quantities of organic wastes; they also consume large supplies of water.

The river moves on to Bihar's capital, Patna, a major producer of agricultural chemicals, where the water undergoes still further alteration. In the last 10 years, concentrations of phosphorus here have increased 15-fold, nitrogen 2-fold, sulfate 3.5-fold and silicate 2.5-fold. Patna produces about 270 million liters of municipal sewage each day, although this city is an exception in that it provides basic treatment to most of its sewage before releasing it into the river.

Further downstream, the large oil refinery at Barauni is notorious for piping huge amounts of oily sludge into the river. Ten years ago at this location, a two kilometer stretch of the river caught fire and burned for 16 hours. Fossil fuel burning produces polynuclear aromatic hydrocarbons (PAHs), known carcinogens that have low water solubility. Instead of flushing out, therefore, the PAHs lodge in sediments—which the Ganges carries in abundance—and settle to the bottom, where they accumulate in aquatic life.

A short distance downstream from Barauni, at the point where the Bata shoe factory dumps its waste, water quality has deteriorated so badly that fish put in the water here in the early 1980s survived only 48 hours, according to a report by the Center for Science and the Environment in New Delhi. A little further on, at the McDowell distillery's mixing zone, fish could survive only *five* hours. The untreated effluents of both industries, but of the distilleries in particular, are ravenous consumers of dissolved oxygen—cutting off the supply of oxygen to fish.

I f Shiva is the god of destruction, the legend that the Ganges passed through his hair now seems to have an ironic significance that its devotees did not anticipate.

AND ON TO THE SEA

When the Ganges enters West Bengal, it branches into the Hooghly, which turns south toward Calcutta. The main channel—now named the Padma—continues on east into Bangladesh, where it is joined by the Brahmaputra en route to the Indian Ocean. Between the two branches, as it nears the end of its journey, the Ganges unburdens itself of much of the sediment it has carried with it for 1,400 miles. The Hooghly has gradually silted up over the centuries, and in some parts it has been reduced to think veins of water amidst masses of sandbars and islands. This has threatened to impair the historical role the Ganges has played as a waterway on which the Bengal region's trade has depended since the third century B.C. In the days of the British East India Company, crates of jute, timber, cotton, and tea were transported down the Ganges-Brahmaputra in steamboats to be sent to European markets.

About 150 large industrial plants are lined up on the banks of the Hooghly at Calcutta. Together, these plants contribute 30 percent of the total industrial effluent reaching the mouths of the Ganges. Of this, half comes from pulp and paper industries, which discharge a dark brown, oxygen-craving slurry of bark and wood fiber, mercury and other heavy metals that accumulate in fish tissues, and chemical toxins like bleaches and dyes, which produce dioxin and other persistent compounds. In the United States, the Environmental Protection Agency has set a standard for suspended solids at 100 particles per liter of water, but the count in the Hooghly is over 6,000. Much of this consists of oily effluents from the port, where ships empty their bilge.

The main branch of the Ganges, the Padma, passes through the Farraka Barrage, a gigantic barrier designed to divert the Ganges waters into the Indian Hooghly branch, and away from Padma. Completed by the Indian government in the early 1970s, it was intended to help flush out the increasing silt deposits in the Hooghly, to improve navigation, and to provide Calcutta with irrigation and drinking water. With the Padma thus depleted, Bangladesh has suffered from water losses in the dry seasons, and the Farraka issue has led to political tension between the two neighbors.

The Padma wends slowly through the Meghna estuary into the Bay of Bengal. The southern part of the delta, between the estuary and the Hooghly, consists mostly of fertile swamps and mangroves, including the Sundarbans National Wildlife Reserve. The Sundarbans tidal forest stretches for about 275 kilometers along the Bay of Bengal coast, and is swept by monsoon floods each year. Home to marsh crocodiles and the endangered Bengal Tiger, it is being poisoned by the pollution washing over it. Moreover, the siltation of the Hooghly and the diversion of the Padma at Farraka have resulted in a diminished flow of freshwater, allowing salt to travel unnaturally far upriver from the Indian Ocean in the dry season. The salinity damages both irrigation and drinking water, and is destroying the deltaic mangroves, which require fresh or less salty brackish water. These mangroves perform important ecosystem functions, by filtering pollution and absorbing excess nutrients from the water, which would otherwise run off onto the neighboring plains.

These highly-evolved ecosystems also protect the coast from the force of the monsoons, by acting as buffers that soak up rainwater rather than allowing it to flood onto the plains unimpeded. In the last 50 years, West Bengal and Bangladesh have continually extended their cities into the mangrove forests, replacing wetlands with enormous landfills. This has left the region defenseless against the monsoon floods that cause immense destruction to life and property along the exposed coast.

Over the final miles to the ocean, the river is now divided into its several usually sluggish but periodically rampaging branches. Fish populations have been decimated. The Farraka Barrage has prevented the spawning of migratory fish, and siltation compounds their problems, making the river bed too shallow for them to lay their eggs. The annual catch of the *hilsa*, a species of Indian salmon, has decreased to as little as 30 percent of past levels below the barrage, and to just 2 percent upstream, in the last 20 years. But even those few fish that remain are now of dubious value, as they contain significant levels of heavy metals such as zinc and lead. If Shiva is the god of destruction, the legend that the Ganges passed through his hair now seems to have an ironic significance that its devotees did not anticipate.

A GRIM FORECAST

Despite the long history of the river's desecration, what has happened to date may pale beside what awaits this region if current practices continue. The population of the basin is projected to reach almost a billion people in the next generation—more than the population of the entire world at the beginning of the 19th century. This would mean 2.5 billion liters of sewage, or double today's quantity, discharged into the river each day by the year 2020. Even more ominous are the forecasts for industrial pollution. According to a report in the *Economic Times*, a Bombay-based daily, industrial discharge into the Ganges is growing at the rate of 8 percent per year. At this rate, by 2020, nearly 2 billion liters of industrial effluents, as well, would enter the river every day—and close to 4 billion by the year 2030.

In any life process, whether that of an individual organism or a large ecosystem, gradually increasing stress does not result simply in gradually increasing impairment; at some point the whole process collapses—as is now happening in the Ganges. If this continues much longer, the Ganges will become incapable of serving its traditional waste-removal function, or of providing usable water for industries or homes. Already, 40 million workdays and millions of rupees in health services are lost each year due to diseases the river carries. With a collapse of basic freshwater services, those losses could explode. Moreover, among the hundreds of rivers and other fresh water bodies of India and South Asia, the abuse of the Ganges is not an isolated case. Nearly 70 percent of India's available water is polluted. Waterborne diseases like typhoid and cholera are responsible for 80 percent of all health problems and one-third of all deaths in India and the rest of the developing world. Only 7 percent of India's 3,000 cities have any kind of sewage treatment facilities.

The link between the river's health and that of the region it sustains has been given short shrift by policymakers. In 1985, the Indian government launched an Action Plan to clean the river, but it failed abjectly—due to pervasive corruption, mismanagement, and technological bungling—and was duly abandoned. Under the plan, a number of waste treatment plants were built, but virtually none of them remain functioning today. A fundamental reason for the failure was that most of those who have a stake in the river's health were never included in the planning. But as conditions have worsened, the prospect of having their life-support system incapacitated may spur concerned industrialists, farmers, public health officials, and ecologists to succeed where the bureaucrats failed. The spiritual role of the river, too, could provide a powerful force for change. Dr. V. B. Mishra, a Hindu priest and professor of hydraulic engineering who leads the Clean Ganga Campaign in Varanasi, tells adherents that the river's sacredness is reason enough to preserve it. Legends of the river's sanctity derive from the same life-supporting properties that now teeter on the brink of collapse.

To observers in other parts of the world, the case of the Ganges may seem uniquely horrific; it may be hard to grasp how people could knowingly put human corpses or raw sewage into the same water they bathe in or drink. Yet what has happened here is fundamentally no different from the continued abuse of ecosystems all over the world. Whether it is the contamination of groundwater by nuclear waste in Russia, the bioaccumulation of toxic chemicals in fish, or the killing of thousands of lakes by acid rain in Scandinavia, the long-range risks are no less alarming.

On the Ganges River, Varanasi, India.

To the ancient peoples of Mesopotamia or the Ganges valley, there was possibly no greater crime than the desecration of a river. Despite all we know about the consequences of our polluting actions, we repudiate this respectful relationship with the resources on which we depend. In an era when science has given policymakers a far stronger grasp of what ancient myths could only suggest, it is a relationship that neither India nor the world can continue to ignore. ■

Water in the Greenhouse

Carbon dioxide, water vapor and other greenhouse gases trap infrared energy emitted from the Earth's surface. If water vapor works as an amplifier — a warmer atmosphere holds more water vapor which makes for a warmer atmosphere — then the Earth will warm much more than if it does not. Computer models that forecast serious global warming count on this amplifying effect.

Sun

Some solar energy is reflected by the Earth and atmosphere.

Water vapor

Carbon dioxide

Atmosphere

Solar energy passes through the atmosphere.

Earth

Some infrared energy is emitted from surface and trapped in atmosphere.

Most of the solar energy is absorbed by the Earth's surface and warms it.

Source: Intergovernmental Panel on Climate Change

Is It Getting Hotter, Or Is It Just the Computer Model?

BY WILLIAM K. STEVENS

As climate experts firm up their view that human activity is seriously altering the atmosphere, one voice stands out in clarion dissent. It is that of Dr. Richard S. Lindzen of the Massachusetts Institute of Technology, a shoemaker's son from the Bronx who has risen through the academic hierarchy as a leading expert on the physical processes of the atmosphere.

Is there truly cause to worry that emissions of waste industrial gases that trap heat like carbon dioxide could disrupt the world's climate?

Dr. Lindzen does not equivocate. "We don't have any evidence that this is a serious problem," he says flatly, with precise diction, in a friendly voice that resonates strongly in his 17th-floor office overlooking Boston across the Charles River. A clutter of folders and papers, coupled with Dr. Lindzen's untrimmed black beard and hornrim glasses, suggest the academic theorist he is.

His opinions attacking the formal consensus about climate change have made the 56-year-old Dr. Lindzen a bete noir to environmentalists who trumpet the dangers of global warming and a champion to political conservatives and industrial interests who minimize the threat. Admirers see him as a force for intellectual honesty in a highly politicized debate. Critics fault him for professing unwarranted sureness in a field of research rife with uncertainty. Many say he is simply wrong.

But everyone takes him with the utmost seriousness because of a reputation for brilliance that got him elected to the National Academy of Sciences at age 37. It is in this sense that his voice stands out from the relatively small group of greenhouse scientists who speak out boldly and publicly in dissent.

Last fall, a panel of scientists convened by the United Nations to advise the world's governments concluded for the first time that greenhouse gases like carbon dioxide are probably responsible, at least in part, for a changing global climate. The panel also predicted that if emissions of the gases are not reduced, the average global temperature will increase by 1.8 degrees to 6.3 degrees Fahrenheit—with a best estimate of 3.6 degrees—by the year 2100. The predicted warming, according to the United Nations panel, would be accompanied by widespread climatic disruption.

Bunk, says Dr. Lindzen. He says the conclusions are based on computerized models of the climate system so flawed as to be meaningless. Everyone recognizes that the models are imperfect, but Dr. Lindzen goes much farther. "I do not accept the model results as evidence," he says, because trusting them "is like trusting a ouija board." Furthermore, he argues, the physics of the atmosphere permit only a minor and untroubling warming despite the buildup of carbon dioxide in the atmosphere.

His assertions have subjected him to a barrage of criticism from the modeling community and its many scientific allies. Dr. Lindzen has "sacrificed his luminosity by taking a stand that most of us feel is scientifically unsound," said a longtime acquaintance, Dr. Jerry D. Mahlman, director of the National Oceanic and Atmospheric Administration's Geophysical Fluid Dynamics Laboratory at Princeton University, which runs one of the computer models Dr. Lindzen scorns. Dr. Mahlman nevertheless describes Dr. Lindzen as a "formidable opponent."

Does Dr. Lindzen feel beaten up on?

"That's a matter of how thick one's skin is," he said over fried calamari at a Cambridge restaurant. It helps, he said, that he gets many calls and letters from silent skeptics in the scientific community who thank him for his stand. They often do not themselves speak out, he says, because it doesn't pay to be a skeptic. "Who needs to be in controversies, who needs any of this?" he said. "And in a time of budgetary restraint, climate has gotten good funding. Why spoil a good thing?"

By the same token, he says, there is a financing advantage in being on the greenhouse bandwagon. Are some people trying to maintain a sense of crisis to get research grants? "Yes," he says, "and it's unconscious and it's natural."

One who says he basically agrees with Dr. Lindzen's view is Dr. William Gray of Colorado State University, best known for his predictions of hurricane activity. "A lot of my

The conclusions are based on computerized models so flawed as to be meaningless.

older colleagues are very skeptical on the global warming thing," said Dr. Gray. He calls Dr. Lindzen's stand "courageous." While some of the criticisms delivered by Dr. Lindzen may have some flaws, said Dr. Gray, "across the board he's generally very good."

Another atmospheric scientist cited by Dr. Lindzen as a fellow skeptic, Dr. John M. Wallace of the University of Washington, said there are "relatively few scientists who are as skeptical of the whole thing as Dick is." Many more, said Dr. Wallace, take the question of climate change seriously but think that assertions of climate change already in progress have been exaggerated, as he does.

The object of the conflicting opinions was born in Webster, Mass., in 1940, after his parents fled Hitler's Germany. His shoemaker father later moved the family to the Bronx, where, Dr. Lindzen says, "I think we were the first Jewish family in an Irish-Catholic neighborhood." There he developed a lifelong enthusiasm for amateur radio and won Regents' and National Merit scholarships at the Bronx High School of Science (class of 1956). He also acquired the middle-class native New Yorker's hardened "G" (as in Lon-GIH-land) that faintly modifies his otherwise straightforward academic accent today.

The scholarships propelled him as a student first to Rensselaer Polytechnic Institute and then to Harvard University, where he was attracted by classical physics, and then atmospheric physics. By his mid-30's he had produced landmark work in atmospheric dynamics, mainly involving "tides," or regular changes in atmospheric pressure, and the periodic shift in direction of high-level equatorial winds that affect global circulation patterns. After various academic posts, he joined the M.I.T. faculty in 1983, where he is the Alfred P. Sloan Professor of Meteorology.

In recent years, while pursuing his main interest of atmospheric dynamics in trying to help "figure out how climate works," he has leveled a variety of criticisms at the idea of serious climatic change, some with telling effect. For instance, he points out, the computer models do not reflect the climate's natural variability very well—a key shortcoming in trying to gauge the human effect on climate, one that is readily conceded by the modelers.

But the Lindzen idea that has attracted most attention is based on a fundamental point of physics: that carbon dioxide and the other waste gases generate only a small amount of warming. Something has to amplify that warming

The computer models do not reflect the climate's natural variability very well.

for the larger amount of warming predicted by the United Nations panel to materialize. The main candidate, whose presumed amplifying effect is built into the computer models, is water vapor—also a heat-trapping gas, and the most powerful one since there is so much of it and it is so pervasive. The theory is that a warmer atmosphere holds more water vapor, thereby increasing the warming even more. Without this amplification, Dr. Lindzen argues, the average global temperature will rise by only about a degree Fahrenheit if atmospheric carbon dioxide is doubled.

"With all due respect to alarmism," he says, "I don't think anyone has argued that's going to be a major change in life as we know it."

The amount of warming produced by the doubling of carbon dioxide has become a standard measure of the climate system's sensitivity to change; the United Nations panel figures it at 3 to 8 degrees. But Dr. Lindzen argues that the models that produced those numbers do not properly reflect the physics of the water vapor question. While it is well known that warmer air generally holds more vapor, he says, "we don't know what determines upper level water vapor," a factor he says is crucial, and central to the predictions of future climate change. He has postulated over the years a number of possible atmospheric mechanisms that might nullify the supposed greenhouse amplification. It was Dr. Lindzen himself who later found the first of three possible mechanisms to be trivial in its effect, but he has advanced others.

Modelers, who insist that the amplifying effect of water vapor is supported by real-world data, sharply dispute Dr. Lindzen on this point and say he has no evidence to prove his nullification hypothesis. But other atmospheric scientists say the issue is not yet resolved. "To be fair," Dr. Lindzen says, "the answer at this stage is that we don't know" what the vapor effect is. And in fact, some important aspects of the issue are left uncertain in the United Nations panel's report.

In the meantime, he is exploring other ways to test the climate's sensitivity to change. One avenue involves volcanic eruptions. If the climate is not very sensitive, Dr. Lindzen says, the cooling effect produced by the haze from eruptions should dissipate quickly; if it is very sensitive, the effect should linger. So far, he says, it appears that the volcanoes are indicating low sensitivity—bolstering, if he is right, his over-all argument about warming.

To some critics, Dr. Lindzen's confidence about the climate's low sensitivity to carbon dioxide emissions embodies more certitude than the facts allow. "I don't know what line from God he has," says Dr. Stephen Schneider of Stanford University, who cites what he sees as the over-precise estimate Dr. Lindzen gives.

Dr. Lindzen replies that he at least gives some reasons for his estimate rather than simply following a "herd instinct" that he says is very common in science. All in all, he says, "I don't think we've made the case yet" that serious climate change is in prospect, and he therefore sees no cause to worry now. To Dr. Mahlman, Dr. Lindzen is saying, "we don't know nearly as much as we need to know, therefore we shouldn't have any concern." This view, Dr. Mahlman asserts, is "deeply fallacious."

Dr. Lindzen traces his decision to begin voicing his doubts to a speaking engagement at Tufts University in the spring of 1989. After he stated his case, he recalled: "One person after another got up, saying scientists can have their doubts but we don't have any. I developed this awful feeling that here was an issue that was running away, developing a reality that transcended the science."

He says he prizes the environment, but that global warming and other issues have prompted environmental groups to go "off the deep end" and produce "a drum roll that gets rid of perspective." One consequence, he says, is that "if you are questioning the basis of global warming, you are definitely treated as someone who hates the earth—and that's a little bit odd, because it is, after all, a scientific question."

Dr. Lindzen has always been a Democrat, too, but he says the global warming controversy has caused him to change parties. The notion that "extremely weak science" could set into motion policies with long-term implications for the economy made him "queasy" about governmental action, he said. In the academic community, he volunteers, laughing, his turn to the Republicans "must have been like coming out as a gay 25 years ago."

In 5 or 10 years, Dr. Lindzen says, direct observations of the climate's behavior might well make it clearer who is right in the greenhouse debate. Could he turn out to be wrong when all is said and done?

"I think it's unlikely," he said, "but it can happen." ∎

A warmer atmosphere holds more water vapor, thereby increasing the warming even more.

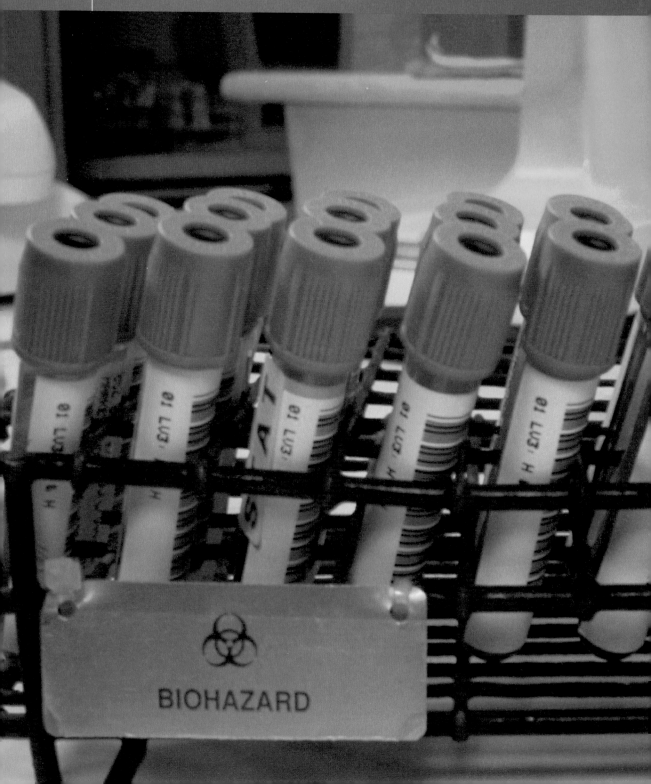

CONTENTS

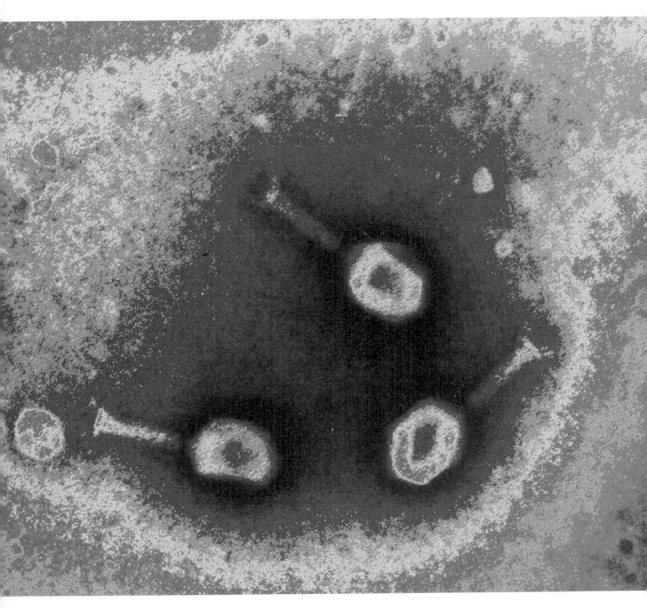

The bacteriophage has a capsid
(head), is polyhedral and tail is helical.
The head contains nucleic acid. The
phage attaches to the host bacteria by
adsorption. This is a chemical attachment including flagella or fimbrae.

Biological Warfare

SCIENTISTS ONCE AGAIN ADVOCATE PITTING VIRUSES AGAINST BACTERIAL INFECTIONS

BY JOHN TRAVIS

When dysentery struck a cavalry squadron resting in Paris in 1915, Felix d'Hérelle, a young bacteriologist at the city's Pasteur Institute, noticed something remarkable: The bloody stool samples of a few of the soldiers contained microscopic agents that could destroy the dysentery bacteria.

In a 1917 report on his finding, d'Hérelle labeled the unseen killers as bacteriophages, or eaters of bacteria, and concluded that they were viruses that infect bacteria. This brash verdict, though ultimately proved correct, ignited fierce debate.

D'Hérelle wasn't the first scientist to describe bacteriophage activity publicly—English physician Frederick W. Twort published such a report in 1915. But d'Hérelle sparked great interest in bacteriophages, or phages, by confidently proclaiming that the viruses could cure dread bacterial diseases sweeping the globe. "He traveled all around the world trying to treat bubonic plague and cholera," says Carl R. Merril of the National Institute of Mental Health Neuroscience Research Center at St. Elizabeths in Washington, D.C.

D'Hérelle even inspired the Sinclair Lewis classic *Arrowsmith*. In the 1925 novel, Martin Arrowsmith is an idealistic young physician who travels to the West Indies to treat bubonic plague with phage therapy. *Arrowsmith*, which challenged the motives of medical researchers, won a Pulitzer prize, and its author became the first person in the United States honored with the Nobel prize in literature.

Unfortunately, the novel's success was greater than that of phage therapy itself. "It was frustrating…. The problem was it worked some times and didn't work other times," says Merril.

Largely because of its inconsistent nature, phage therapy never caught on in the United States. Then in the

Sinclair Lewis

1940s, physicians embraced penicillin and other newly dis-covered antibacterial drugs.

"Antibiotics took over, and phage therapy got dropped like a stone," says Richard M. Carlton of Exponential Bio-therapies, a biotech firm in New York.

Phage therapy is still practiced today but only by a few physicians in Europe and the former Soviet Union, and then usually as a last resort, notes d'Hérelle biographer William C. Summers of Yale University School of Medicine.

Phage is the only antibacterial agent — actually, the only drug of any kind — that makes more of itself as it works… As a result, a single dose of phage should, theoretically, be all that is required to defeat an infection.

Some scientists now argue that d'Hérelle's dream deserves another look, especially as drug-resistant bacteria pose an ever-increasing threat. A few deadly strains of bac-teria today are susceptible to only one antibiotic, van-comycin, and investigators don't expect it to remain effec-tive for very long, Merril notes.

In Merril's opinion, modern researchers now have the knowledge and tools to avoid the pitfalls of past phage therapy.

"This is just too good an agent to abandon. Phage is no longer the black box it was to d'Hérelle. If it doesn't work in some cases, we can now understand the molecular basis of why it fails. We should be able to engineer and manipulate phage to make it into a highly effective antibacterial agent," he says.

The destructive ability of a phage stems from the way it reproduces. After injecting its genetic material into a bac-terium, the virus usually commands the internal machinery of the microbe to mass-produce copies of itself. The new phages flood the interior of the bacterium and eventually lyse, or burst, its cell wall, spreading to other bacteria and repeating the cycle.

Phage is the only antibacterial agent — actually, the only drug of any kind — that makes more of itself as it works, observes Carlton. As a result, a single dose of phage should, theoretically, be all that is required to defeat an infection. Under the right conditions, a single phage produces more than a million copies of itself in a day. (This exponential growth inspired the name of the phage therapy company Carlton now heads.)

So what prevented the success of phage therapy? Modern investigators cite a number of obstacles. D'Hérelle and other scientists of his era didn't have the technology to purify phages completely, notes Merril. Even recent investigators may not have taken enough care to purify their phages, he contends.

Researchers generate phages by growing them inside bacteria and then letting them burst out, explains Merril. That process creates bacterial debris, which often clings to a phage, impairing its ability to infect. The debris can also include endotoxins, poisonous bacterial substances that cause illness.

"You can kill people with those alone," says Merril, who notes that with modern equipment, investigators can purify phages easily. Merril and his colleagues, for example, place their lab-grown phages in tubes containing a salt solution. Then they spin the tubes in a high-speed centrifuge. The bacterial debris and the phages have different densities, so they end up at different levels in the solution, which enables researchers to pluck out the phages.

Early proponents of phage therapy may also have thought that all bacterial infections are equally vulnerable to phages. That's not necessarily true. Because they hide away inside cells, some bacteria may escape encounters with phages, notes Merril. Other bacteria, he adds, infect parts of the body that would be difficult for bloodborne phages to reach.

Another historical stumbling block for phage therapy,

says Merril, has been the speed with which a treated person or animal gets rid of most administered phages. This swift clearance — within hours — often gives phages too little time to infect bacteria.

More than 20 years ago, Merril and his colleagues found an explanation for this expeditious removal of phage. A consensus had emerged that preexisting antibodies attach themselves to phages and facilitate clearance, recalls Merril. His group, however, demonstrated that mice without such antibodies clear phages just as speedily. Furthermore, they established that the elimination of phages actually stems from the reticuloendothelial system, a cell-mediated defense system found largely in the spleen and liver.

Merril didn't follow up on this line of investigation until a few years ago, when he read about the rise of drug-resistant bacteria. He began to wonder if there might be a way to isolate phages that could avoid the reticuloendothelial system.

An idea popped into Merril's head. What if researchers injected billions of phages into mice, waited a day or so, then isolated any phages left in the rodents' blood? Investigators could allow the few remaining viruses to reproduce in the lab, then inject them into mice in order to repeat the selection strategy. After several repetitions of this procedure, it should be possible to cull a population of phages ignored by the reticuloendothelial system.

Merril's idea has now borne fruit. When the investigators injected more than 100 billion unselected phages into a mouse, fewer than 100 phages were found in a blood sample taken 2 days later — a drop of nine orders of magnitude. After just one selection cycle, phage concentrations generally dropped by only four orders of magnitude within 18 hours of injection. By the end of 10 selection cycles, there emerged a population of phages whose concentrations rarely dropped by more than one order of magnitude in 18 hours, reported

Merril and his colleagues in the April 16 PROCEEDINGS OF THE NATIONAL ACADEMY OF SCIENCES (PNAS). "We have clearly solved the clearance problem," says Carlton.

The researchers also believe they can explain the evasiveness of their bacteriophages. While examining one long-circulating phage, Merril's group found that a protein on the outer shell of the virus differed by a single amino acid from its counterpart on normal phages. A second long-circulating phage, isolated from another selection series, shared the same mutation.

The viral coat mutation substitutes lysine for glutamic acid, says Merril. He and his colleagues are still studying how this change alters the ability of the reticuloendothelial system to capture the mutant phage.

Nonetheless, the investigators have already obtained evidence that long-circulating phages may offer a more effective therapeutic option than normal phages. When they injected mice with lethal quantities of the *Escherichia coli* bacterium, treatment with normal *E. coli*-specific phages did save the lives of the rodents, but the animals got quite sick before recovering. In contrast, mice treated with long-circulating strains of the *E. coli* phage survived and had few side effects from the phage therapy. "They were just slowed down a bit, as if they were under the weather," says Carlton.

As promising as Merril believes phage therapy is, he stresses that the new strategy for selecting long-circulating phages is just a small step toward a comeback. If investigators do try to revive d'Hérelle' dream, as Merril hopes they will, they should be mindful that the phages they choose for therapy might do more harm than good. Diphtheria, notes Merril, actually stems from a phage gene utilized by the diphtheria bacterium. The gene produces an enzyme that is toxic to humans.

"We know that phages can carry genes that cause disease themselves. With modern techniques, we can cut those genes out," says Merril.

Under the right conditions, a single phage produces more than a million copies of itself in a day.

The message of Merril and his colleagues—that phage therapy should be systematically reexamined in light of science's vastly improved understanding of phages and bacteria—has so far received a warm reception.

"I read with great enthusiasm this paper. I believe it will induce, maybe a little late, new interest in this area," comments David Schrayer of Brown University in Providence, R.I. Schrayer, who immigrated to the United States from the former Soviet Union, once worked on phage therapy at a Russian bacteriophage institute that d'Hérelle had helped establish.

Far too many questions remain for bacteriophage therapy to be seen today as a viable alternative to antibiotics.

The PNAS report was also accompanied by an encouraging commentary from Nobel laureate Joshua Lederberg, an infectious disease specialist at Rockefeller University in New York. "The paper is important as a reopening of an interesting idea," Lederberg told *Science News*.

He cautions, however, that far too many questions remain for bacteriophage therapy to be seen today as a viable alternative to antibiotics. Even if the new selection strategy identifies phages that sneak by the reticuloendothelial system, will an eventual antibody response eliminate those long-circulating phages? "That's a legitimate concern," admits Carlton.

In addition, bacteria often mutate to evade the attacks of phages, notes Lederberg. Merril acknowledges the problem but points out that phages are also continually evolving new tricks in their campaign against bacteria.

"It's a biological warfare that's probably been going on since life evolved on Earth. And there's no reason we shouldn't use it to our benefit. It will work. It's just a matter of investing the time and money to build up the armament of phages to do what we need to do," contends Merril. ∎

The next morning, on opening the incubator, I experienced one of those rare moments of intense emotion which reward the research worker for all his pains: at the first glance I saw that the broth culture, which the night before had been very turbid, was perfectly clear: all the bacteria had vanished, they had dissolved away like sugar in water. As for the agar spread, it was devoid of all growth, and what caused my emotion was that in a flash I understood: what caused my clear spots was in fact an invisible microbe, a filtrable virus, but a virus parasitic on bacteria.

Another thought came to me also: "If this is true, the same thing has probably occurred during the night in the sick man, who was in serious condition. In his intestine, as in my test tube, the dysentery bacilli will have dissolved away under the action of their parasite. He should now be cured."

I dashed to the hospital. In fact, during the night, his general condition had greatly improved and convalescence was beginning.

— **Felix d'Hérelle**, recalling his discovery of bacteriophages

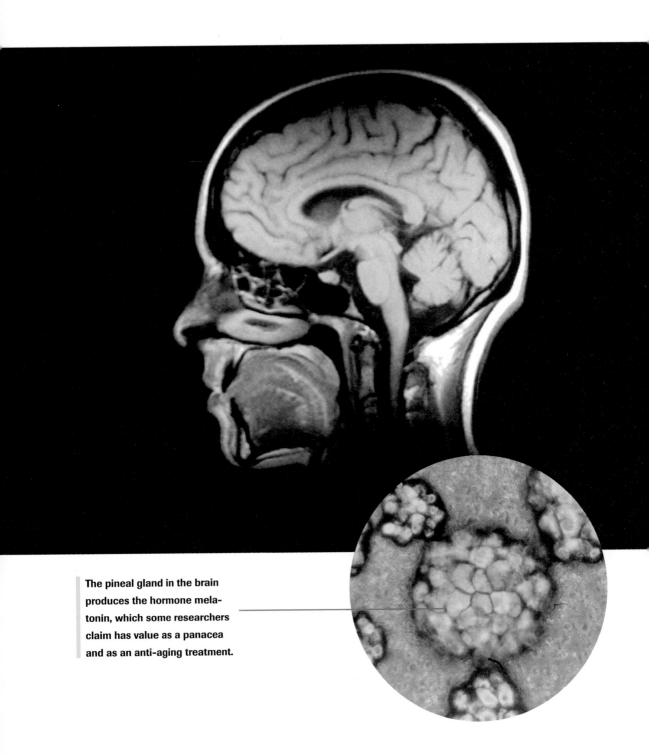

The pineal gland in the brain produces the hormone melatonin, which some researchers claim has value as a panacea and as an anti-aging treatment.

Melatonin:

A Fad or an Important New Drug?

BY JOHN T. BURNS

Melatonin, a hormone that is produced by the pineal gland in the brain, became the object of much interest in 1996 when two books on its effects were published: *Melatonin: Your Body's Natural Wonder Drug*, by Russel J. Reiter, Ph.D., and Jo Robinson, advertises on its cover "breakthrough discoveries that can help you combat aging, boost your immune system, reduce your risk of cancer and heart disease, get a better night's sleep." *The Melatonin Miracle*, by Walter Pierpaoli, M.D., Ph.D., and William Regelson, M.D., has as its subtitle *Nature's Age-Reversing, Disease-Fighting, Sex-Enhancing Hormone*. Both books contain medical disclaimers recommending that readers consult their physicians before taking melatonin. Moreover, such remarkable findings are by no means proclaimed by all researchers in this rapidly developing field of study.

Josephine Arendt of the University of Surrey, for example—a pioneer in the application of melatonin to human medicine—has taken issue with these two books. She states with regard to melatonin, "Several books on the subject have made grossly exaggerated claims for its value, portraying it as a panacea and as an 'anti-aging' treatment. These claims are distortions of current knowledge of the physiological functions of melatonin and its therapeutic potential." A February 5, 1996, *Time* magazine article entitled "Lost Fountain of Youth" concluded that "the claims for melatonin are running far ahead of the science" and raised the question of whether such claims fit into the category of those made by the purveyors of snake oil. Some knowledgeable researchers are concerned that unforeseen side effects may be associated with taking melatonin. In fact, melatonin is available in Great Britain and Germany only by prescription, in contrast to its widespread availability in the United States in health-food stores.

ROLE OF THE PINEAL GLAND

The true role of the pineal gland and its hormone melatonin in physiology is only beginning to be understood. Until the middle of the twentieth century, the pineal gland was shrouded in mystery and misinformation. The earliest mention of the pineal in literature occurs in the *Veda* of ancient India. It was thought to be the supreme "chakra," or center of spiritual force. The pineal was named for its pine-cone shape by the Greek physician Galen (c. A.D. 130-200), which gave it sufficiently important status that it was noted by later anatomists. René Descartes (1596-1650) was so struck by the pineal's conspicuous location in the center of the brain that he hypothesized that it was the seat of the soul. For Descartes, a founder of the mechanistic view of the universe, to be so moved to make such an exception for the pineal suggests the intensity of the debate that has surrounded this organ. A more common view held until the 1960s was that the pineal was a vestigial organ that no longer had any function in vertebrates. It also was said to be functionally related to a third eye that is found in some animals, such as the sphenodon lizard of New Zealand. The function for such a third eye in the middle of the forehead of lizards remains largely a mystery. It has been suggested that the third eye monitors the changing seasonal photoperiod, synchronizes circadian rhythms, or may be involved in regulating behavior tied to thermoregulation.

The 1968 book *The Pineal* by Richard Wurtman, Julius Axelrod, and Douglas Kelly summarizes virtually all that was known by scientists about the pineal gland to that date. It notes that the pineal is sometimes destroyed by tumors in children who become sexually developed at a very early age. Also, the blanching effect of pineal extracts on the skin of amphibians is cited. Joseph Bagnara's research in the early 1960s on the skin-blanching effect helped stimulate interest in the pineal and melatonin. Surprisingly, a few vertebrates —such as owls, anteaters, sloths, and armadillos—are said not to have pineal glands. Perhaps in these species other tissues carry out the functions of the pineal. With age, the pineal develops odd-looking, mulberry-shaped calcium deposits, the significance of which remains a mystery.

Roger Hoffman and Russel Reiter in the mid-1960s did experiments with the Syrian hamster that demonstrated an important role for the pineal in regulating the seasonal changes in the reproductive system of hamsters. Normally, hamsters exposed to a seasonally changing photoperiod

Galen (c. A.D. 130-200)

experience a regression in their reproductive systems as the days become shorter in the late fall and early winter. Significantly, these researchers discovered that hamsters that had been pinealectomized (i.e., had their pineals surgically removed) did not show the normal seasonal regression of their reproductive systems. Thus, it was demonstrated that the pineal had an important function in a common laboratory mammal. Further research by other scientists revealed that a substance called melatonin, produced in the pineal (as well as in some other tissues)—when given late in the day to Syrian hamsters kept on long daily photoperiods—inhibited their reproductive development. It was soon realized that melatonin is normally released from the pineal at night and serves functions related to the biological clocks of vertebrates. For example, in the Syrian hamsters it was eventually realized that the fall regression of the reproductive system was dependent on the seasonally changing biological rhythms of melatonin production and release. However, much research was required to fill out the story.

Sue Binkley and other researchers concentrated on learning about the function of the pineal gland in birds such as the house sparrow. They found that in house sparrows light reaches the pineal directly through the thin skull of the bird. When the birds are pinealectomized, under certain conditions (constant dark) their normal daily rhythms of locomotor activity become arrhythmic. Such a fundamental effect of pinealectomy on daily activity patterns was not found in mammals that were studied. Additional experiments by Binkley and others reveal that when the pineal is removed from the brain and placed in tissue culture in a dish, it still functions with a daily rhythm in its production of melatonin, in synchrony with the light-dark cycle of the laboratory. Therefore, in birds, the pineal is said to be a biological clock and to be important in directly responding to environmental light-dark schedules by its rhythmic production of melatonin.

In mammals the story is different. In these vertebrates the pineal does not respond directly to light, perhaps in part due to the thickness of the mammalian skull. Instead, the pineal is dependent on other parts of the brain to provide it with information about the daily environmental light-dark cycle. Robert Moore and others found that nerve pathways separate from those involved in vision transmit information about the light-dark cycle to a specific area of the hypothalamus called the suprachiasmatic nucleus (SCN). In mam-

A few early studies reported that even massive doses of melatonin in humans have few effects other than depressing body temperature and inducing sleep.

mals the SCN serves as a biological clock, and this part of the brain controls the melatonin production by the pineal gland. Therefore, the control of melatonin production is fundamentally different in birds and mammals.

EARLY STUDIES

Although the study of the physiology of melatonin and the pineal continues in experimental animals, some investigators are already using what knowledge about melatonin is available to improve human health. Much of that effort centers on the fact that melatonin and the pineal are involved in the control of circadian rhythms. So far all vertebrates that have been studied, whether diurnal or nocturnal, have a release of melatonin from the pineal during the night portion of the daily light-dark cycle. Thus, a general function of melatonin may be that it signals the tissues of the body that the organism is in the dark phase of the light-dark cycle.

The rationales for taking such supplements are diverse, and the variety of medical reasons that it has been recommended probably reflects the current lack of knowledge of the true functions of melatonin.

A few early studies reported that even massive doses of melatonin in humans have few effects other than depressing body temperature and inducing sleep. Melatonin depresses the body temperature, and it has been observed that people fall asleep more easily when the body temperature is falling. The normal low in body temperature coincides with the nocturnal peak in melatonin release. Given that this has been the primary observed effect, some researchers believe that it is safe for adults to take melatonin supplements. The rationales for taking such supplements are diverse, and the variety of medical reasons that it has been recommended probably reflects the current lack of knowledge of the true functions of melatonin. In fact, researchers sharply differ in their opinions about the advisability of even taking melatonin.

One of the early applications of melatonin therapy has been its use to treat jet lag. This application seems to be based on a fairly solid experimental base of data that shows that melatonin can be given just before the subject wishes to be able to sleep—to adjust, for example, to the sleeping schedule of the population at a new travel destination. Such use of a melatonin supplement would be limited, in most cases, to occasional use for only a few days. Josephine Arendt has made clinical studies of the use of melatonin to treat sufferers from jet lag. For such studies to be valid, placebo treatments as well as melatonin treatments have to be included. Typically the circadian rhythms of melatonin excretion in the urine are monitored for days before, during, and after the period of travel. Less expensive experiments can be done by placing volunteers in isolated living units where the light-dark cycle can be manipulated to mimic travel across time zones. Arendt reports frequent amelioration of jet-lag symptoms in many, but not all, "travelers" who receive melatonin.

Shift workers also are exposed to sometimes abrupt changes in their daily schedules, especially regarding the time to awaken or to fall asleep. Again, melatonin has been successfully used to reduce the difficulty of adjusting to new schedules. However, the symptoms caused by shift work may be difficult to quantify in the case of psychological effects, and even the more easily measured physiological responses, such as gastrointestinal disorders and fatigue, may have to be monitored for extended periods. It is important to realize that night workers who are off work on the weekend and are active during the daylight hours on the weekend usually do not show much physiological adaptation to the night work. That is, their temperature rhythms and dexterity rhythms still tend to reach low levels during the night. In general, melatonin would be taken shortly before one wanted to sleep. However, in the case of night workers, the circadian phase of the physiology of the worker may be unknown, complicating the question of melatonin's usefulness in this situation. It is a fact, moreover, that *when* a drug is taken, with reference to the timing of internal rhythms, can be just as important as *how much* is taken (the dosage). Even the most enthusiastic proponents of taking melatonin say that taking it during the daytime probably should be avoided and that it normally should not be given to children.

There is evidence that melatonin supplements can aid the synchronization of circadian rhythms in visually impaired people, those with delayed sleep phase syndrome, and the elderly with insomnia. Visually impaired people may have trouble keeping their rhythms, such as the sleep-wake cycle, in synchrony with the normal light-dark cycle.

Melatonin has been successfully used to reduce the difficulty of adjusting to new schedules.

This can cause serious problems with family, school, or job. Taking melatonin at the right time seems to help synchronize such rhythms. People with delayed sleep phase syndrome (the inability to fall asleep soon after going to bed) and elderly insomniacs are reportedly helped by taking melatonin in the evening.

POTENTIAL BENEFITS, POSSIBLE SIDE EFFECTS

As might be expected, because research in this area is in its infancy, the overall effects of melatonin on reproduction are far from clear. Early studies showing evidence of reproductive responses in Syrian hamsters being inhibited by melatonin have been substantiated by many researchers. There is some evidence that melatonin combined with progesterone can be used as a contraceptive in women, based on studies in the Netherlands. Supposedly, an estrogen-free birth control pill would not have some of the side effects of pills containing estrogen, such as increased risk of breast cancer. Some studies with mice, however, report a contradictory, rejuvenating effect of melatonin on sexual development and behavior. The extrapolation from mice to humans is sometimes difficult. Pierpaoli and Regelson's *The Melatonin Miracle* claims that the pineal and its nightly production of melatonin are responsible for REM (rapid eye movement) sleep and, therefore, erotic dreams. It is further claimed that fluctuating melatonin levels are necessary for the adequate production of sex hormones that maintain physiological and behavioral sexual processes. Clearly, much more information is needed to document fully the role of melatonin in reproduction. Certainly the possible importance of melatonin in controlling this process argues for caution in the use of melatonin supplements.

Extravagant claims are being made that melatonin may have future applications for the treatment of many conditions, including immune disorders, cancer, and heart disease. Many of the claims, however, are based on limited results, often (again) involving only laboratory animals. Georges Maestroni and others studied the immune systems of mice given melatonin and found that the mice resisted disease better than control mice. Russel Reiter finds that melatonin is a powerful antioxidant, which may be important in its alleged anticancer effects. Also, the toleration of chemotherapy is said to be improved with melatonin treatment in both mice and women. The damaging side effects of X-ray therapy are said to be reduced after taking melatonin.

Extravagant claims are being made that melatonin may have future applications for the treatment of many conditions including immune disorders, cancer, and heart disease.

Melatonin has been reported to lower both harmful cholesterol and blood pressure in human patients. Additionally, it is claimed that natural melatonin levels are lower in patients with coronary heart disease. Researchers, however, stop short of recommending melatonin to prevent heart disease because of the complexity of the problem of treating heart disease and the very limited amount of information on melatonin's effects.

There are some reports that the pineal gland is influenced by electromagnetic fields (EMFs) and magnetic fields. Reiter suggests that people make an effort to avoid EMFs in the home and workplace. In his book *Melatonin* he lists common sources of EMFs and gives numerous suggestions for reducing one's exposure to EMFs. Reiter cites studies that have suggested a link between geomagnetic storms and various medical statistics, including the incidence of epileptic seizures, homicides, and heart attacks. It is suggested that geomagnetic storms may trigger such events by influencing the pineal and altering its normal production of melatonin. With even the possibility of there being such effects, one would surely hesitate to experiment with taking melatonin.

More conservative researchers such as Alfred Lewy, who has done fundamental research on melatonin's ability to reset circadian rhythms, question the advisability of people taking melatonin without medical supervision and for ill-defined reasons—as is occurring today in the United States. Lewy's research shows that melatonin may have very different effects, depending on exactly when it is taken during the daily cycle of activity and sleep. That is, melatonin may have powerful effects in resetting the biological clock, and our understanding of the function of the biological clock in humans is in its infancy.

While the future may hold important new medical uses for melatonin, the careful process of gathering data from clinical studies on humans is necessary before the general public and physicians will have the information they need to make informed decisions about taking melatonin. Certainly anyone taking melatonin should be under careful medical supervision. ∎

Even the most enthusiastic proponents of taking melatonin say that taking it during the daytime probably should be avoided and that it normally should not be given to children.

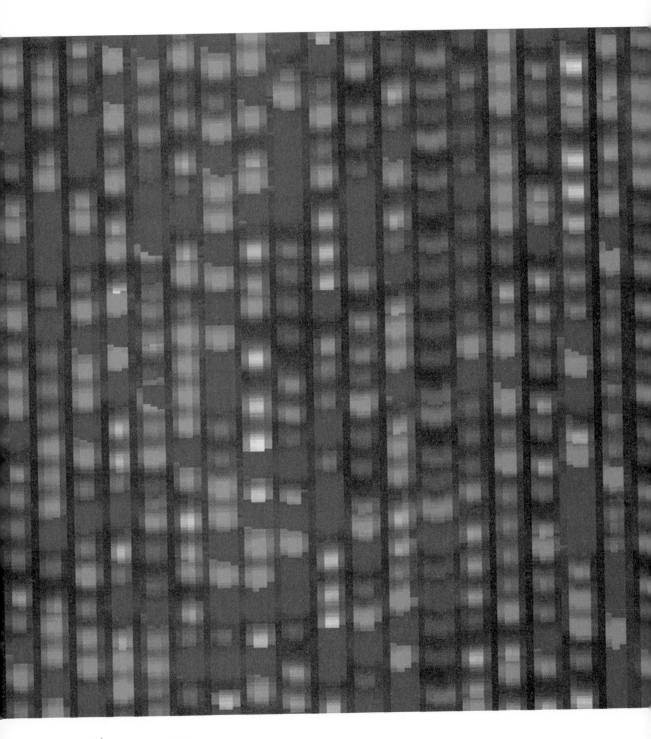

Vanishing Flesh

MUSCLE LOSS IN THE ELDERLY FINALLY GETS SOME RESPECT

BY JANET RALOFF

I f you're 35 to 40, although you're feeling fit as ever, you have probably begun losing skeletal muscle, the tissue that provides your strength and mobility.

Slow, inexorable muscle wasting occurs even in healthy individuals who engage in regular aerobic exercise, but it usually goes unnoticed for decades. In fact, the body hides its loss by subtly padding affected areas with extra fat. So maintaining your weight perfectly over time does not mean muscle isn't vanishing, notes Steven B. Heymsfield of St. Luke's-Roosevelt Hospital Center in New York.

This phenomenon didn't even have a name 8 years ago. At that time, while speaking at a conference on aging, Irwin H. Rosenberg wondered aloud whether its anonymity accounted for the paucity of research on it—and for the medical community's apparent lack of concern over its role in crippling society's elders.

Several recent studies have indicated that while thinning bones render the elderly especially vulnerable to fractures, it's the unsteadiness caused by muscle wasting in the legs that leads to falls. To the extent that it makes walking, stair climbing, and getting in and out of chairs difficult, muscle loss can not only rob aging adults of their independence but also steer them into unhealthful, sedentary lifestyles.

"So that we could begin taking this problem seriously, I suggested, half tongue in cheek, that we give it a name—sarcopenia," recalls Rosenberg, director of the Agriculture Department's Jean Mayer Human Nutrition Research Center on Aging at Tufts University in Boston. He hoped the Greek moniker's classical ring would give it the cachet to catch on.

The tactic worked.

Sarcopenia, which means "vanishing flesh," has begun

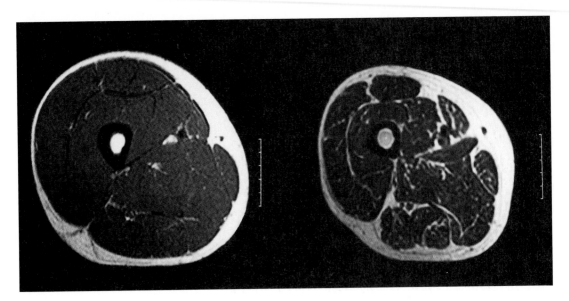

Magnetic resonance image (MRI) of a thigh cross section from a 25-year-old man (left) and a 65-year-old man (right). Fat, in white, surrounds skeletal muscle, encircling the bone. Though the thighs are of similar size, the older man shows a growing buildup of fat around and through the muscle, indicating substantial muscle loss.

popping up in medical texts and gerontology papers. It even appears in a solicitation for new research proposals just issued by the National Institute on Aging (NIA) in Bethesda, Md. The institute convened a conference 4 weeks ago on techniques for studying sarcopenia, with the goal of spurring more research in the area. Next spring, NIA plans to launch an 8-year study of how this muscle loss affects activity and recovery from disease in 3,000 otherwise healthy septuagenarians.

At its annual meeting in October, the American Aging Association has scheduled a session on sarcopenia. And Miriam E. Nelson of the Tufts center has written a book for the general public, due out next year, describing exercises that her studies show can fight the ravages of muscle loss.

Sarcopenia is well on its way to becoming a household word, like osteoporosis, concludes geriatrician Tamara Harris of NIA.

Gilbert Forbes of the University of Rochester (N.Y.) School of Medicine holds the world's record for the longest chronicle of age-related muscle loss in a single individual. Since he was 44, Forbes has measured his own fat-free mass on at least 150 separate occasions spanning 37 years. He has another 27 years' worth of data on a colleague, begun when that man was 53.

Skeletal muscle comprises about half of a person's lean body weight. Because the weight of the two other major components—bone and viscera (organs)—does not drop much over time, Forbes' measurements offer an indirect gauge of vanishing muscle.

Those data, reported at the Experimental Biology '96 meeting in Washington, D.C., this past April, indicate that Forbes experienced a fairly constant 1 kilogram per decade loss of muscle, roughly twice the rate of his heavier, more muscular colleague.

To get a speedier estimate of sarcopenia within the general population, Ronenn Roubenoff and Joseph Kehayias of the Tufts center have just finished measuring skeletal muscle in Boston area adults. By comparing people of different ages but similar builds, they're looking to identify when muscle loss begins and how quickly it proceeds.

"The data we have clearly show a decline from the thirties onward," Roubenoff told *Science News*. Though men tend to start with more muscle, they appear to lose about the same percentage as women over time. Despite large individual variability, he says, the trends indicate "that if you're a healthy elderly person in your seventies, you're down about 20 percent [in skeletal muscle] from where you were at age 25 or 30."

To the extent that it makes walking, stair climbing, and getting in and out of chairs difficult, muscle loss can not only rob aging adults of their independence but also steer them into unhealthful, sedentary lifestyles.

Moreover, there are some indications that sarcopenia's ravages accelerate with time. So far, these associations "are primarily anecdotal," Harris says. However, she adds, there haven't been many attempts to look into it.

Eric T. Poehlman of the Baltimore Veterans Affairs Medical Center and his colleagues are among the few who have tackled this question. They reported finding just such a trend in the Nov. 1, 1995 ANNALS OF INTERNAL MEDICINE.

For 6 years, they followed 35 healthy but sedentary women who were in their mid to late forties at the start of the study. The investigators monitored such factors as physical activity, calories burned during periods of rest, and where their bodies store fat. Over this period, half of the women entered menopause.

While all the volunteers maintained a fairly constant weight, those who became menopausal lost an average of 3 kg of lean tissue during the study, six times the loss seen in the women of the same age who did not enter menopause. The menopausal women also became less active over the course of the study, a factor that can itself spur muscle loss.

This study didn't continue long enough to establish whether the acceleration of sarcopenia at menopause represents a permanent change. But Poehlman says his data clearly indicate that menopause "throws you into a downward spiral of muscle loss and inactivity—two things you don't want to happen."

Studies indicate that exercise regimes that focus on high-intensity resistance training of the arms and legs go a long way toward countering disabling frailty in the elderly.

One hallmark of menopause is a drop in a woman's production of the sex hormone estrogen. Might such a change accelerate sarcopenia? "It's possible," says endocrinologist Clifford J. Rosen of the Maine Center for Osteoporosis Research and Education at St. Joseph Hospital in Bangor.

Estrogen helps modulate the body's production of a hormone, insulinlike growth factor 1 (IGF-1), that is important for muscle growth and development, Rosen notes. Growth hormone controls concentrations of IGF-1 even more directly. Like estrogen, growth hormone declines dramatically with age in both men and women.

Rosen therefore suspects that age-related drops in growth hormone, estrogen, and other hormones may play a driving role in sarcopenia.

To test that idea, he's conducting a yearlong trial with 200 frail men and women over the age of 65. Half receive daily supplements of growth hormone, the others a placebo. If the study shows that the treatment halts muscle loss or aids an individual's ability to regain muscle strength with exercise, it may hold out the prospect of hormone therapy, he says.

Charlotte A. Peterson of the McClellan Memorial Veterans Hospital in Little Rock, Ark., suspects that some share of sarcopenia may also trace to problems involving satellite cells, the body's poorly understood muscle repair crews. Her data indicate that here again, IGF may play a role.

A large community of these satellite cells surrounds skeletal muscle. They do nothing until a muscle needs to grow or experiences damage — such as a bruise or those minor rips that cause aches the day after exercise. Then the satellite cells spring into action, migrating to where they're needed.

Some multiply and turn into new muscle, which eventually fuses to the old muscle. Others return to their quiet state to await the next crisis. "We're trying to figure out what signals which satellite cells to do what," Peterson explains.

What is clear, she says, is that the performance of satellite cells wanes with age. Her work with rats has shown that within just a few weeks, muscle damage in a 3- to 6-month-old young adult completely disappears. But when an elderly 24- to 28-month-old animal sustains the same damage, the satellite cells' repair proceeds much more slowly and often incompletely.

Exercise is critical in the prevention of sarcopenia.

The real problem, she notes, may be not the satellite cells themselves but rather the body's difficulty in communicating with them. Other researchers have shown that when they transplant muscle and its satellite cells from an old animal into a young one, the muscle again heals rapidly.

Insulinlike growth factors "seem to be really important in controlling satellite cell function," Peterson says. Her preliminary evidence indicates "that satellite cells from older animals mount a less robust IGF response following injury." This suggests, she says, "that it's production of the growth factor may be impaired."

Age-related neurological changes may also play a pivotal role in sarcopenia.

Over decades, the body loses nerves, including those that branch out from the spinal cord into skeletal muscle throughout the body. As one of these nerves dies, a neighbor sends out branches to rescue the muscle fibers that had been abandoned. Without such a new nerve connection, that muscle would eventually shrink and die.

But there's a limit to how much a nerve can grow, according to studies by neurologist Jan Lexell of Lund University Hospital in Sweden. "It's somewhere around two to three times its original size," he says. "So it can double the number of muscle fibers that it innervates" but probably no more. When surviving nerves are no longer numerous enough to rescue all of the abandoned muscle fibers, he says, sarcopenia becomes inevitable.

It's never too late to start muscle training, which goes a long way toward prevention of age-related diseases.

Studies that have attempted to quantify the loss of these muscle-innervating nerves find that somewhere between one-quarter and one-half of them die off between the ages of 25 and 75. Moreover, Lexell observes, because the rate of nerve loss "speeds up after age 60," persons approaching 90 are likely to have suffered dramatically more loss.

His studies indicate that the first muscle fibers to go are those used the least—rapidly-contracting fibers that serve as a sort of muscular overdrive. The body calls on them to execute the most intense and rapid activities, such as heavy lifting and sprinting. The progressive loss of different types of muscle "accounts for part of the slowing of our movements with age," he says, and much of the frailty.

What all these studies confirm, Rosenberg maintains, is that although sarcopenia may represent a universal symptom of aging today, it should not be accepted as normal. Instead, he argues, it should be considered a newly recognized disease—amenable to prevention and treatment.

In fact, a series of studies at his center indicates that exercise regimes that focus on high-intensity resistance training of the arms and legs go a long way toward countering disabling frailty in the elderly. Lexell agrees, noting that this type of exercise wakes up languishing overdrive muscles by challenging them to gradually and steadily lift or move increasingly heavy weights.

Older people who have done weight lifting over the last 15 to 20 years will have muscles the same size as someone who is 20 and sedentary," he notes.

It's never too late to start that muscle training, according to studies over the past few years led by Nelson and Maria A. Fiatarone of the Tufts center. In one 10-week study of 100 frail nursing home residents between the ages of 72 and 98 (SN: 6/25/94, p. 405), individuals more than doubled the strength of trained muscles and increased their stair-climbing power by 28 percent when they exercised their legs with resistance training three times a week.

Nelson's group then prescribed a less rigorous training regimen, with workouts only twice a week, in a year-long study with 50- to 70-year-old women. Not only did those who exercised increase their strength throughout the study, but they also gained skeletal muscle. Women who remained sedentary declined on both measures.

Moreover, this training offers payoffs that go well beyond sarcopenia, notes William J. Evans of Pennsylvania State University in University Park. A physiologist, he collaborated with the Tufts team on several of their exercise studies. While those women assigned to an exercise group in the year-long study gained a little bone over the course of their training, he notes that those who remained sedentary lost about 2 percent of their bone.

In another study, his group found that elderly men and women who performed strength training for 3 months burned 15 percent more calories over the course of a day than their sedentary counterparts. The difference was traced not so much to their increased exercise but to a boost in their metabolism, which should fight sluggishness and weight gain, he says.

In fact, he notes, those elderly adults who follow through on weight training tend to voluntarily increase their activity. In some cases, this training also enabled them to forsake wheelchairs for a walker or cane.

That's one reason the Tufts center is fighting sarcopenia so actively, Rosenberg says. Muscle loss is robbing the elderly of their freedom. "We want to give it back." ∎

Elderly adults who follow through on weight training tend to voluntarily increase their activity. In some cases, this training also enabled them to forsake wheelchairs for a walker or cane.

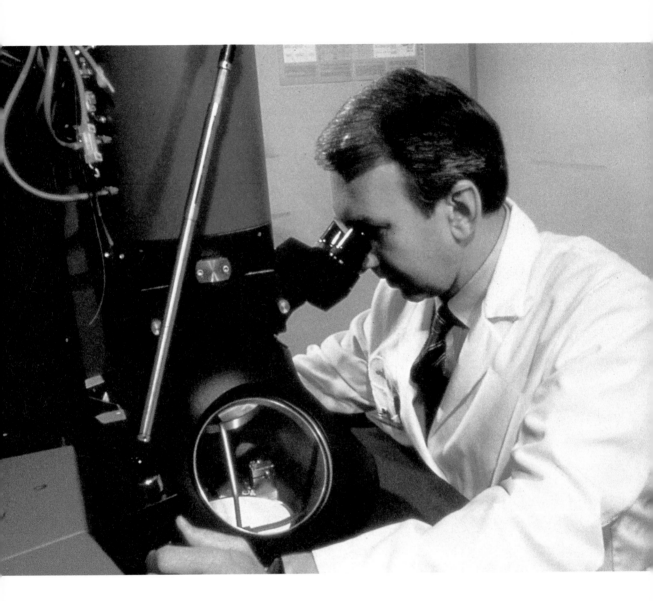

What's in the Vault?

AN IGNORED CELL COMPONENT MAY OFTEN ACCOUNT FOR WHY CHEMOTHERAPY FAILS

BY JOHN TRAVIS

Can you imagine exploring the anatomy of the human body and missing the heart, the organ that sends life-giving blood coursing through the body? Of course not. Or not noticing the brain, the custodian of memories and creator of thoughts? Don't be ridiculous.

Yet cell biologists may soon have to acknowledge an equally unimaginable oversight in their field. For decades, their powerful microscopes have failed to spot a basic cell component of animals and perhaps any organism with a nucleus. Known as vaults, the barrel-shaped particles are three times the size of ribosomes, the easily seen protein-making factories of cells.

Vaults were unearthed 10 years ago only by accident, even though they exist by the thousands in the cells of rats, humans, chickens, sea urchins, and even slime molds. Almost as surprising, a decade after they were spotted, vaults remain largely a mystery, their role uncertain and their existence disregarded by most cell biologists.

Investigators may not be able to ignore these obscure objects much longer: Cancer researchers have identified a tantalizing link between vaults and the frequent failure of chemotherapy to destroy tumors.

Nancy Kedersha laughs when remembering how she stumbled upon vaults in the mid-1980s. Then at the University of California, Los Angeles (UCLA), Kedersha and her colleague Leonard H. Rome were studying coated vesicles, protein-covered fatty spheres that convey molecules around the interior of cells. Kedersha was struggling to purify these microscopic moving vans, carefully separating the coated vesicles from other contents of the cell. "I wasn't trying to discover anything. I was just trying to clean up my coated vesicle preparation," recalls the cell biologist.

Kedersha turned to negative staining, a microscopy method as simple as it is messy. When using an electron microscope, biologists normally dust cells with chemical stains intended to highlight the contents. In negative staining, they flood their samples with stain.

If her preparation contained only stained vesicles and the stain-filled fluid around them, Kedersha would view a sea of black when she looked at it through a microscope. But if it were contaminated with objects that shrug off the stain, that sea would be dotted with white islands. Rome likens the strategy to finding an invisible person by looking for an unexplained shadow in the beam of a spotlight.

To Kedersha's surprise, unstained ovoid objects appeared among her coated vesicles. Since some of the stain settled into furrows on top of the unexpected shapes, the negative staining revealed fine details of the exterior of these mysterious interlopers, including arches that reminded Rome and Kedersha of the ceilings in medieval cathedrals. The two investigators thus christened the curious items vaults.

The researchers quickly discovered why they, and other scientists, had never noticed vaults before. The stains used in imaging cells generally latch onto fatty molecules in the membrane of a cellular component or mark the nucleic acids that make up DNA and RNA. But vaults consist almost entirely of proteins, which traditional stains leave untouched. "In transmission electron micrographs, they're practically invisible," says Rome.

Since they reported the existence of vaults in 1986, Kedersha, now at the Cambridge, Mass., biotech firm ImmunoGen, and Rome have developed a detailed account of these objects. The main constituent of vaults is a protein called the major vault protein (MVP). An individual vault is apparently built of 96 copies of this protein. RNA is another integral, though hidden, part of vaults. Each appears to contain 16 short RNA strands tucked inside of the barrel-like container created by the major vault proteins.

Measuring some 55 nanometers by 30 nanometers, vaults sometimes look in microscopic images like pairs of unfolded flowers, each half of the vault made of eight petals attached to a central ring by a small hook. Those images suggest that vaults open and close as a natural part of their function in the cell, says Rome.

The researchers have precious few clues to the role of vaults in the cell. The best lead comes from their unique shape. "I'm a firm believer in form following function. Nature is trying to tell us something by this incredible structure. And the one thing we might surmise from the structure [of vaults] is that they might contain something," says Rome.

That shape also hints that vaults may pick up their unknown cargo at the nuclear membrane, the barrier that separates the cell's cytoplasm from its nucleus. The nucleus is a fluid-filled sac containing DNA and the machinery required to translate the instructions encoded by that DNA into molecules called messenger RNA. These mRNA strands, as well as other molecules, must somehow get out of the nucleus. The portals they use are membrane structures called nuclear pore complexes. Remarkably, says Rome, vaults match almost perfectly the size and shape of pores formed by these complexes.

Furthermore, some researchers have observed what they call plugs filling nuclear pore complexes. While Rome acknowledges that many investigators discount the existence of plugs, labeling them experimental artifacts, he believes that plugs may be the same as vaults. Some images of vaults, he notes, show them lolling around the cytoplasm in the vicinity of nuclear pore complexes.

"It's a perfect match to me. My opinion is that vaults either dock at the pore complex or dock at the pore complex and are the plugs. I think they're moving things from the nucleus into the cytoplasm," says Rome. Suggesting one type of cargo, Rome says that brief strands of vault RNA may serve as attachment sites for mRNA, which the vaults would then ferry around the cell.

Vaults might have languished in obscurity for many more years, studied only by Rome, Kedersha, and a few other adventurous souls, if it were not for a discovery made last year by a group of researchers led by Rik J. Scheper of

Free University Hospital in Amsterdam. Until recently, Scheper and his colleagues were oblivious to the existence of vaults. The group had focused its research efforts on cancer, particularly the troublesome phenomenon of tumor cells that can escape destruction by chemotherapeutic drugs.

Such drug resistance frequently causes chemotherapy to fail, say Scheper. Many forms of cancer are either naturally unyielding to drugs or develop resistance in the course of therapy, probably because tumor cells mutate into resistant forms that survive and proliferate.

For decades, cell biologists powerful microscopes have failed to spot a basic cell component of animals and perhaps any organism with a nucleus. Known as vaults, the barrel-shaped particles are three times the size of ribosomes, the easily seen protein-making factories of cells.

In the last few years, investigators have begun to unravel the molecular mechanisms that guard cancer cells from drugs. They have discovered that some cancer cells resistant to several commonly used drugs dramatically increase the production of proteins that pump various drugs out of a cell's interior. In particular, two recently identified proteins, P-glycoprotein (Pgp) and multidrug-resistance-associated protein (MRP), serve this protective function.

Not all cancer cells depend upon Pgp or MRP. Since 1993, Scheper's group has investigated a protein that many drug-resistant lung cancer cells produce in unusual abundance. Early indications are that this protein, known as lung-resistance-related protein, or LRP, may be the most effective predictor of whether a particular cancer will respond to chemotherapy, says Scheper.

His group recently joined forces with researchers at the National Cancer Institute to examine a large variety of cancer cells stored there. Production of LRP was found in 78 percent of the cancer cells, notes Robert H. Shoemaker of NCI's Developmental Therapeutics Program in Frederick, Md. The presence of LRP, more so than that of either Pgp or MRP, provided the most accurate indication of whether the cells were susceptible to chemotherapeutic drugs, the researchers report in the Jan. 17 INTERNATIONAL JOURNAL OF CANCER.

Furthermore, Scheper and his colleagues have examined the tumor cells of people with ovarian cancer or acute myeloid leukemia. In both types of cancers, the investigators found that people whose tumors made LRP had not responded well to chemotherapy or survived as long as people whose tumors had no LRP. "It looks like [LRP production] is a predictor of a poor response to chemotherapy, but it's still too early for regular clinical screening," comments Scheper.

Scheper's research took an extraordinary turn last year, when his group finally found the gene that codes for LRP. That gene turned out to be the gene for the human version of the major vault protein. "It shocked us," says Rome, recalling his reaction when he first learned of Scheper's discovery, later reported in the June 1995 NATURE MEDICINE.

The connection between vaults and drug-resistant cancer cells gained more support earlier this year. Since the synthesis of LRP may not in itself mean that a complete vault forms. Rome's and Scheper's groups joined together to examine the number of actual vaults in drug-resistant cancer cells. At the RNA Society meeting in Madison, Wis., Valerie A. Kickhoefer, a UCLA colleague of Rome's, reported that drug-resistant cancer cells do indeed make more vaults than other cancer cells do—as much as 16 times the normal amount.

How vaults may confer drug resistance upon cancer cells remains a matter of speculation. If vaults transport molecules, especially if they ferry compounds away from the nuclear membrane, cancer cells may employ them to oust

DNA-damaging drugs from the nucleus or to convey other toxic drugs away from their intended targets elsewhere in the cell.

Scheper cautions that no one has yet proved that vaults are responsible for drug resistance in cancer. That, investigators agree, would require proof that the elimination of vaults from resistant cells robs them of their protection or that the addition of vaults to susceptible cells confers resistance.

While the identification of LRP as the major vault protein suggests that cancer cells can commandeer vaults for their own ends, the discovery doesn't resolve the lingering mystery of what vaults do in normal cells. Rome still holds that vaults move about the cytoplasm, periodically docking at nuclear pore complexes to pick up strands of mRNA for transport. Yet Kedersha has evidence that vaults may also dwell inside the nucleus.

Moreover, she and Kathy Suprenant of the University of Kansas in Lawrence champion an alternative theory about the cargo of vaults. They note that vaults are far larger than any mRNA they might carry. "You don't need anything this big to move mRNA around," says Kedersha.

Instead of carting mRNA, Kedersha and Suprenant suggest, vaults may help form and haul the two subunits that make up ribosomes, the organelles that translate the information encoded by mRNA into strings of amino acids.

Suprenant was led to join the small band of scientists studying vaults by her research on microtubules. These hollow filaments crisscross the interior of a cell and provide it with support. Working with cells from sea urchins, Suprenant and her colleagues recently isolated unusual complexes that contain microtubules, ribosomes, other proteins, and mRNA. One protein in these complexes turned out to be the sea urchin's version of the major vault protein. Prompted by that discovery, the investigators took a closer look at the complexes. "Lo and behold, there are vaults," says Suprenant.

Moreover, the vaults are intimately associated with the ribosomes from the complexes. "If you purify vaults from the preparation, there are ribosomes. If you purify ribosomes, there are vaults around," says Suprenant. She and her colleagues have also found that antibodies to the sea urchin's vault protein stain the cell's nucleolus, the site inside the nucleus where the two subunits of ribosomes form.

To Suprenant and Kedersha, the circumstantial evidence linking vaults to ribosomal assembly and transport is compelling. "Ribosomal subunits are assembled inside the nucleus, then they exit the nucleus in a manner that's completely unknown. Presumably, they go through the nuclear pore complex, because how else could they get out? There must be something that takes them across the membrane. It turns out vaults have an interior that's the right size to shuttle the ribosomal subunits across the nuclear envelope," remarks Suprenant.

Rome remains unconvinced by the arguments of Suprenant and Kedersha, noting that estimates of the vaults' interior volume are only speculation based on their exterior size. Moreover, no one has found a complete vault particle inside the nucleus, counters Rome.

As this collegial debate shows, the most rudimentary questions about vaults remain unanswered a decade after their discovery. Do vaults actually transport something, and if so, what? Where do vaults go in the cell? These pressing questions should be answered more quickly now that vaults have been associated with cancer.

"We'll get a whole new group of people anxious to find out what vaults do," predicts Rome. ∎

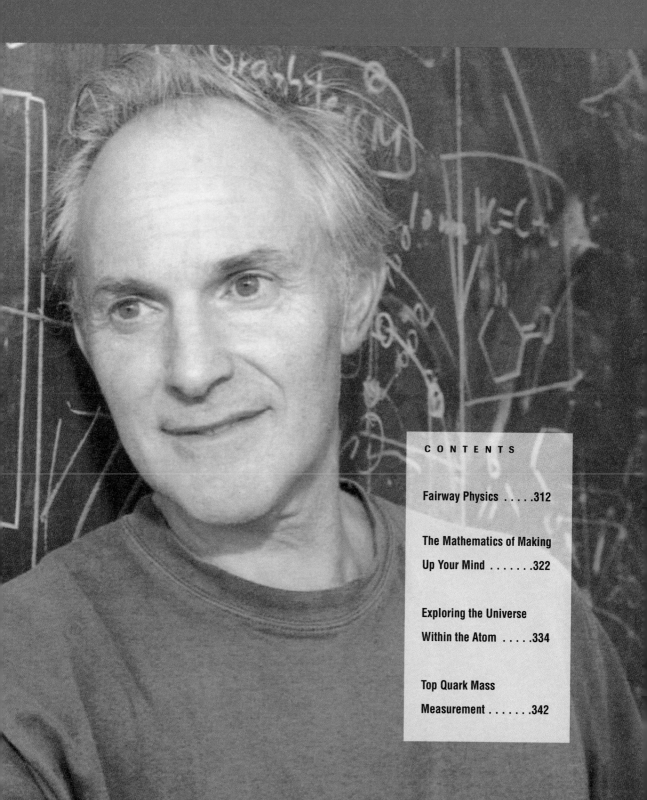

CONTENTS

Fairway Physics

BY JEFFREY KLUGER

They talked about a lot of things when Edmund Muskie died earlier this year, but his hole in one was not among them.

It was late 1968 when Muskie got his ace, and at that time, the former governor, sitting senator, and future secretary of state was running for vice president. Late 1968, as any active politician appreciated, was not the best historical moment to be running for any office. The Southeast Asian military offensive was at its most offensive; American cities were "experiencing unrest" (a term the press considered more polite than "on fire"); and the Chicago convention had wound up looking like a Shriners convention. And yet one evening in the midst of this, Muskie scheduled a television appearance, and the first thing he was asked about was his hole in one.

Even as a political naïf, I remember being taken aback by this. Here we were, if not on the eve of the apocalypse, then certainly approaching the late brunch, and all the usually inquisitorial media wanted to discuss with the Democratic vice presidential candidate was his triumph on the links. "Après le déluge," they seemed to be saying, "golf!"

And yet the remarkable thing was, no one—not the Democrats, not the Republicans, not Muskie himself—objected. The questioners in this interview wanted to ask about holes in one, the audience wanted to listen, and that appeared to be that. I began to suspect then that there was more to this golf thing than I knew.

I was right. In the United States alone an estimated 24 million people call themselves regular golfers. In 1994, the last year for which figures are available, this near nation-state spent more than $2 billion on golf clubs, $10 billion on greens fees and club memberships, and over $2 billion on miscellaneous merchandise. And hidden in this last figure is

PHYSICAL SCIENCE | **313**

possibly the most remarkable statistic of all: in 1994, as in most years, the American golf industry manufactured and shipped around 850 million golf balls—about 3.2 for every man, woman, and child in the country.

Perhaps more than anything else, it is the ball that is the central totem of the game of golf. But it's not just the people on the links who find the little pill an object of reverence; it's the people in the labs as well. Packed inside a golf ball's 2.4-cubic-inch interior and spread across its 8.86-square-inch face are more parts per million of science than in virtually any other piece of sports equipment ever invented. What a golf ball lacks in a football's size, a baseball's lore, and a bowling ball's mass, it may make up in sheer scientific complexity.

To appreciate the contemporary golf ball, one might appreciate its historical roots—and they are roots that go deep. The first known appearance of a golflike game was roughly 2,000 years ago when the Romans invented a club-and-ball sport they called paganica. While the Romans, with their powerful military, were among the world leaders in the sophisticated field of club technology, ball manufacturing was a different matter, and the earliest known paganica balls were little more than stitched, feather-stuffed skins that later came to be known, appropriately enough, as featheries. Built of only the finest ancient materials, the average feather ball could last a sportsman a lifetime, provided he didn't do anything stupid with it like hit it with a club. This tended to make it fall apart and required the ancient player to run all the way back to the ancient pro shop to buy another one.

Though the featherie had its shortcomings, the Romans —with such workaday concerns as sacking and pillaging to keep them busy—did not have time to invent an alternative. Not until the nineteenth century, when more-contemporary Italians dreamed up the gutta-percha, or "guttie" ball, did golf make its next strides forward. The guttie ball was a solid one-piece golf ball made of the dried gum of the Malaysian sapodilla tree. This was a perfectly fine material for a golf ball with the exception that when the temperature drops too low, sapodilla gum grows a bit brittle—a lesson the cold-weather golfer learned the hard way when he hit a shot on the tenth hole and found his guttie ball flying off in the direction of the eleventh, twelfth, and thirteenth. Happily for fellow duffers who were tired of coming home from a day on the links with more shrapnel wounds than muscle aches, the guttie ball was later replaced by balls made of natural rubber and, then, synthetic rubber, both of which led to the modern balls in use today. While all these balls differed dramatically in design, one thing they had in common was that at some point they felt the wrath of a club. That is the moment when the sport of golf started to turn into the science of golf.

"The act of swinging a golf club and striking a ball seems like a graceful one," says Joseph Stiefel, physicist and golf ball designer with the Spalding Corporation in Springfield, Massachusetts, "but at the level at which club head meets ball, it's also a pretty complex and violent one."

To understand how complex and violent, Stiefel recommends starting off by imagining a perfect, platonic golf swing with a club speed of, say, 100 miles an hour. For most of us, this isn't easy. I haven't played golf often, but when I have, the only thing about my game that stood a chance of reaching 100 miles an hour was the perfect, platonic Pontiac in which I drove to the perfect, platonic country club, hoping all the while I wouldn't meet a perfect, platonic policeman. For accomplished players, however, a 100-mile-an-hour swing is by no means uncommon; for the ball, that can make things by all means unpleasant.

When a moving seven-ounce club head collides with a stationary 1.62-ounce ball, the first thing that happens is that the ball is temporarily flattened, losing about a third of its usual diameter. The club head, for its part, responds to the impact by sacrificing not size but speed, going from 100 miles per hour to just 81. Since energy can be neither created nor destroyed but only altered (and then only within 30 days of purchase), the 19 miles per hour the golf club seems to lose isn't lost at all but merely transferred to the compressed ball in the form of elastic energy. With the help of this kinetic infusion, the so-far passive golf ball suddenly becomes active.

"A ball will remain compressed for only so long before it springs back into shape," Stiefel says. "When it does, it pushes backward on the club head. This tiny push is enough to slow the golf club down further—to about 70 miles per hour—at the same time that it speeds the ball up, causing it

to fly away from the club at about 135 miles per hour."

To be sure, not all golf balls will display such pop. Just how well any given ball jumps off the club depends on what's known as its coefficient of restitution. The coefficient of restitution, for all its multisyllabic heft, is nothing more than a term scientists use to talk about bounciness. Why they don't just say bounciness is unclear, but from a community of people who say "high viscosity" when they mean "gooey," "high adhesion" when they mean "sticky," and "dissertation pending" when they mean "My dog ate my homework," some obfuscation is inevitable. Nonetheless, the coefficient of restitution is a deceptively simple idea.

"When a ball is dropped from a given height," says Michael Sullivan, Spalding's senior director of research, "the material it's made of will largely determine how high it bounces, and that height will be the measure of its coefficient of restitution." A rubber ball dropped from 100 inches may, for example, bounce back up to 60, which would give it a rough coefficient of restitution of .600. A billiard ball may bounce only 10 inches, for a rough coefficient of .100. A piece of clay, which would hit the floor and simply stay there, scores a perfect zero on the coefficient-of-restitution scale. (To calculate a true coefficient of restitution, Stiefel explains, these rough figures must be square-rooted or cube-rooted or root-rooted or *something*, but for anyone not planning on going into the golf ball manufacturing field this afternoon, rough numbers are probably okay.)

As soon as scientists devised the coefficient-of-restitution test, they realized that golf balls had been flunking. The featherie and the guttie ball had low to modest coefficients of restitution. When rubber balls were introduced in the twentieth cen-

tury, the rough number climbed above .600—better, but still a little leaden for many golfers' tastes. It was only in the 1970s that golf balls achieved true state-of-the-art spring, thanks to a substance known as polybutadiene.

Essentially a petroleum-based polymer, polybutadiene had been little more than a chemical curiosity until the late 1960s, when the *über*ball known as the Superball hit the toy market. Resembling a squash ball, the Superball was advertised as the ultimate rubber ball, and its bounce lived up to its billing, achieving a coefficient of restitution reaching the middle 800s. Not surprisingly, parents of that era were reluctant to buy children so high-octane a toy, and with good reason. Fully 30 years after the introduction of the product, suburban communities across the country still conduct occasional drills, as Superballs bounced in mid-1968 suddenly reappear menacingly over the horizon. Even the name of the company that manufactured the Superball—Wham-O—vaguely suggested mayhem, though other names reportedly under consideration (including Oops, Smash, and I Hope You Had Coverage for That) would almost certainly have been worse.

Predictably, a ball that could be bounced in Central Park and wind up in Fenway Park soon caught the eye of the golf industry. At Spalding, a chemist named Bob Molitor began toying with polybutadiene and immediately discovered that while a ball made of the polymer was more than strong enough to be bounced, it was a little too soft to withstand the punishment it would take when hit by a club-wielding golfer. To toughen the stuff enough to make it fit for the links, Molitor decided to fortify it with an unlikely material: zinc. Just what would make even the most optimistic industrial chemist conclude that the performance of any piece of sporting equipment could be improved by an element drawn from the ductile metals section of the periodic table is unclear ("Holy cow, Nolan Ryan really put some zinc on that pitch!"), but Molitor was evidently onto something.

"Polybutadiene, like all polymers," explains Sullivan, "is made of molecules arranged in long strands. What Molitor envisioned doing was mixing zinc salt with polybutadiene and allowing it to attach to bonding sites along the strands. This would cause the molecules to become cross-linked — they would essentially attach to one another in a ladderlike configuration — which would help strengthen the material."

To Molitor's delight, that's exactly what happened, leading to a new form of fortified polybutadiene that could survive even the hardest blow from the fastest club. When all the ciphering for the true coefficient of restitution had been done, the new golf ball bounced back with a kangaroo-style .890. Before long, Spalding had converted most of its golf balls to polybutadiene, and soon the rest of the industry followed suit, formally consigning the ordinary rubber ball to the same sporting goods dustbin in which the guttie ball and featherie had long resided.

But just because the interior of the golf ball had been reinvented did not mean all was well with the exterior—particularly with that most identifiable feature of the exterior: the dimple. While the presence of the golf ball dimple has always been something of a given in the sporting goods world, the purpose of it hasn't. In a recent, utterly unscientific survey I conducted of a sample group known as Drivers of New York City Cabs I've Been in Recently, the three most common answers to the question "What is the purpose of a golf ball's dimples?" were:

1) "Uh, something to do with grip?"
2) "Uh, something to do with appearance?"
3) "Ero B Mahxatah?"

Not surprisingly, number three is the closest to being correct. When a golf ball in flight plows through the atmosphere, it leaves a sort of semi-airless trench behind it. Since nature abhors even partial vacuums, it immediately tries to fill them, and in the case of the golf ball, that means that air and suspended particles in the vicinity are going to be drawn toward the low-pressure wake. One other — less expected — thing affected by the partial vacuum is the golf ball itself, which is pulled subtly backward by the trail it's

created. Over the course of the ball's flight, this insistent tug
acts like a brake, dragging the ball down to Earth sooner
than it would otherwise have fallen. In the early part of the
twentieth century, when golf balls were still smooth, designers discovered that the balls that suffered least from this
phenomenon appeared to be the oldest ones, those with the
most pits and gouges in their surface. Somehow the exterior
flaws seemed to be able to snag and hold the air as the ball
passed through it, keeping it swaddled in atmosphere
throughout its flight.

"A ball that travels through the atmosphere wrapped in
a corona of air leaves not a vacuum trail in its wake but simply a stream of more air," Stiefel says, "and this can help
keep it aloft. When designers realized this, the idea of
putting flaws in the ball on purpose—dimples, in other
words—was born."

As a general rule, the more dimples a ball has the better it flies, provided those dimples are about .15 inch in
diameter, the average size shown to favor flightworthiness.
Sprinkling the dimples evenly over the face of the golf ball
gives a total dimple population of about 336. For decades
the 336-dimple ball held sway, but in recent years manufacturers have discovered that the size of an effective dimple
can vary by one-hundredth or two-hundredths of an inch,
meaning that the number of dimples can vary, too, by 50 to
100 per ball.

"In recent years," says Sullivan, "more and more golf
balls with 400 and even 500 dimples have appeared on the
market, with new ones being tested all the time."

Some of the most dramatic testing is taking place not

at Sullivan's and Stiefel's own Spalding, but across the state in Fairhaven, where the competing Acushnet company manufactures the popular Titleist ball. Standing in a wing of the Acushnet factory is the industry's—and, indeed, the world's—only wind tunnel designed exclusively for golf balls. While wind tunnels have always been helpful in designing such things as passenger jets and missiles, their record with consumer products is a little spottier. It was the aerodynamic ideal established by wind tunnels, after all, that was at least partly responsible for the finned family cars of the 1960s, a time when the average automobile had all the sleekness of the average shopping mall. Despite this history, the Acushnet wind tunnel seems just the thing if you're trying to build the perfect golf ball.

"The tunnel we use to study our balls is far smaller than ordinary wind tunnels—about 40 feet long with a 75-horsepower fan," says Steve Aoyama, Acushnet's product research manager. "At one end is the fan, at the other is an opening from which the fan draws in air, and in the center is a 36-inch-by-18-inch test chamber along with an observation room for engineers. In order to test our products, we suspend a prototype ball over the test chamber, get the fan going, drop the ball in, and see what happens."

On the surface, this sounds pretty scientific, but unless I'm missing a Newtonian step here, what should happen is that the ball will—as physicists like to say—fall down. And indeed that is what happens, but in the instant it is falling, a lot of other things are going on, too.

"Before the ball is dropped," Aoyama says, "we set it spinning with the same RPMs it would achieve when hit by a golf club. As it's falling, a battery of high-speed cameras take its picture. To the untrained eye, the path the ball takes to the floor does not look like much, but the trajectory can actually tell you a lot about the ball's lift and drag properties. When the pictures are digitized and entered into a computer, the computer analysis helps us change the ball's dimple pattern to improve those properties accordingly."

How much the golf ball's dimple pattern—or its polymer core or its coefficient of restitution—will continue to change is uncertain, but what is certain is that they *will* change. Even after two millennia, it is this mutability that probably most distinguishes the golf ball from practically every other ball used in every other sport. Unless tennis tournaments are suddenly sponsored by depilatory makers, tennis balls are unlikely to get any less fuzzy. Unless bowling leagues suddenly become popular in the squid community, bowling balls are unlikely to develop many more holes. Unless Olympic coaches begin serving frosty mugs of androgens during qualifying trials, shot puts are unlikely to get any heavier. The golf ball, however, and thus the game of golf in general, are works in progress. Now if only they could do something about the checkered pants. ∎

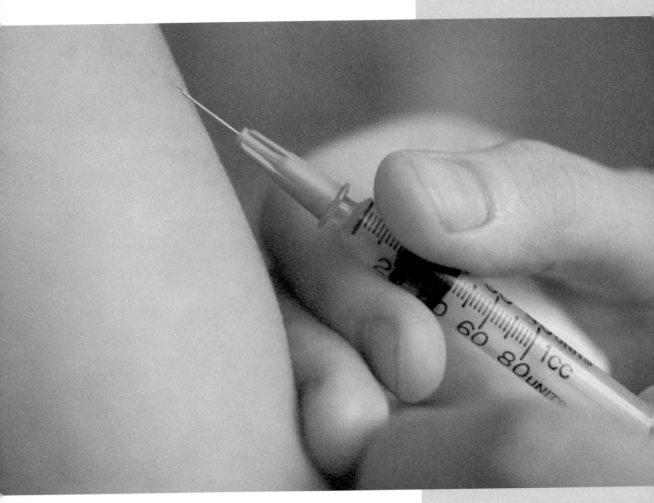

Bayes's Theorem, *n.* (*Statistics*) the fundamental result that expresses the CONDITIONAL PROBABILITY $P(E \mid A)$ of an even E given an even A as

$$P(E \mid A) = P(A \mid E)\frac{P(E)}{P(A)};$$

more generally, where E_n is one of a set of E_i that constitute a PARTITION of the sample space,

$$P(E_n \mid A) = \frac{P(A \mid E_n)\ P(E_n)}{\sum_i [\,P(A \mid E_i)\ P(E_i)\,]}$$

The Mathematics of Making Up Your Mind

BY WILL HIVELY

With a wee bit of guidance from an obscure eighteenth-century clergyman, statisticians are figuring out how to factor subjective judgments into their objective equations.

Two or three times a week, while a life hangs in the balance, James Brophy makes a quick decision. Brophy is a cardiologist at Centre Hospitalier de Verdun, in suburban Montreal, which treats about 300 heart attack victims a year. As they arrive, Brophy orders roughly half of them—the ones who made it to the hospital quickly enough—to be injected with one of two clot-busting drugs, streptokinase or tissue plasminogen activator (t-PA). All cardiologists agree that both drugs work well: more than 90 percent of all patients who receive either medication survive. Where they disagree is on the question of which of the drugs they should use. To be sure, thick reports convey the results of clinical trials designed to test the relative merits of the two drugs. But unfortunately the meaning of the data is confusing.

Like every other cardiologist—and, most certainly, like every patient—Brophy would like to know which drug is superior. And to that end, he's waded through a pile of tricky statistics, skirted deep philosophical questions involving how we can know anything at all, and teamed up with Lawrence Joseph, a biostatistician at McGill University. Last year they published a controversial paper advising other doctors how to cut through the statistical fog. To make a rational choice, Brophy and Joseph declared, physicians of the late twentieth century should learn the mental techniques of an obscure eighteenth-century Englishman: the Reverend Thomas Bayes.

Despite his clerical title, the Reverend Thomas Bayes' most enduring work is mathematical, not spiritual. In 1763 he proposed a procedure, known as Bayes' theorem, for evaluating evidence. Early in this century, with the rise of modern statistics — a different set of procedures for evaluating evidence — Bayes' theorem fell out of favor. Recently, however, some researchers have returned to Bayesian ideas.

Mathematicians, by and large, don't find Bayesian procedures very exciting. The people who use them tend to be analysts working on practical problems that require someone to make a risky decision based on imperfect information: evaluating the health risks of radioactive pollutants, for example, even though precise exposure records may be lacking and the effects of low doses are not well understood; or estimating the reliability of backup diesel generators at nuclear power plants, though there have been very few real-life emergencies. One of the Big Three auto companies even paid a statistician good money to design Bayesian software that forecasts warranty claims for new-model cars, although no data yet exist on the long-term performance of those cars.

Bayesian procedures, in theory, are tailor-made for these kinds of "messy" problems, which often involve complex science, uncertain evidence, and quarreling experts — the sort of mess a cardiologist might face when choosing between streptokinase and t-PA. "I've used these drugs," says Brophy, "and participated in clinical trials." But his limited experience didn't count for much, and two large trials, run in 1990 and 1993, one involving some 20,000 patients and the other almost 30,000, proved equivocal. Streptokinase did slightly better in one, t-PA in the other. "Essentially," says Brophy, "they found no big difference between the two drugs."

There *is* one big difference, though. T-PA costs about $1,530 a pop, streptokinase $220. In Canada and Europe, most doctors give streptokinase. In the United States, most doctors give t-PA. "In the States, you might be a lot more worried about whether someone will sue you if you don't use what the literature says is the 'best' drug," speculates Lawrence Joseph.

According to current wisdom, expensive t-PA probably does work better. T-PA, after all, is an enzyme found naturally in blood-vessel linings. Streptokinase, by contrast, is a foreign enzyme derived from streptococcus bacteria, and it can sometimes trigger an immune response. What's more, t-PA acts only at the site of a clot; streptokinase triggers blood-thinning reactions everywhere in the body.

But until a few years ago, the clinical evidence for that supposed superiority was still missing. Then Genentech, t-PA's manufacturer, joined with four other companies in sponsoring a third clinical trial — a *huge* trial this time, with over 40,000 patients — called GUSTO (Global Utilization of Streptokinase and Tissue Plasminogen Activator in Occluded Arteries). When the results were published in 1993, they looked so good for t-PA that the trial's leading researchers declared the drug "clinically superior" to streptokinase on the basis of this trial alone. The earlier trials, they said, had been flawed.

At the time, Brophy, who had gone back to school for his Ph.D. in epidemiology and biostatistics, was studying statistics with Joseph at McGill. When he learned about Bayes' theorem, it changed his way of thinking about such trial results — or rather, it added precision to a way of thinking he'd always used but had previously considered outside the realm of statistics. It mixed personal beliefs right in with the math. Ignorant ideas or expert opinions, the predilections of monsters or saints — anything at all could go in, and Bayes' theorem would turn out a rational conclusion.

According to standard procedures, an analyst should look objectively at the data from any one study. In evaluating a large clinical trial, for instance, he might say that patients taking drug x survived more often than patients taking drug y, so x is better than y. Everyone who looks at the same data should reach the same conclusion. A Bayesian, however, might look at the evidence and think, "Aha! Just as I suspected: it's a toss-up between those drugs." Another Bayesian might decide that y is better than x.

How are such different conclusions possible? Each Bayesian analyst evaluates the same evidence, using Bayes' theorem. Yet each may also bring other information to bear on the problem. According to many Bayesians, statistics should reflect everything we know about a given question — all relevant prior experience. Each analyst must judge, subjectively, which experience is relevant — folklore? similar clinical trials? — and how much that prior evidence should sway belief in the latest results.

Bayes' theorem does not *require* an analyst to weigh evidence subjectively, but it allows him to do so. And that, say critics, shifts the foundation of the analysis from rock-solid mathematics to the quicksand of personal opinion.

Detractors call the Bayesian method an exercise in arbitrary thinking—a soft, subjective brand of statistics.

The Reverend Thomas Bayes himself is a shady figure. The first time he surfaced as a mathematician, he was already dead. Posthumously, in 1764, the British Royal Society published Bayes' theorem about probabilities. Essentially it was a formula for updating any kind of belief when confronted with new evidence. Bayes described it originally in words that mathematicians and philosophers still struggle to interpret: "The *probability of an event* is the ratio between the value at which an expectation depending on the happening of the event ought to be computed, and the value of the thing expected upon its happening."

Fortunately, Bayes had an editor. To illustrate how the method worked—how he *thought* it worked—the editor added an appendix containing a charming example: "Let us imagine to ourselves the case of a person just brought forth in this world" and left alone to observe it. "The Sun would, probably, be the first object that would engage his attention; but after losing it the first night he would be entirely ignorant whether he should ever see it again." Our new person, dreading the uncertainty, decides to compute the probability of sunrise.

During his first night, this babe in the woods might decide that the probability of the sun's coming back is not good. That's called a prior probability. Bayes' theorem explains how a babe should update this belief if he runs across new evidence—in this case a sunrise. He starts with his prior probability, adds the new evidence, cranks it all through a computing machine, and out comes an updated "posterior probability"—the new belief.

You can do it yourself with a simple computer: a bowl and some balls. Start out with, say, one white and one black ball in the bowl, representing "sun will return" and "sun will not return." The odds your computer will give for sunrise are the odds of picking a white ball from the bowl.

At the beginning, you have no idea what to expect; your prior belief is completely arbitrary. Some Bayesians recommend starting, always, with even odds—one white ball and one black. Others don't mind more subjective choices. But let's say you start out with a neutral belief in the face of global catastrophe: 50-50 odds that the sun will return. Every time you see a sunrise, you add a white ball to the bowl. After two sightings, the odds look better for a third sunrise: two to one in favor (67 percent probability). After three sightings, the odds are three to one in favor (75 percent probability), and so on. Every day, as the sun keeps returning, you keep raising the probability it will return yet again. After a while, the initial, arbitrary odds hardly matter. The white balls overwhelm the black balls of doubt, just as evidence should always overwhelm superstition.

When should you give up this cumbersome routine and declare sunrise practically dead certain? Whenever it suits you; there's no rule for stopping.

Starting out with subjective beliefs is the whole point of Bayesian statistics; it liberates analysts from the "statistical slavery" of bean counting.

Early in the nineteenth century the great French mathematician Pierre-Simon Laplace translated Bayes' sketchy ideas into usable formulas. With his work, statistical thinking grew out of its mathematical infancy. Some Bayesians, in fact, say their method should probably be called Laplacean. But no matter whose name is attached, Bayes' brand of statistics reigned supreme for a century. Then, near the end of the nineteenth century, the English statistician Sir Ronald Fisher developed simpler and more objective procedures for analyzing data, and by the 1920s almost everyone was using them. With Fisher's methods, a researcher could determine whether the results from any one study were significant. If they were, there would be no need to look at other studies, no need to update an arbitrary prior belief, and no need for the Reverend Thomas Bayes. Everyone could just believe the evidence at hand.

Nowadays when the results of some new study earn the label "statistically significant," we take this as a mathematical seal of approval. It means we can almost certainly believe the new evidence. Fisher's work gave rise to this notion, clarifying the advantage of large trials. If you flip a coin four times and get three heads, is that significant? Would you conclude that the probability of getting heads is 75 percent? Probably not. Those results could well be a fluke—a random long run. If you flip a coin 1,000 times, you would expect most random long runs, such as 3 or even 30 heads in a row, to be balanced by similar long runs of tails. You would expect, overall, results much closer to 50 percent heads and 50 percent tails. The larger your number of coin flips, the more significant your results are likely to be, and the more confident you can be that they are true.

Fisher and several others developed formal tools for calculating significance. One measure of an experiment's significance is called the p-value, another is called the confidence interval, and yet another is popularly known as the margin of error. These are all ways of comparing the results actually found in the trial with the numbers you would expect from pure chance. The larger a trial, an experiment, or an opinion poll, the smaller your p-value, confidence interval, or margin of error. If you are looking for small differences between drugs, you need a small margin of error, which means a large clinical trial.

Fisher applied his methods to classic probability problems, such as Gregor Mendel's famous experiments with peas. When Mendel wanted to know if wrinkling was an inherited characteristic, he grew smooth and wrinkled peas, crossbred them, and looked at the second generation. If about three-fourths of the peas in the second generation were wrinkled, that would suggest wrinkling was inherited as a dominant character; if about one-fourth were wrinkled, it was a recessive character. Any other ratios would rule out inheritance, according to Mendel's genetic hypothesis.

These kinds of experiments reduce the statistician's role, essentially, to pea counting. You don't make any judgment about including, say, similar trials with old, wrinkled beans; you just keep counting thousands of peas until you reach some arbitrary level of significance that satisfies all critics. Lawrence Joseph believes that analysts who use these procedures on such cut-and-dried problems "do not in any way, shape, or form need to know anything about anything. They just take the data, plug them in, and get an answer."

That's fine for peas but not for new cars, which do not roll off the assembly lines with long-term maintenance data ready to plug in. Nor will standard methods work for estimating the reliability of backup diesel generators, which hardly ever get used. And trials with human, of course, raise questions far more complex and statistically messy than the heritability of smoothness or wrinkles. "Had you asked

Fisher to analyze a clinical trial back then," Joseph continues, "he may not have thought his methods were good for
that. We'll never know, but the types of problems he was
looking at are very different from what Bayesians are looking at today"—problems like choosing between streptokinase and t-PA.

GUSTO showed that when t-PA was administered
rapidly and combined with aggressive follow-up therapy, it
clearly came out on top: 93.7 percent of patients who
received t-PA survived, versus 92.7 percent of those who
received streptokinase. A 1 percent difference may seem
small, but in cardiology it can mean a lot. In the United
States alone, half a million people die of heart attacks every
year. Of course, not all those people make it to the emergency room in time for the drugs to work, but if they did,
and if 1 percent more of them survived, that would mean
5,000 lives saved. One percent, in fact, happened to be the
cutoff point the researchers who conducted the new trial had
chosen as proof of t-PA's "clinical superiority." One additional life saved, they said, among every 100 patients injected would justify the higher cost of t-PA. This is, of course, as
Joseph grouses, a subjective opinion.

The larger your number of coin flips,
the more significant your results are
likely to be, and the more confident
you can be that they are true.

Aside from that quibble, GUSTO met the gold standard for clinical trials: a very large number of patients—41,021 of them—randomly assigned to groups that received one drug or the other. The 1 percent difference looked real. If streptokinase and t-PA were equally effective, you would almost never see a difference in survival rates as large as 1 percent. By the laws of probability, for a trial that large, there was only one chance in 1,000 that t-PA would perform so much better if it was merely as good as streptokinase. So the conclusion seemed unassailable, according to standard, classical statistics: reach for the t-PA, and shell out the extra bucks.

Most practicing physicians would accept GUSTO as a decisive. But Brophy could not bring himself to ignore the earlier trials. In his gut, he could not believe t-PA was that much better than streptokinase. "If you're having to put close to 100,000 people into these trials," he says, "you don't need to be a Bayesian analyst to say, jeez, there's probably not a big difference between them, right?"

He and Joseph decided to reanalyze all the data on streptokinase and t-PA. In March 1995 they published their conclusions in the *Journal of the American Medical Association*. Their widely read article, "Placing Trials in Context Using Bayesian Analysis," was more than a comparison of two drugs. It was an all-out pitch for Bayesian methods. Brophy and Joseph wanted to change the way doctors think about clinical trials. Five pages deep in their paper, after some light mathematical skirmishing, they dropped a bombshell.

By any standard significance test, the 1 percent superiority of t-PA seems almost as certain as a law of physics. But according to Brophy and Joseph, the probability of t-PA's being clinically superior is at best 50-50, if you consider GUSTO evidence alone. And if you have any belief at all in earlier results, the odds for clinical superiority drop rapidly to "negligible."

Any doctor who reads the article can start with a subjective prior belief and then use the published data to reach a personal Bayesian conclusion. Brophy and Joseph explain how to do it. One option, for example, is to start with no prior beliefs, like a standard statistician, and accept only the GUSTO results. Surprisingly, this yields no better than a 50 percent probability that t-PA is clinically superior. That's because t-PA's 1 percent better survival rate has a margin of error. The small size of the margin doesn't matter. What matters is that if you ran the same trial again, with 41,000 new patients, t-PA might surpass 1 percent or fall short. In a truly random clinical trial, the odds are 50-50 that a new trial would go either way.

Since the GUSTO result of 1 percent is also the cutoff point for t-PA's clinical superiority, the odds are only about 50-50 that t-PA is actually clinically superior, on the basis of GUSTO alone. A non-Bayesian analyst could have figured this out. If the GUSTO researchers had picked any other value for clinical superiority, the odds would have come out differently. As it was, the researchers chose a small value for clinical superiority and yet barely squeaked in with their results. So the strongest degree of belief anyone can reasonably have in t-PA's minimal superiority is merely, shall we say, halfhearted.

This discouraging conclusion does not contradict the impressively high significance of the GUSTO study. Significance is one thing and clinical superiority is another, although it's easy to confuse them—as Brophy suspected some doctors would do when reading the GUSTO study. Given the GUSTO results, say Brophy and Lawrence, the probability is that if you ran 1,000 trials, t-PA might do better 999 times. But how often would it do 1 percent better? The answer, at best, is about half those times. You can be 99.9 percent certain that t-PA is better than streptokinase and, at the same time, only 50 percent certain it's clinically superior.

That's if you start with no prior belief, like a babe in the woods. If you assign more credibility—any whatsoever —to earlier trials, the clinical superiority of t-PA looks less likely. Brophy and Joseph illustrate three options: 10 percent, 50 percent, and 100 percent belief in the results from two earlier trials. You can choose any degree of belief as your starting point—it's your own subjective judgment.

If you choose 10 percent, it means you are giving the earlier evidence only one-tenth the statistical weight of the GUSTO evidence. If you accept earlier results at the maximum value, 100 percent, you are skeptical that the differences between trials—the rapid administration of t-PA, the follow-up therapy, and so on—mean very much. You are willing to take the results from all three trials at face value and lump them together. That option yields the lowest probability, nearly zero, that t-PA is clinically superior.

But why stop at an impartial, equal belief in all three trials? Brophy and Joseph drop a hint that the GUSTO data might count for less. Physicians participating in the study knew which drug they were giving—it was not a blind trial—and patients who got t-PA were "apparently" 1 percent more likely to have a coronary bypass operation as well.

This kind of give-and-take is typical of complex scientific problems. Contradictory conclusions are also typical; you can see them every day in newspapers. On January 4, for example, the Associated Press wire service reported this new evidence on global warming: "The world's average surface temperature for 1995 was 58.72 degrees Fahrenheit, or 0.7 degree higher than the average for 1961-1990, said Phil Jones of the Climatic Research Unit at the University of East Anglia in England." It was the highest average surface temperature ever recorded for a single year.

Three experts commented on the new statistic. "'This is the culmination of a whole series of findings which demonstrate that the world is warming,' said Michael Oppenheimer, an atmospheric scientist at the Environmental Defense Fund. 'The question is no longer whether the climate is changing, the question is now what are we going to do about it.'" Oppenheimer's prior belief in other evidence clearly influenced him to accept this new information about surface temperature at face value.

Kevin Trenberth of the National Center for Atmospheric Research in Boulder, Colorado, "cautioned that the British study may exaggerate the amount of overall warming." It seemed to him perhaps a fluke. This could be an argument for counting more peas.

The third expert, climatologist Patrick Michaels of the University of Virginia, referred to specific prior evidence. "'There is now a statistically significant difference,' he said, 'between the temperatures measured in that [British] land-based record and temperatures measured by satellites.'" He gave the satellite evidence more weight; satellites have better coverage. "'The net temperature trend in the satellite record, which just finished its 17th year, is actually slightly negative,' he said. 'I think in the long run you're just going to see increasing conformation of the hypothesis that the warming would not be nearly as large as it was forecast to be.'"

To Joseph, this all represents ad hoc interpretation that would be vastly improved by Bayesian analysis. Of course, no one expects a researcher to reel off impeccable Bayesian logic while talking to a reporter. But Joseph sees a deeper problem, which demonstrates the glaring deficiency of standard procedures. First some "objective" data arrive on the scene, almost completely out of context. Then some "interpretation" smacks the new evidence around. This happens even in scientific journals. Researchers pull prior evidence from all over the map, "but it's never done at a formal level," Brophy complains. "The difference in a Bayesian analysis is that it forces you to consider the prior information formally, and formally put it into your analysis." That way, "at least you could check the subjectivity." And subjectivity always exists, or scientists would never disagree. "It is the degree that subjectivity is apparent," Joseph says, "that makes for good science."

Most Bayesians would say that your prior "degrees of belief" should not be pulled from thin air. Some say they should not be pulled from anywhere; since they believe Bayesian statistics should be no more subjective than the classical kind, they favor using a standard value, such as giving each set of data equal weight. Others, like George Washington University statistician Nozer Singpurwalla, one of the more passionate Bayesian revivalists, say that starting out with subjective degrees of belief is the whole point of Bayesian statistics; it liberates analysts from the "statistical slavery" of bean counting.

As for Brophy, he is still at Centre Hospitalier de Verdun, going about his grueling business. In his spare time he is also still working on his Ph.D. Along the way, as part of a project for only one class, he may have changed the way clinicians will interpret data from clinical trials — or at least one of the largest trials in medical history. He personally rates the chances of t-PA's being clinically superior to streptokinase as "no better than 5 or 10 percent." At that rate, t-PA might save only one more life among every 250 heart attack victims. Would that person's life be worth the extra $327,500, say, that it would cost to give all those patients the more expensive medicine?

"As a physician," Brophy says, "your primary responsibility is toward your patient. You also have to give a little thought to the next patients coming in. Maybe your hospital is going broke and can't treat them down the line. These are hard questions to face. People would rather not."

And that, in the end, may be the biggest problem the Bayesians face. Their procedure forces people to examine their beliefs, as Joseph says — and possibly change them. People would rather not. ∎

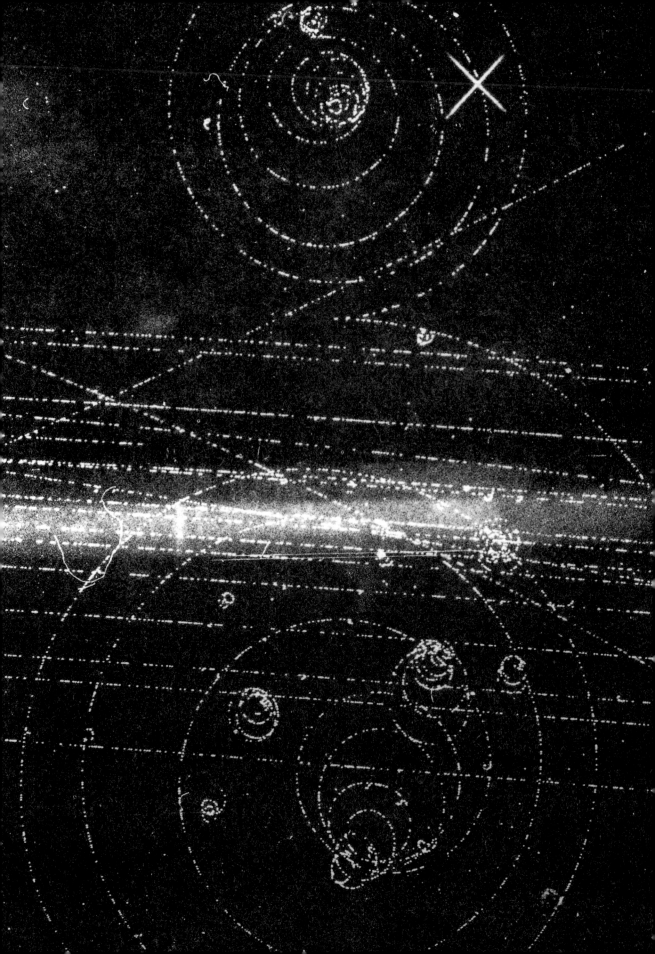

EXPLORING THE UNIVERSE WITHIN THE ATOM

BY ROSE SECREST

In 1996 physicists made use of recent technological advances to increase their knowledge of atomic structure. Discoveries made using powerful particle accelerators, high-speed computers, lasers, and other advanced equipment answered many questions about the fundamental nature of matter but created new mysteries to be solved.

NEW TOOLS FOR STUDYING SUBATOMIC PARTICLES

The world's largest center for nuclear research upgraded one of its most important instruments in July of 1996. The Large Electron-Positron (LEP) collider at the Center for European Nuclear Research (Centre Européen de Recherche Nucléaire, CERN) in Geneva, Switzerland, was increased from an energy of about 91 gigaelectronvolts (GeV) to about 161 GeV. The LEP, formerly used to produce Z particles, will now be used to produce W particles as well. By studying Z and W particles, researchers hope to gain a better understanding of the subatomic interaction known as the weak force.

Meanwhile, plans were made for an even more powerful accelerator at CERN. In March of 1996 officials of the United States Department of Energy and the National Science Foundation agreed to work with European scientists and engineers to build the Large Hadron Collider (LHC). The LHC and its two main particle detectors, estimated to cost about $4 billion, are expected to take about ten years to construct. Once completed, the LHC will be used to produce proton-proton collisions with an energy of about 14,000 GeV. Researchers hope this enormous amount of energy will allow them to detect a hypothetical particle known as a Higgs boson, which is believed to be responsible for determining the mass of other particles.

While this gigantic accelerator is being built, other scientists are working on the possibility of building an accelerator that could fit on a tabletop. Lasers are used to produce bursts of light as short as 100 femtoseconds (one femtosec-

PHYSICAL SCIENCE | 335

ond equals one-millionth of one-billionth of a second) and containing a power of up to 100 trillion watts. Donald P. Umstadter and coworkers at the Center for Ultrafast Optical Science at the University of Michigan in Ann Arbor use these lasers to produce a beam of electrons with an energy of one GeV after about one centimeter of acceleration. If the acceleration path can be increased to a few meters, researchers may be able to reach energies equivalent to conventional accelerators several kilometers long.

Although not as dramatic as an accelerator, a new instrument known as the Gammasphere is also being used to study atomic structure. This device is used at the Lawrence National Laboratory in Berkeley, California, to detect gamma rays emitted by rapidly spinning nuclei produced during high-energy collisions of ions. The Gammasphere consists of a metal sphere more than 2 meters in diameter and contains more than one hundred sensors. Because these nuclei spin so quickly, they often have unusual shapes resembling footballs or pancakes.

PARTICLE ACCELERATORS: NEW ANSWERS, NEW QUESTIONS

Particle accelerators, the most important devices used to study subatomic physics, enabled scientists to make new discoveries about the structure of matter in 1996 but raised at least as many questions as they answered. Because of the difficulty of extracting useful information from the immense amount of data produced by accelerators, these discoveries were often announced only after years of analysis.

Based on observations made in 1992 and 1993, physicists at the Fermi National Accelerator Laboratory (Fermilab) in Batavia, Illinois, made a startling announcement in February 1996. The Tevatron accelerator at Fermilab, which collides protons and antiprotons at an energy of up to 1,800 GeV, appeared to produce evidence that quarks, normally thought to be the smallest subunits of matter, may contain even smaller components. Most scientists believe that the results from the Tevatron can be explained by the uncertainty of the complex calculations needed to interpret them. If the existence of particles smaller than quarks is confirmed, it will be a revolutionary discovery.

Data from 1993 were used by researchers at the International Business Machines (IBM) Corporation's

Fermi National Accelerator Laboratory (Fermilab), Illinois.

Thomas J. Watson Research Center in Yorktown Heights, New York, to announce evidence for the discovery of a hypothetical particle known as a glueball in early 1996. Glueballs are made up of particles known as gluons, which are believed to hold quarks together. A special high-speed computer took more than two years to calculate the mass of the lightest possible glueball in what was said to be the largest single numerical calculation in the history of computing. The calculated mass of 1.707 GeV matches well with a particle seen to have a mass of 1.71 GeV.

Other physicists were fortunate enough to be able to obtain results without waiting so long. In January of 1996 a team of researchers led by Walter Oelert of the Institute for Nuclear Physics in Jülich, Germany, was able to announce the first synthesis of atoms of antimatter after only three weeks of observations. Although scientists have been able to produce antiprotons and antielectrons (positrons) for years, no one had been able to bring them together to form antiatoms. Using the Low Energy Antiproton Ring (LEAR) at CERN, the researchers were able to create atoms of antihydrogen that lasted forty-billionths of a second before being destroyed by contact with ordinary atoms. The team hopes to be able to isolate antiatoms for several hours in order to study their properties.

A unique event in accelerator physics was announced in April of 1996, when physicists at Fermilab described a single particle collision out of millions of observations which could not be fully explained by the standard model of subatomic particles. Instead, it seemed to fit an extension of the standard model known as supersymmetry, which postulates the existence of several hypothetical particles such as the selectron and the photino. Researchers hope to discover more evidence for supersymmetry at the LEP collider at CERN.

The standard model of particle physics was also challenged in May of 1996, when scientists at the Los Alamos National Laboratory in New Mexico reported evidence that neutrinos, usually thought to be massless, may possess a very small amount of mass. Neutrinos are extremely common particles but are difficult to study because they rarely interact with other forms of matter. Neutrinos exist as electron neutrinos, muon neutrinos, tau neutrinos, and the corresponding antineutrinos.

The Los Alamos researchers used particle accelerators to produce high-energy protons that collided with water molecules to produce pions, which decayed into muons and muon neutrinos. The muons decayed into positrons, electron neutrinos, and muon antineutrinos. A small fraction of the various neutrinos and antineutrinos produced by these decays were then detected using a large tank of mineral oil surrounded by photodetectors. Out of three years' worth of data, twenty-two electron antineutrinos were detected, which should not have been produced by this process. Scientists believe that some muon antineutrinos were transformed into electron antineutrinos, which could take place only if neutrinos have mass. The mass of a neutrino is estimated to be less than one-millionth of the mass of an electron. If confirmed, the existence of this tiny mass would greatly increase current estimates of the mass of the universe.

Another discovery made using particle accelerators also had important implications for astronomy. Physicists believe that immediately after the Big Bang the universe consisted of a superhot mixture of unbound quarks and gluons known as a quark-gluon plasma. At a conference held in Heidelberg, Germany, physicists from CERN announced results suggesting that microscopic quark-gluon plasmas had been created during high-energy particle collisions. These collisions, performed at CERN's Super Proton Synchrotron, involved lead nuclei hitting lead targets with an energy of 3,600 GeV.

Researchers led by Louis Kluberg of the École Polytechnique in Palaiseau, France, measured the rate at which these collisions formed J/Psi particles. They found only half as many of these particles as expected. This suggested that some J/Psi particles were broken down in quark-gluon plasmas. Researchers studying other particles formed during these collisions found similar evidence. The Relativistic Heavy Ion Collider, scheduled to begin operating at the Brookhaven National Laboratory in Upton, New York, in 1999, is expected to produce more quark-gluon plasmas. By studying the properties of these plasmas, physicists hope for a better understanding of the beginning of the universe.

Particle accelerators can also be used to create new elements. In February of 1996 Sigurd Hofmann and coworkers at GSI, the center for heavy ion studies in Darmstadt, Germany, detected a single atom of element 112. The new element was created by the fusion of a high-energy zinc ion with a lead atom and decayed after less than a millisecond. Elements 110 and 111 were created at GSI in 1994, and the institute hopes to create elements 113 and 114 in the near future. Atomic theory predicts that element 114 should be much more stable than other new elements. The GSI researchers hope to confirm this prediction.

In a similar experiment, physicists at the State University of New York in Stony Brook announced in May of 1996 that they had created atoms of the naturally occurring but rare and highly unstable element francium by fusing oxygen and gold atoms. They were able to keep these atoms in a glass bulb by using an array of lasers to hold them in place, allowing their radioactive decay to be studied in detail.

THE STRANGE WORLD OF QUANTUM MECHANICS

In 1996 important discoveries were also made in the branch of subatomic physics known as quantum mechanics. Quantum effects, which are rarely apparent under ordinary circumstances, often seem to contradict common sense.

In a structure known as a quantum dot, for example, a team of physicists led by Raymond C. Ashoori of the Massachusetts Institute of Technology (MIT) in Cambridge discovered unusual electron behavior. A quantum dot, composed of semiconductors, is like an artificial atom but contains much more empty space than an ordinary atom. This extra space allows subtle quantum effects to be seen. When exposed to a magnetic field, some of the electrons inside a quantum dot appear to attract each other, unlike ordinary electrons, which always repel each other.

A similar discovery was made by a team of physicists from the University of Nottingham in the United Kingdom and the University of Tokyo in Japan using a device known as a tunnel diode. This device traps electrons in a space known as a quantum well, consisting of a thin layer of gallium arsenide between two layers of aluminum gallium arsenide. The electrons bounce back and forth inside the quantum well. When exposed to a magnetic field, the motion of the electrons becomes extremely complex. Within this apparent chaos, however, can be found repeating patterns of electron movement known as quantum scars. These quantum scars cause the tunnel diode to undergo abrupt changes in electrical current, an effect that may have practical applications in electronic devices.

Quantum effects were also studied using an unusual state of matter known as a Bose-Einstein condensate. Created for the first time in 1995, Bose-Einstein condensates consist of thousands or millions of atoms that are all in the same quantum state. They are created by cooling atoms of rubidium, sodium, or lithium to a temperature below two microkelvins. This forms a dense cloud of supercold gas which behaves as if it were a single particle. In 1996 researchers at several institutions began producing Bose-Einstein condensates in amounts sufficient to investigate their properties. Wolfgang Ketterle and his colleagues at MIT produced the first direct images of a Bose-Einstein condensate by using laser light of a color that was able to penetrate the gas cloud without disturbing it. The cloud acted as a lens, forming an image of itself.

Perhaps the strangest discovery made in 1996 involving quantum effects was an experiment in which an atom

The National Institute of Standards and Technology, Boulder, Colorado.

was made to exist in two places at once. Physicists at the National Institute of Standards and Technology in Boulder, Colorado, used a laser to produce a supercold atom of beryllium. They then used a rapid series of laser pulses to cause the atom to vibrate in such a way that it briefly appeared simultaneously in two positions eighty nanometers apart. This seemingly impossible result confirms certain aspects of quantum theory.

Some scientists have been working on methods of putting quantum mechanics to work. Quantum effects make it possible for a hypothetical quantum computer to perform calculations much more quickly than a conventional computer. Although quantum computers are impossible to build using present-day technology because their components must be kept perfectly isolated from the rest of the universe, scientists study their hypothetical operations in order to better understand computer science and quantum mechanics.

In early 1996 Lov K. Grover of the ATT Bell Laboratories in Murray Hills, New Jersey, described a technique that would greatly reduce the time needed for a quantum computer to find a single piece of information in a random list. For a search that would normally take fifty thousand steps, this method would require only one hundred steps. Meanwhile, scientists at the ATT Bell Laboratories and at the IBM Thomas J. Watson Research Center have devised methods to prevent errors from distorting information in quantum computers.

On June 17, 1996, Harald Weinfurter and coworkers at the University of Innsbruck in Austria announced that they had achieved the first use of quantum mechanics in communication. This process involved splitting a beam of ultraviolet laser light into two beams of opposite polarization containing pairs of photons linked by quantum effects. One beam went to the sender of the message and the other to the receiver. The sender manipulated the polarization of the photons in the first beam and sent it on to the receiver. The two beams interfered with each other to form distinctive patterns based on whether the linked pairs of photons were both horizontally polarized, both vertically polarized, or opposite. In this manner each pair of photons could be encoded in three ways. Because of this triple coding the researchers were able to transmit letters of the alphabet using fewer pairs of photons than the single, binary-coded photons normally used in electronic communication.

OTHER METHODS OF ATOMIC RESEARCH

Not all research into subatomic physics in 1996 involved particle accelerators or quantum mechanics. Many discoveries were made using less dramatic but no less important technology.

Richard A. Webb and his colleagues at the University of Maryland in College Park were studying magnetically induced electric currents in tiny gold rings at low temperature when they found that an unexplained current, less than one-billionth of an ampere, persisted when the magnetism was turned off. The researchers speculate that similar currents may be responsible for distorting information in miniaturized electronic components.

A new method of manipulating particles was discovered in 1996. In April Jun-ichi Fujita and his colleagues at the NEC Fundamental Research Laboratories in Tsukuba, Japan, announced that they had used a hologram to diffract a stream of supercold neon atoms onto a detector plate. The atoms were diffracted in such a way as to produce a series of images of the letter F one micrometer high. This technique may be used in the future to print microscopic computer circuits. ∎

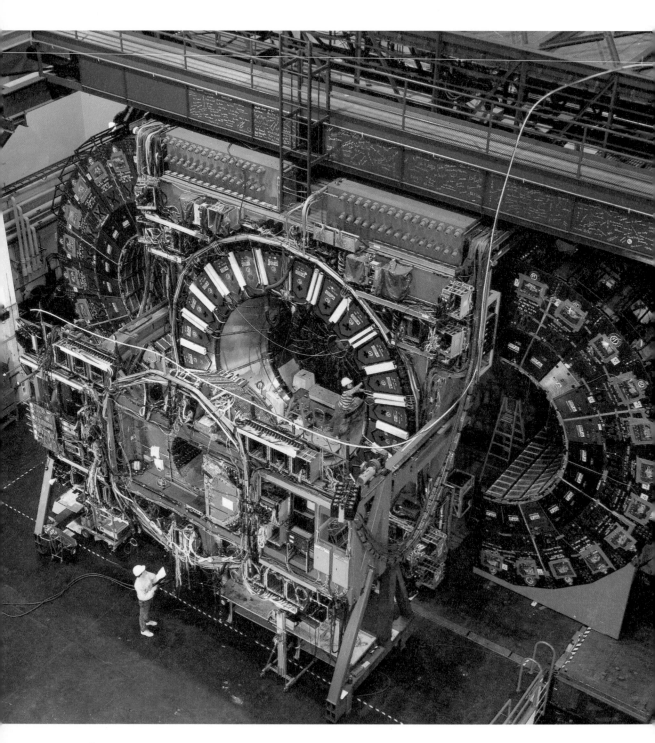

Top Quark Mass Measurement

BY JOSEPH L. SPRADLEY

n August of 1996, a group of researchers at the Fermi National Accelerator Laboratory in Batavia, Illinois, announced an accurate determination for the mass of the top quark at a meeting of the American Physical Society's division of particles and fields. Surprisingly, this achievement took little more than a year since the discovery of the top quark was announced at Fermilab on March 2, 1995. Two large teams of physicists had collected data for three years to find the top quark, the last of six basic building blocks in the quark theory of matter. One of those teams, working with the Collider Detector at Fermilab (CDF), has now identified some one hundred top quarks, making it possible to define the top-quark mass within a few percentage points. "Now it's a precision measurement," said William Carithers, cospokesman for the international CDF team of some 450 members.

In fact, the precision of the top-quark mass is now greater than that for any of the other five quarks discovered over the last quarter of a century. "I thought we were going to have to wait another five years to know it that well," said Chris Quigg, a Fermilab particle theorist. Physicists need this precision, along with the mass of the associated W-particle, as a guide to find the Higgs particle and thus solve one of the major mysteries of particle physics today. In the standard model of quark theory, the Higgs particle is needed to explain how elementary particles gain their particular masses. The second top-quark team has now used their D-Zero detector at Fermilab to improve the accuracy of the W-particle mass. These precision mass values imply that discovery of the Higgs particle may be within reach of existing particle accelerators, which would reveal new details in the Big Bang theory of creation itself.

HISTORICAL BACKGROUND

Since the earliest Greek philosophers, atoms have been viewed as indivisible units of matter. In 1808 the English scientist John Dalton found some of the first evidence that each element is made up of its own distinctive atoms. However, when the English physicist Joseph John Thomson identified electrons as negatively charged particles in 1897, he recognized that they must be subatomic particles that combine with positive matter to make up an electrically neutral atom. By bombarding atoms with radioactive alpha particles (charged helium atoms) in 1911, the English physicist Ernest Rutherford was able to analyze the alpha-particle scattering to show that atoms consist of a very small positive nucleus surrounded by orbiting electrons.

By 1932 Rutherford and his students had shown that the nucleus is made up of protons with positive charge (+e) equal and opposite to that of the electron (−e), and neutrons with about the same mass as protons but no electrical charge. Also in 1932 at the California Institute of Technology (Caltech), Carl Anderson discovered the first antimatter particle, the positive counterpart of the electron called the positron. In the same year at the University of California, Ernest Lawrence developed the cyclotron, in which charged particles could be accelerated in circles to high energies for probing the structure of matter. After World War II, large particle accelerators began to produce sufficiently high energies that colliding particles could create many new kinds of particles by converting energy into mass as suggested by Albert Einstein's theory of mass-energy equivalence ($E = mc^2$).

By 1960 several hundred new subatomic particles and their antiparticles had been studied and were classified into three families: leptons (light particles such as electrons, muons, and neutrinos), mesons (intermediate-mass particles that transmit the strong nuclear force between particles), and baryons (heavy particles such as protons and neutrons). In 1964 at Caltech, Murray Gell-Mann developed a theory that successfully accounted for the properties of all mesons and baryons by assuming that they were composed of smaller particles he called "quarks," with the unusual feature of having fractional charges. His theory required three quarks, designated by u, d, and s for up, down, and strange (with charges of +2e/3 for u and −e/3 for d and s), and three antiquarks (with charges of −2e/3 or +e/3). All baryons had three quarks in differing combinations (proton = uud, neutron = udd, etc.), and all mesons consisted of quark-antiquark pairs.

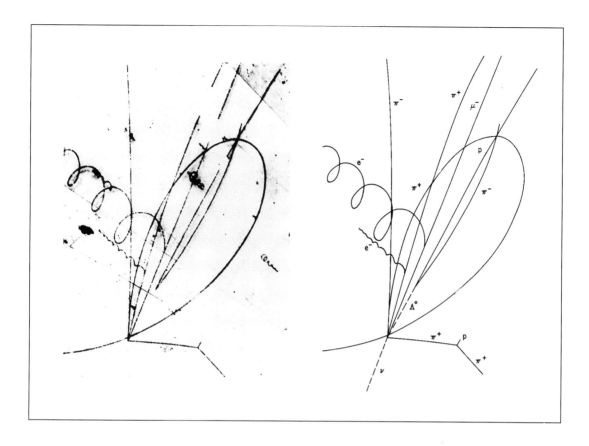

The three-quark theory predicted several new particles and was confirmed by showing that the proton consists of three pointlike objects in the scattering of high-energy electrons from protons at the Stanford Linear Accelerator Center (SLAC) in 1968. However, new mesons discovered in 1974 at SLAC and at Brookhaven National Laboratory (New York) required a fourth quark, called the charmed quark (c-quark), to account for the properties of these mesons. The c-quark has a charge of $+2e/3$ and is related to the s-quark as the u-quark is related to the d-quark.

In 1977 at Fermilab, a group led by Leon Lederman discovered evidence for a fifth quark, called the bottom quark (b-quark). Fermilab operates the largest proton accelerator in the world, with a Main Ring that is four miles in circumference. By smashing protons with energies of 500 billion electronvolts (gigaelectronvolts, or GeV) into a fixed nuclear target, they were able to identify a new meson called the upsilon particle with properties matching a bottom quark-antiquark pair. The b-quark has a charge of $-e/3$ and a mass-energy equivalence of 4.25 GeV (4.5 proton masses).

Quark theory suggested that the b-quark should be related to a sixth quark with charge $+2e/3$, called the top quark (t-quark). Because even higher energies would be required to produce the top quark, Fermilab began the construction of another beam tube in the four-mile ring called the Tevatron, in which counter-rotating antiprotons could be accelerated for head-on collisions with protons from the Main Ring. By 1986 these proton-antiproton collisions reached energies of 1.8 trillion electronvolts (TeV) in the 5,000-ton Collider Detector at Fermilab (CDF). This energy was enough to produce top quarks, but the CDF could detect only a few of the decay reactions expected from t-quarks. Under Fermilab director John Peoples, a second detector of a similar size was completed in 1992, called the D-Zero, which was sensitive to other t-quark decay reactions.

Because the Higgs particle is the key to mass formation by elementary particles and the process of symmetry breaking, a central idea in all unified theories, its discovery is crucial for understanding the universe and the early stages of creation. Precise determination of the top-quark mass contributes to this goal.

The CDF detector, completed in 1985, can be moved on tracks into the path of the Tevatron. It deflects colliding particles with a strong electromagnet and can distinguish charged particles as small as the electron from their distinctive tracks and energy content. The D-Zero, built in 1992, intercepts both the Main Ring and the Tevatron and is designed for better detection of the muon, a lepton some 207 times more massive than the electron. The top quark itself is too short-lived for direct detection, but these massive Fermilab detectors are designed to detect them indirectly by measuring their decay products. According to the standard model of quark theory, most top quarks decay into a bottom quark, the next heaviest of the quarks, and a W particle, which carries the weak force of radioactivity in much the same way that the photon transmits the electromagnetic force. Because quarks cannot exist alone, the bottom quarks bind themselves to other particles, which produce distinctive jets of particles that trigger the detectors.

The top-quark search was conducted with these detectors by two international teams, each with about 450 experimenters. On March 2, 1995, both teams announced their independent discovery of the top quark. The search was complicated by the fact that collisions producing top-quark events are accompanied by similar background events resulting from other particle interactions Initially, the CDF group reported 33 top-quark events under conditions in which only eight such events would be expected without a top-quark decay. These data permitted an estimate of the mass-energy equivalence for the top quark of 176±13 GeV. The D-Zero group reported seventeen top-quark events with an expected background of only four non-top-quark events, giving an estimated mass-energy equivalence of 199±30 GeV. The probability of this many events without a top-quark decay was about one in a million. The estimated mass-energy values overlap within the range of their uncertainties, but were not precise enough to predict the theoretical mass-energy range in which to search for the Higgs particle.

MASS OF THE TOP QUARK

The precision measurements of mass at Fermilab have resulted from longer-running times of the Tevatron colliders and new methods of data analysis. The new data set includes nearly an additional year of runs, right up until the Tevatron was shut down for an upgrade early in 1996. From three years of data and 5 trillion collisions, the CDF should have produced about 500 detectable top quarks and their antimatter counterparts. By August of 1996, CDF researchers had identified the distinctive signature of the top quark in about 100 collisions.

To determine the top-quark mass, its other primary decay products had to be accurately accounted for also. The W particle, which decays into other leptons or quark jets, was evaluated by the D-Zero group with the more precise mass-energy equivalence of 80.37 ± 0.15 GeV (75 proton masses). The CDF group divided the top-quark events according to the relative ambiguity in their identification of the bottom jets and analyzed them in different ways to minimize the effect of background events. In this way the background events in the more ambiguous samples did not contaminate the good samples in arriving at the final result. The top mass was then calculated by adding up the energy in all of the decay products and averaging over the selected events. The bottom line on the top-quark mass-energy was 176.8 ± 6.5 GeV (166 proton masses).

Even with the current degree of precision for these masses, the range of possible masses for the Higgs particle is still fairly wide. This range depends even more sensitively on the W-particle mass than on the top-quark mass. The combined result narrows the energy requirement for producing the Higgs particle to a range of about 50 to 500 GeV, centered at about 150 GeV. If the mass of the Higgs particle lies in the lower part of this range, it could be seen at the Center for European Nuclear Research (Centre Européen de Recherche Nucléaire, or CERN) in Geneva, Switzerland, with the new upgraded LEP-II collider (27-kilometer Large Electron-Positron ring). If the mass is larger, experimenters will have to wait for a possible future upgrade of the Tevatron at Fermilab or for the Large Hadron Collider at CERN, due for completion in the year 2006.

IMPORTANCE OF THE TOP QUARK

The discovery of the top quark strongly supports the quark theory, which in its modern revised form predicted six quarks matched with six leptons as the basis of all known matter. In 1970 at Harvard University, Sheldon Glashow and his associates predicted the charmed quark to explain why certain expected particle reactions never occur. Their theory suggested a paired symmetry between quarks and leptons, with the u- and d-quarks matched with the electron and its neutrino, and the s- and c-quarks paired with the muon and its neutrino. The muon neutrino was distinguished from the electron neutrino in 1962 by Lederman and his associates, then at Columbia University, and the 1974 discovery of the c-quark confirmed Glashow's revised quark theory. The discovery at Stanford in 1975 of a new lepton heavier than the muon, called the tau lepton, suggested the possibility of a tau neutrino and implied the existence of a third generation of quark pairs. The discoveries at Fermilab of the bottom and top quarks completed this symmetry.

In 1983 David Schramm and his associates at the University of Chicago used evidence from astronomy concerning the density of matter in the universe to show that no more than three types of neutrino can exist if they have less than 10 MeV of mass-energy equivalence. This cosmological argument was confirmed in 1990 by the first measurements at CERN's LEP collider and at the Stanford Linear Collider (SLC). Present evidence suggests that no more than six quarks and six leptons are needed to explain the known forms of matter. However, additional particles (known as bosons) are involved in transmitting forces between particles. The standard model of quark theory requires eight bosons, called "gluons," to carry the strong force that binds quarks together. Efforts to understand the relation between particles and forces are called unified field theories, but none has been completely successful yet.

Unified field theories indicate that all the forces of nature, including gravitation, electromagnetism, the weak force, and the strong force, were a single unified force in the early universe when the vacuum of space itself may have possessed energy. In 1964 at the University of Edinburgh, Peter Higgs introduced the idea that a force field permeating space can give the vacuum a positive energy. As the universe expanded after the Big Bang, this type of "Higgs field" and its associated Higgs particle could account for the "symmetry breaking" that split the single unified force at high energy into the several forces at low energy that are seen today, some 15 billion years later.

The Collider Detector at Fermilab.

The electroweak theory, a successful unified theory of the electromagnetic and weak forces, explains the breakdown of the electroweak force by the action of a Higgs particle at about 1 picosecond (trillionth of a second) into creation, giving the W and Z particles (charged and neutral forms of the weak-force particle) their masses. Because the Higgs particle is the key to mass formation by elementary particles and the process of symmetry breaking, a central idea in all unified theories, its discovery is crucial for understanding the universe and the early stages of creation. Precise determination of the top-quark mass contributes to this goal. ∎

WARNING
DO NOT PUSH ON DOOR
TO TILT SAMPLER, IT MAY
DETACH UNEXPECTEDLY

7672A AUTOMATIC SAMPLER

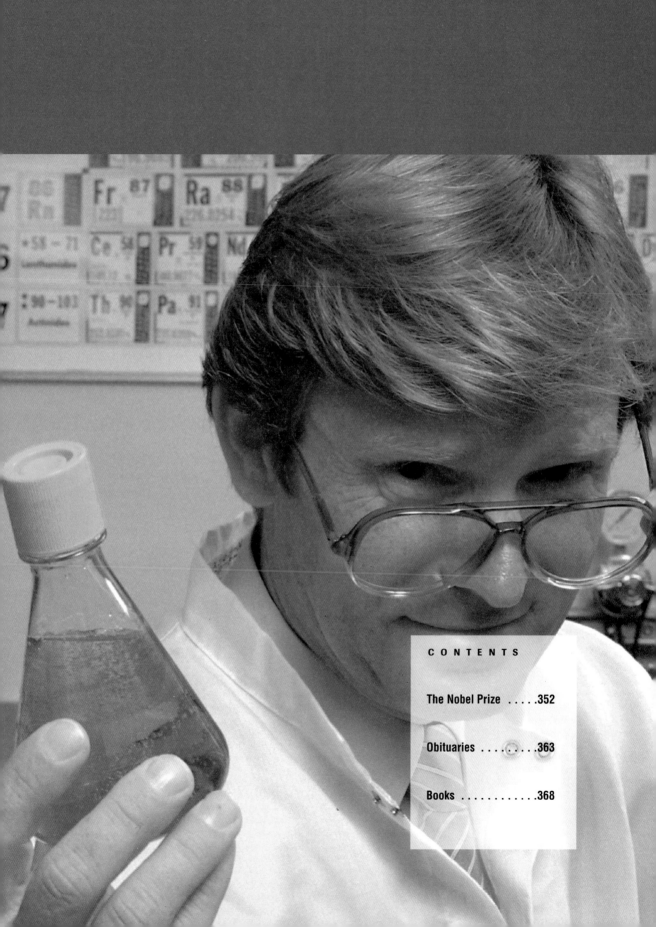

The Nobel Prize

BY JEFFRY M. JENSEN

Physiology or Medicine

On October 7, it was announced that the 1996 Nobel Prize in Physiology or Medicine was won by Peter C. Doherty, an Australian citizen working at St. Jude Children's Research Hospital in Memphis, Tennessee, and Rolf M. Zinkernagel, a Swiss citizen working at the Institute of Experimental Immunology of the University of Zurich in Switzerland. The Royal Swedish Academy of Sciences singled out these pioneering immunologists for their work in determining how the immune system identifies foreign invaders. The Nobel Prizes were first awarded in 1901. As envisioned by Alfred Nobel, the scientific prizes were to be awarded to nominees whose research benefited humankind. It usually has been the physiology or medicine prize in which the general public shows the greatest interest. The general public more easily can identify the direct correlation to their lives with this prize. Most of the recipients of the Nobel Prize in Physiology or Medicine have worked directly in the human health arena as either physicians or scientists. Biomedical research has become a growing industry in the second half of the twentieth century and the 1996 winners, Doherty and Zinkernagel, have continued in this trend.

The two researchers began working together in the mid-1970's at the John Curtin School of Medical Research in Canberra, Australia. In their research with mice, it was discovered that the lymphocytes or white blood cells need to recognize both foreign and self molecules in order to destroy the foreign invaders. This research helped to add some clarity to the understanding of how the cellular immune system functions. The mice experiments tried to determine how the immune system, most specifically T-lymphocytes, is able to protect the mice against the meningitis virus. Doherty is a veterinary surgeon by training and Zinkernagel is a specialist in tropical diseases. For many decades, scientists have tried to unravel the mystery of how the immune system will reject one molecule and not another. By working in Australia, Doherty and Zinkernagel were able to do their research in relative isolation. Through diligent work that was not distracted by outside pressures, they were able to conclude that the rejection response of the immune system is related to the body's defense system that protects it against viruses. The white blood cells are on guard against changes in the "self" protein. This self protein diligently identifies the cells that belong in the body. When alterations occur, such as a virus invading a cell, then the self protein marks that cell for destruction. There are different kinds of white blood cells, including t- and b-lymphocytes. These lymphocytes fight against infection by destroying invading microorganisms and infected cells. The researchers recognized that it was necessary for the lymphocytes to simultaneously distinguish between what needs to be destroyed and what does not. Something had to exist in the immune system which allowed for this distinction to occur.

In 1974, Doherty and Zinkernagel published their findings in the journal *Nature*. The impact on immunological research was immediate. The concept of simultaneous recognition was determined to be an essential component of the immune system. The white blood cells can destroy a target only after recognizing what is "self" and what is "nonself." With a better understanding of the immune response system, scientists hope to manipulate the system. If scientists can slow down the response system, then they can impact autoimmune diseases such as diabetes and rheumatoid arthritis. If scientists are able to speed up the response system, then it may be possible for them to better fight against such diseases as cancer. With a better understanding of how the response system reacts to viral diseases, there may be hope in the near future to treat such deadly diseases as AIDS. The discovery also has helped with organ transplants, since rejection of the new organ is a major concern.

The chairperson of the Nobel medicine committee stated that Doherty and Zinkernagel's work also has led to "successful vaccines for animals" which means that "it must not be far away before you can do the same with humans." Although the two researchers only worked together for three years, their discovery shed a bright light on how the immune system distinguishes a friend from an enemy. In a statement issued by the Nobel Foundation, it was pointed out that this discovery has "guided attempts to use the immune system to hunt down and destroy microscopic cancer cells that have escaped from tumors. It has also helped scientists as they design ways to suppress harmful immune system attacks on the body's own tissue, as seen in multiple sclerosis and diabetes."

PETER C. DOHERTY was born on October 15, 1940, in Australia. He completed his undergraduate studies at the University of Queensland in Australia. In 1970, Doherty received his Ph.D. from the University of Edinburgh in Scotland. From 1963 to 1967, he worked as a veterinary officer for the Animal Research Institute in Brisbane, Australia. Doherty then went to work as a scientific officer for the Department of Experimental Pathology at Moredun Research Institute in Edinburgh, Scotland. During the mid-1970's, he was a research fellow in the Department of Microbiology at the John Curtin School of Medical Research of the Australian National University in Canberra, Australia. In 1975, Doherty became an associate professor at the Wistar Institute in Philadelphia. He left Wistar in 1982 to become the head of the Department of Experimental Pathology at the John Curtin School of Medical Research. He remained there until 1988 when he took the position of chairman of the Department of Immunology at St. Jude Children's Research Hospital in Memphis, Tennessee. In 1992, he also became an adjunct professor in the Departments of Pathology and Pediatrics at the University of Tennessee's College of Medicine in Memphis.

ROLF M. ZINKERNAGEL was born on January 6, 1944,

in Basel, Switzerland. From 1962-1968, he studied for his medical degree at the University of Basel. He went on to become a postdoctoral fellow at Basel in the Laboratory for Electron Microscopy and then a postdoctoral fellow at the University of Lausanne. From 1973 to 1975, Zinkernagel was a visiting fellow in the Department of Microbiology at the John Curtin School of Medical Research of the Australian National University in Canberra. He moved to Southern California in the late 1970's and worked at both the Research Institute of Scripps Clinic in La Jolla and the University of California at San Diego. In 1979, he became an associate professor in the Department of Pathology at the University of Zurich. Zinkernagel became a full professor there in 1988 and the head of the Institute of Experimental Immunology at the University of Zurich in 1992.

Rolf. M. Zinkernagel

Physics

On October 9, it was announced that the 1996 Nobel Prize in Physics had been won by three American physicists: David M. Lee and Robert C. Richardson of Cornell University in Ithaca, New York, and Douglas D. Osheroff of Stanford University in Stanford, California. The Royal Swedish Academy of Sciences singled them out for their discovery of superfluid helium-3, which was a major breakthrough in low-temperature physics. Since 1901 when the first Nobel Prizes were awarded, American scientists have won more than fifty prizes in the category of physics. Each year, the Nobel Committee for Physics reviews the accomplishments of some one hundred nominees. It is an exhaustive process and takes many months before the names of the finalists can be turned over to the Royal Swedish Academy of Sciences for the final selection to be made.

In a low-temperature laboratory at Cornell University, Lee, Richardson, and Osheroff discovered that helium-3—a helium isotope—could be transformed into a superfluid state at a temperature near absolute zero (approximately minus

459.67 degrees Fahrenheit). When matter is in a superfluid state, the atoms will behave in a coordinated way, making it possible for the liquid to flow without any friction to slow it down. In 1908, the Dutch physicist Heike Kamerlingh Onnes first changed helium-4 into a liquid form. During the 1930's, the Soviet physicist Pyotr Kapitsa experimented with liquid helium and was able to explain certain concepts relating to superfluidity. For his work in low-temperature and plasma physics, Kapitsa received the 1978 Nobel Prize in Physics. Since the 1930's, superfluid helium 4 has proved to be a useful scientific too. While superfluid helium-4 has become commonly used, it was not until the discovery made by the Cornell researchers in 1972 that helium 3 was ever observed in a superfluid state. It only had been theorized that helium 3 could be transformed into a state of superfluidity. During the 1972 experiments, Osheroff was a graduate student at Cornell, and Lee and Richardson were his thesis advisers.

The research team had been looking for a completely different phenomenon when Osheroff accidentally observed helium-3 in a superfluid state. They had hoped to witness a phase transition whereby a specific magnetic state would occur in frozen helium-3 ice. At approximately two one-thousandths of a degree above absolute zero, helium 3 was converted into a superfluid state. Superfluidity can be compared to the phenomenon of superconductivity. In superconductivity, electric current flows nonstop without ever losing any energy. It is thought that superfluid helium-3 behaves in a similar manner since it flows in a frictionless state. It has been theorized that the lack of friction in helium-3 after it has been transformed to a superfluid state may actually give scientists a glimpse of the physical transitions that took place just after the big bang. By studying the properties of superfluid helium-3, scientists may be better able to eventually understand the creation of the universe.

The three Cornell researchers were first recognized for their work in superfluidity in 1976 when they won the Simon Memorial Prize of the British Physical Society. In 1981, they were awarded the Buckley Prize of the American Physical Society. N. David Mermin, a leading physicist, has written that the discovery "transformed the direction of theoretical and experimental research in low temperature physics, stimulating advances in our understanding of the hydrodynamics of intricately ordered systems, the microscopic theory to degenerate Fermi-systems, and the range of phenomena accessible to nuclear magnetic resonance probes and...the superfluidity widely believed to be present in rotating neutron stars." It has been agreed upon by the research community that further study into superfluid helium-3 is mandatory. Theoreticians have pointed out that in quantum physics sometimes the study of microscopic systems, such as superfluid helium-3, can lead to a greater understanding of macroscopic systems, such as the creation of galaxies.

DAVID MORRIS LEE was born on January 20, 1931, in Rye, New York. In 1952, he received a B.A. from Harvard University in Cambridge, Massachusetts, and, in 1955, Lee received his M.S. from the University of Connecticut. He continued his studies at Yale University in New Haven, Connecticut, and received a Ph.D. in physics there in 1959. Lee served in the United States Army from 1952 to 1954. After receiving his Ph.D., he became an instructor at Cornell University. In 1968, he became a Professor of Physics at Cornell. During his tenure at Cornell, Lee also has taught or lectured at various other leading research centers, including Brookhaven National Laboratory, the University of Florida, the University of California at San Diego, and Beijing University in China.

David Morris Lee

ROBERT COLEMAN RICHARDSON was born on June 26, 1937, in Washington, D.C. In 1958, he received a B.S. in physics from Virginia Polytechnic Institute, and in 1960, Richardson received a M.S. in physics from the same institution. He earned his Ph.D. in physics from Duke University in 1966. After receiving his Ph.D., Richardson went to work at

Cornell University as a research associate. In 1975, he became a Professor of Physics at Cornell. Since 1987, Richardson has been the Floyd R. Newman Professor of Physics there. He became the director of the Laboratory of Atomic and Solid State Physics at Cornell in 1990. Richardson has continued to focus his research on low-temperature physics. He is the co-author, with Eric N. Smith and a number of Cornell graduate students, of the book *Experimental Techniques in Condensed Matter Physics at Low Temperatures* (1988).

Douglas Dean Osheroff

DOUGLAS DEAN OSHEROFF was born on August 1, 1945, in Aberdeen, Washington. In 1967, he received a B.S. in physics from the California Institute of Technology in Pasadena. Osheroff continued his studies at Cornell University where he received his M.S. in physics in 1969 and his Ph.D. in physics in 1973. From 1972 to 1987, he was a member of the technical staff at AT&T Bell Laboratories. He was the head of the Solid State and Low Temperature Research Department there from 1981 to 1987. In 1987, Osheroff left Bell Laboratories to become a Professor of Physics and Applied Physics at Stanford University. He was also one of the recipients of a MacArthur Foundation grant in 1981. These grants have been labeled the "genius" grants. In addition to being a world-renowned authority in superfluidity, Osheroff is an award-winning teacher. While at Stanford, he won the Walter J. Gores Award for Excellence in Teaching.

Chemistry

On October 9, it was announced that the 1996 Nobel Prize in Chemistry had been won by Robert F. Curl, Jr., and Richard E. Smalley, both Americans working at Rice University in Houston, Texas, and Harold W. Kroto, a British citizen working at the University of Sussex in Brighton, England. They were singled out by the Royal

Swedish Academy of Sciences for their discovery of a new family of carbon molecules, which they named "buckminsterfullerenes." The name was shortened to "buckyballs" or "fullerenes." The carbon molecules were given these odd names in the first place because of their resemblances to the geodesic domes designed by the world famous architect R. Buckminster Fuller. Since World War II, American chemists have won more chemistry prizes than chemists from any other country. The Nobel Committee for Chemistry has the primary responsibility to the Royal Swedish Academy of Sciences for final approval. The committee's choice usually is submitted to the Academy by late September or early October. All attempts are made for the winners to be notified prior to the public announcement made at a press conference in Stockholm.

The 1996 winners first made their discovery in 1985. Before experiments had been performed by Curl, Smalley, and Kroto in Smalley's laboratory at Rice University, only six crystalline forms of the element carbon had been identified. The six forms included two types of diamond, two types of graphite, chaoit, and the sixth form known as carbon (VI). The last two forms mentioned were discovered in 1968 and 1972 respectively. On September 1, 1985, Kroto arrived at Rice University to join the research team that included Curl and Smalley in order to carry out experiments on carbon molecules. The first experiment was performed over an eleven day period in Smalley's laboratory. Two graduate students, James R. Heath and Sean C. O'Brien, were also members of the research team. The Nobel committee acknowledged their contribution to the discovery, but they did not share in the prize. The experiment itself consisted of directing an intense laser light at carbon atoms found in a sheet of common graphite. After the carbon atoms had been released by a pulse of laser light, they were mixed with a stream of helium gas. The gaseous carbon then bunched into clusters. The scientists directed the clusters into a vacuum chamber where they could be cooled to just above absolute zero.

After this was done, it was then possible for the scientists to analyze the carbon clusters with mass spectrometry.

While some of the clusters found had seventy carbon atoms, the majority of the clusters contained carbon with sixty atoms. The C^{60} (or carbon with sixty atoms) was found to be very stable. This stability suggested to the research team that the molecular structure was symmetrical. To the common eye, it looked like a soccer ball. The spherical carbon molecules (the C^{60}) were truncated icosahedrons, meaning that they had twelve hexagonal surfaces and twelve pentagonal surfaces. The Royal Swedish Academy of Sciences noted in its citation that before this discovery had been made "no physicist or chemist had expected that carbon would be found in such a symmetrical form other than those already known."

While the 1985 experiments produced only small amounts of C^{60}, in 1990 two other research scientists, Donald R. Huffman of the University of Arizona in Tucson and Wolfgang Krätschmer of the Max Planck Institute for Nuclear Physics in Heidelberg, Germany, discovered a process whereby they could produce buckyballs in large quantities. Because buckyballs could superconduct, lubricate, and absorb light, scientists argued that buckyballs promised a number of useful applications. Further scientific investigation has made it possible for the new carbon molecules to be chemically modified. Researchers also have been able to fill C^{60} with other atoms.

Credit must be given to Curl, Smalley, and Kroto for their initial research. They were bold in declaring what they thought they had found. The more cautious research community was not convinced that a new family of carbon molecules had been discovered. The results of their research were first published in the journal *Nature* in 1985. Since then, more research has been done and buckyballs or fullerenes have found acceptance and given rise to great excitement among scientists. Out of this discovery, a new branch of chemistry has been constructed. The Royal

Swedish Academy of Sciences stated that Curl, Smalley, and Kroto had led the way to new developments "in such diverse areas as astrochemistry, superconductivity, and materials chemistry and physics." At this point in time, the possibilities for how buckyballs could be manipulated seem almost limitless. While no practical applications have yet to be produced, the future looks bright, and researchers are working toward the day when many useful applications become linked directly to the discovery of buckyballs.

ROBERT FLOYD CURL, JR., was born on August 23, 1933, in Alice, Texas. He received a B.A. from Rice Institute in 1954 and a Ph.D. from the University of California at Berkeley in 1957. During 1957-58, Curl was a research fellow at Harvard University. He left Harvard in 1958 to become an assistant professor of chemistry at Rice. During his tenure at Rice, Curl also has held concurrent positions at leading research facilities throughout the world, including Oxford University in England and the Institute of Molecular Science in Okazaki, Japan.

Robert F. Curl, Jr.

RICHARD ERRETT SMALLEY was born on June 6, 1943, in Akron, Ohio. He received his B.S. degree from the University of Michigan in 1965, his M.A. from Princeton University in 1971,and his Ph.D. in chemistry from Princeton in 1973. From 1965-1969, Smalley worked as a research chemist for Shell Chemical Company. In 1973, he became a research associate at the University of Chicago. He remained at the University of Chicago until 1976 when he took the position of assistant professor at Rice University. Smalley became a Professor of Chemistry at Rice in 1981 and a Professor of Physics there in 1990. He also has held numerous concurrent positions at leading American research centers, including Princeton University and Brookhaven National Laboratory.

HAROLD WALTER KROTO was born on October 7,

Harold Walter Kroto

1939, in Wisbech, Cambridgeshire, England. In 1964, he received a Ph.D. in chemistry from the University of Sheffield. He was a research scientist at Bell Telephone Labs in New Jersey during 1966-1967. Kroto began working at the University of Sussex in 1967. In addition to his position at Sussex, he was a visiting professor at the University of British Columbia in Canada in 1973, at the University of Southern California in Los Angeles in 1981, and the University of California at Los Angeles in 1988-1992. He has continued to be actively involved in C^{60} research. Since 1990, Kroto has been the chairperson of the editorial board of the *Chemical Society Reviews*.

Obituaries

BY JEFFRY M. JENSEN

ALYEA, HUBERT NEWCOMBE (October 10, 1903, Clifton, New Jersey – October 19, 1996, Hightstown, New Jersey). Attending Princeton University, he received his A.B. in 1925, his A.M. in 1926, and a Ph.D. in chemistry in 1928. He worked at the Kaiser Wilhelm Institute in Berlin, Germany, before returning in 1930 to be an instructor at Princeton. Alyea remained at Princeton for forty-two years until he retired in 1972. As a chemistry professor there, he became famous for his theatrical teaching methods. At one point, Walt Disney attended one of Alyea's lectures. Disney went on to make the 1960 movie *The Absent-Minded Professor*, which was based on Alyea's eccentric mannerisms. He developed a system called Tested Overhead Projection Series (TOPS) which allowed for his audiences to view his experiments more closely. TOPS has been widely used throughout the world as an effective teaching tool. After his retirement in 1972, Alyea became an Emeritus Professor of Chemistry at Princeton. He continued to lecture and contribute articles to scientific publications. His wife, Evelyn, did not survive him, but he is survived by a son, Frederick, and a granddaughter.

BEAN, CHARLES P. (November 27, 1923, Buffalo, New York – September 30, 1996, Fairfax, Virginia). He received his B.S. in physics from the University of Buffalo in 1947. He continued his studies at the University of Illinois where he received a Ph.D. in physics in 1952. Bean worked for General Electric for thirty-four years. He left them in 1985 to teach at Rensselaer Polytechnic Institute in Troy, New York. Bean is best remembered for his theory of superconductivity. Superconductivity is the flow of electricity through a substance where there is almost no resistance. His theoretical model explained the kind of superconductor that has been used in magnetic resonance imaging machines. During his career, Bean also published influential articles concerning magnetism. In 1976, he was elected to the National Academy of Sciences and, in 1977, he was elected to the

American Academy of Arts and Sciences. Bean retired in 1993, but he continued to teach at Rensselaer as a professor emeritus. He died of an apparent heart attack. His wife, Elizabeth, died in 1990, but he is survived by three daughters and two sons.

Seymour R. Cray

CRAY, SEYMOUR R. (September 28, 1925, Chippewa Falls, Wisconsin–October 5, 1996, near Colorado Springs, Colorado). He served in the United States Army during World War II. He was a member of an infantry communications platoon and saw action during the Battle of the Bulge. After the war, Cray attended the University of Minnesota where he received a B.S. in electrical engineering and a M.S. in mathematics. On the recommendation of one of his instructors, he went to work after graduation for Engineering Research Associates in Minneapolis. While working at Engineering Research Associates, Cray excelled at computer design. A solitary worker and not one to put up with corporate bureaucracy, he finally left Engineering Research Associates in order to work for Control Data. While there, Cray led the design of many landmark computing machines, including the first transistor-based computer. In 1972, he left Control Data and formed his own company, Cray Research. His new company became a leader in the making of supercomputers. For his work as a computer industry pioneer, he has been called the father of the supercomputer. Cray died of severe head injuries that he had sustained in a car accident. He was treated at Penrose Community Hospital and died there after a two-week stay. He is survived by his wife, two daughters, and a son.

ERDOS, PAUL (March 26, 1913, Budapest, Hungary–September 20, 1996, Warsaw, Poland). He was the only child of a Jewish family. His parents were both mathematicians, and Erdos was a mathematical prodigy, amazing visitors with various multiplying feats at the age of three. His parents were protective of him since his older sisters had died of scarlet fever prior to his birth. He was taken out of public school so that his parents could teach him at home. Mathematics became his whole life. Never marrying, Erdos led a nomadic life. He never lived in one place for very long. Moving from university to university or conference to conference, he lived off the kindness of friends or the honorariums that he received. Erdos is one of the most prolific mathematicians of the twentieth century. He published more than 1,500 articles. His mathematical specialty was number theory. Erdos also founded the field of discrete mathematics. Known for his generosity, he gave away much of the money he earned to other more needy mathematicians. In 1983, Erdos won the Wolf Prize for mathematics. Living like a pilgrim, he died of a heart attack while attending a conference in Warsaw.

GOLDBERG, STANLEY (August 4, 1934, Cleveland, Ohio – October 16, 1996, Washington, D.C.). In 1960, he received a B.S. from Antioch College and, in 1961, he received a A.M.T. from Harvard University. He continued his studies at Harvard and earned a Ph.D. in education in 1969. Goldberg went on to teach at a number of institutions, including Antioch College, the University of Zambia, Hampshire College, and the University of Maryland in Baltimore. In the area of history, Goldberg specialized in the study of military science. He became a consultant to the Smithsonian Institution's National Museum of American History in 1983. A few years later, he became a consultant to the National Air and Space Museum. As a member of the advisory board of the air and space museum, Goldberg was involved in the controversy over the exhibition of the Enola Gay, the airplane that dropped the atomic bomb on Hiroshima. Eventually, Goldberg resigned from the advisory board over the mishandling of the exhibition in 1994. He published *Understanding Relativity: Origin and Impact of a Scientific Revolution* in 1984. Goldberg is survived by his wife, Susan, and three children from his first marriage.

GROVER, GEORGE MAURICE (June 7, 1915, Garland, Utah – October 24, 1996, Albuquerque, New Mexico). He was awarded an undergraduate degree from the University of Washington in 1941 and went on to receive his Ph.D. in nuclear physics from the University of Michigan in 1950. Grover then went to work at the Los Alamos National Laboratory in New Mexico. While working at Los Alamos, he solved the problem of how to transfer heat out of a nuclear reactor. Grover is considered the inventor of what is known as the heat pipe. To generate electricity in space by using a nuclear reactor, his heat pipe had to efficiently transfer heat out of the reactor. The invention proved to be so efficient that it became widely used in space and on earth to maintain level temperatures. He left Los Alamos in 1971. Suffering from Alzheimer's disease, Grover died at a nursing home in Albuquerque. He is survived by a son.

KUHN, THOMAS SAMUEL (July 18, 1922, Cincinnati, Ohio–June 17, 1996, Cambridge, Massachusetts). He was a trained physicist who taught at the Massachusetts Institute of Technology. In 1962, he published the influential work *The Structure of Scientific Revolutions*. In his book, Kuhn advanced the theory that scientific knowledge does not expand at a steady pace when a revolutionary discovery gains prominence. He differentiated between normal science and revolutionary science. In revolutionary science, researchers abandon one paradigm for a new one that incorporates the revolutionary change. His paradigm-shift theory has been used widely in disciplines outside of science, including politics and business. Kuhn suffered from cancer and died at home.

PORTER, RICHARD WILLIAM (March 24, 1913, Saline, Kansas–October 6, 1996, near Cheverly, Maryland). In 1934, he received a B.S. from the University of Kansas. He continued his studies at Yale University, where he received a Ph.D. in electrical engineering in 1937. After receiving his doctorate, Porter went to work for General Electric. During World War II, he had supervised the development of aircraft equipment. After General Electric was awarded an Army contract in 1944, Porter was put in charge of the development of guided missiles. Although he had no previous experience with rockets, he became one of the leading experts over the next few years. He showed himself to be a talented scientific administrator. During the mid-1950's, Porter was put in charge of the nation's space program. He continued to be involved in the space program in an advisory capacity into the 1980's. His wife, Edith, died in June. Porter was on a train bound for New York when he suffered a heart attack. He is survived by two daughters and a son.

SHULMAN, ALEXANDER G. (June 22, 1915, Toronto, Ontario, Canada–July 7, 1996, Los Angeles, California). During the 1950's, he pioneered the treatment of burns with ice water. Shulman discovered that ice water was more effective in treating a burn on his own hand than was the conventional application of butter or grease to the burn. He used his own experience to construct a new treatment procedure. Shulman would use ice water to successfully treat more than one hundred burn patients. In 1960, he published his findings in the *Journal of the American Medical*

Association. Shulman moved to Los Angeles where he was chief of surgery at Midway Hospital. Before retiring in 1995, Shulman was the director of the Liechtenstein Hernia Institute in Los Angeles. He died of cancer at his home.

SNELL, GEORGE DAVIS (December 19, 1903, Bradford, Massachusetts – June 6, 1996, Bar Harbor, Maine). As a boy, he excelled in mathematics and science. Snell did his undergraduate work at Dartmouth College. He continued his studies at Harvard University where he received a Sc.D. in 1930. For one year, he taught at Brown University in Rhode Island. Snell gave up teaching in order to concentrate on research. As a National Research Council fellow, he studied the genetic effects of X-rays on mice at the University of Texas in Austin. He remained there for two years. In 1935, Snell joined the research staff at Roscoe B. Jackson Memorial Laboratory in Bar Harbor, Maine. During his years there, he did extensive genetic research. In 1980, Snell won the Nobel Prize in Physiology or Medicine for his work in how tissue transplantability is affected by genetics. He shared the prize with Baruj Benacerraf and Jean Dausset.

George Davis Snell

SQUIRE, LUCY FRANK (1915, Washington, D.C. – September 15, 1996, New York, New York). She received her undergraduate degree from George Washington University. In 1940, Squire received her medical degree from the Women's Medical College of Pennsylvania. She completed her residency in radiology at Massachusetts General Hospital in Boston in 1945. She decided to join the faculty of the University of Rochester. In 1964, Squire published a textbook *Fundamentals of Radiology*. It has been a popular textbook and has been updated periodically over the years. During the mid-1960's, Squire started teaching part time at Massachusetts General Hospital and at Downstate Medical Center in Brooklyn. The Brooklyn center changed its name to the State University of New York Science Center. From 1972 to 1993, she was a professor of radiology at the center. Squire dies at her home in Manhattan after suffering a heart attack. ∎

Books

BY WENDY E. SACKET

ANIMALS AND PLANTS

Buchmann, Stephen L., and Gary Paul Nabhan. *The Forgotten Pollinators*. Washington, D.C.: Shearwater/Island Press, 1996. 302 pp. Illustrated.

> Entomologist Buchmann and ethnobotanist Nabhan provide a fascinating investigation of the relationships between plant species and the birds, mammals, lizards, and insects that serve as their pollinators. Noting that one-third of the food consumed by humans around the world comes from animal-pollinated plants, the authors explore the devastating impact of habitat destruction on the planet's ecological and economic health.

Conniff, Richard. *Spineless Wonders: Strange Tales from the Invertebrate World*. New York: Henry Holt, 1996. 256 pp. Illustrated.

> A science writer known for producing nature documentaries for *National Geographic* and the Discovery Channel and for publishing articles in various popular magazines, Conniff has produced an enlightening and entertaining book about the lives and habits of dragonflies, eels, earthworms, fire ants, leeches, moths, mosquitoes, squid, tarantulas, and other invertebrate species that make up more than 99 percent of all living animals found on Earth.

Davis, Wade. *One River: Explorations and Discoveries in the Amazon Rain Forest*. New York: Simon & Schuster, 1996. 384 pp. Illustrated.

> Based on his own explorations and those of his mentor (Harvard ethnobotanist Richard Evans Schultes), Wade Davis has written a thought-provoking study that documents the changes wrought by rubber exploration, strip mining, deforestation, and other forms of environmental (and cultural) destruction in the Amazon rain forest from the 1930's through the 1980's. Demonstrating a superb clarity of expression and attention to detail, Davis invites readers to consider the quandary scientists confront in trying to document the rapidly disappearing biological and cultural riches of the vast Amazon region.

Hillyard, Paul. *The Book of the Spider: From Arachnophobia to the Love of Spiders*. New York: Random House, 1996. 208 pp. Illustrated.

> Hillyard draws on his background as a spider specialist at the Natural History Museum in London to provide this eclectic survey of the folklore, literature, history, and science of spiders. Aimed at general readers, Hillyard's work discusses the lifestyle and characteristics of various spider species, with chapters devoted to spider webs and silk production, varieties of spider venom, the phenomenon of arachnophobia, and efforts made to conserve spider species and preserve their habitats.

Novacek, Michael. *Dinosaurs of the Flaming Cliffs*. New York: Anchor Books, 1996. 352 pp. Illustrated.

As one of a handful of Western scientists permitted to conduct fieldwork in Mongolia's Gobi Desert in the 1990's, Novacek provides a lively account of his experiences as a member of joint Mongolian-American expeditions to search for dinosaur fossils. Accompanied by effective illustrations, Novacek gives readers a glimpse of the excitement and the hazards his teams faced and introduces basic concepts of vertebrate paleontology and related scientific fields.

Patterson, Gareth. *With My Soul Amongst Lions: A Moving Story of the Struggle to Protect the Last Adamson Lions*. New York: St. Martin's Press, 1996. 228 pp. Illustrated.

An environmental activist committed to protecting the legacy of Joy Adamson and the descendants of the lions she helped rehabilitate, Patterson describes the risks he and his animal companions faced in their efforts to avoid the dangers posed not only by poachers and big game hunters but also by politicians and landowners in Botswana, Zimbabwe, and South Africa. Concerned about the fate of all African wildlife, Patterson makes a compelling case for the creation of a wild animal reserve that would include land from all three countries, thus furnishing much-needed protection and space for these magnificent creatures to live without the artificial constriction of national boundaries.

Poole, Joyce. *Coming of Age with Elephants: A Memoir*. New York: Hyperion, 1996. 288 pp.

Poole's memoir gives readers an opportunity to understand her work as a behavioral scientist from many vantage points. In addition to providing an interesting account of her fieldwork in studying the behavior of African elephants, she describes the sexism that she encountered as a woman working in a largely male-dominated profession. Readers will also appreciate her clear-sighted exploration of the ethical and environmental issues related to her work with elephants.

Quammen, David. *The Song of the Dodo: Island Biogeography in an Age of Extinctions*. New York: Scribner, 1996. 702 pp.

Noted essayist David Quammen has produced an elaborate and wide-ranging discussion of evolutionary theory and species extinction in connection with some of the most isolated regions of the world: islands. To Quammen, the disappearance of many island-based plant and animal species serves as an omen, since their extinction signals the potentially grim fate of humankind. Instead of depressing his readers, however, Quammen uses his topic as an opportunity to explore the richness of the natural world and the intellectual fervor of the scientists who have studied it, providing hope for the future.

Wrangham, Richard, and Dale Peterson. *Demonic Males: Apes and the Origins of Human Violence*. Boston: Houghton Mifflin, 1996. 332 pp. Illustrated.

Wrangham and Peterson draw on their credentials as an anthropologist and an animal behavioralist, respectively, to explore the evidence of aggression and violence found in the behavior of chimpanzees and other primates closely related to human beings. They also bring to light evidence of how these primates have developed certain social mechanisms for containing such aggressive behavior, particularly as seen among the bonobo, or pygmy chimpanzee. The authors provide an engrossing account that should be read together with Frans de Waal's *Good Natured: The Origins of Right and Wrong in Humans and Other Animals*. (1996)

ASTRONOMY AND SPACE SCIENCE

Goodstein, David L., and Judith R. Goodstein. *Feynman's Lost Lecture: The Motion of Planets Around the Sun*. New York: W. W. Norton, 1996. 224 pp. Illustrated.

The Goodsteins, who were colleagues and friends of Feynman, here present a lecture on the Copernican cosmological theory given by Feynman at Caltech, along with chapters by Feynman on Newtonian physics and the scientific revolution. They conclude their book with a collection of reminiscences about Feynman, who was well known for his colorful and eccentric personality.

Gribbin, John, and Mary Gribbin. *Fire on Earth: In Search of the Doomsday Asteroid*. New York: St. Martin's Press, 1996. 256 pp.

John and Mary Gribbin, authors of *Schroedinger's Kittens and the Search for Reality* (1995), draw together historical evidence and scientific theories about the astonishing effect that asteroids and other astronomical events have had during the course of Earth's biological history.

Krupp, E. C. *Skywatchers, Shamans, and Kings: Astronomy and the Archaeology of Power*. New York: John Wiley & Sons, 1996. 384 pp. Illustrated.

Drawing on his scientific credentials as director of Los Angeles' Griffith Observatory, Krupp presents an intriguing synthesis of scientific and cultural history, demonstrating how shamanistic practices, cosmology, and astronomy have been intertwined with political power in world cultures ranging from the ancient Maya, Egyptians, and Chinese to the indigenous peoples of the Arctic region, the American plains, and central and southern Africa.

Mather, John, and John Boslough. *The Very First Light: The True Inside Story of the Scientific Journey Back to the Dawn of the Universe*. New York: Basic Books, 1996. 326 pp. Illustrated.

Mather, an astrophysicist and NASA project scientist, and Boslough, a freelance writer, collaborate in the history of NASA's involvement with the design, construction, launch, and interpretation of data gathered by the Cosmic Background Explorer (COBE), whose space mission began in 1989. Intended to measure cosmic background radiation, COBE found evidence that appears to support the Big Bang theory of cosmic creation.

Parker, Barry. *Chaos in the Cosmos: The Stunning Complexity of the Universe*. New York: Plenum, 1996. 310 pp. Illustrated.
> Tracing the historical origins of chaos as a scientific theory, Parker provides a detailed and accessible explanation of how chaos theory helps explain astronomical features ranging from the rings of Saturn to the geography of the universe as we know it.

Zubrin, Robert, with Richard Wagner. *The Case for Mars: The Plan to Settle the Red Planet and Why We Must*. New York: Free Press, 1996. 352 pp.
> Zubrin and Wagner make a persuasive argument for a fast-track mission to settle on Mars. Their plan calls for NASA and other space agencies to work together to send a crew of astronauts together with self-contained living quarters directly to the surface of Mars, where they would draw upon the planet's natural resources to create a permanent Earth outpost.

EARTH AND ENVIRONMENT

Ellis, Richard. *Deep Atlantic: Life, Death, and Exploration in the Abyss*. New York: Alfred A. Knopf, 1996. 400 pp. Illustrated.
> Combining folklore, fiction, nautical history, and modern science, Ellis presents an engaging account of humans' fascination with the ocean deep and how Jules Verne's fantastic story of underwater exploration has given rise to the deep-sea submersibles that have mapped the Atlantic seafloor and retrieved artifacts from the *Titanic*.

Maslow, Jonathan. *Footsteps in the Jungle: Adventures in the Scientific Exploration of the American Tropics*. Chicago: Ivan R. Dee, 1996. 293 pp. Illustrated.
> In making a case for preservation of tropical regions in the Americas, Maslow takes readers on a journey through the life adventures of thirteen scientist-explorers, ranging from Alexander von Humboldt at the end of the eighteenth century to the tropical naturalists and explorers of the late twentieth century.

Outwater, Alice. *Water: A Natural History*. New York: Basic Books, 1996. 224 pp. Illustrated.
> An environmental engineer by profession, Outwater was inspired to pen this overview of water resources after working as a consultant on the cleanup of Boston Harbor. Explaining why the elimination of industrial pollution alone is insufficient to purify the contents of America's waterways, Outwater describes the destruction of animal and plant habitats and other disruptions of the natural water cycle that have occurred and explores environmental solutions to these manmade problems.

Palmer, Tim. *America by Rivers*. Washington, D.C.: Island Press, 1996. 272 pp. Illustrated.
> Palmer, an outdoor enthusiast and longtime river researcher, presents a keenly observed

account of the environmental and biological conditions of America's rivers. Combining a wealth of practical knowledge about the distinctive features of various rivers and a love of river lore, Palmer's work describes the interaction of cultural, historical, and geographical forces that have shaped the course of American waterways.

HUMAN SCIENCES

Black, Kathryn. *In the Shadow of Polio: A Personal and Social History*. Reading, Mass.: Addison-Wesley, 1996. 288 pp. Illustrated.

> Having witnessed her mother's own struggle with polio, Black examines the life stories of her mother and other polio sufferers in the context of the history of the disease, particularly the changes brought about with the advent of the Salk and Sabin vaccines. With her journalist's acumen, Black has written an absorbing story— one that helps readers understand the disease's impact on individual families.

Calvin, William H. *How Brains Think: Evolving Intelligence, Then and Now*. New York: Basic Books, 1996. 192 pp.

> In this entry in the Science Masters series for nonspecialists, Calvin concisely summarizes current knowledge about the inner workings of the human brain. While admitting the continuing mysteries surrounding the origins of human intelligence, Calvin does a fine job of explaining prevalent theories about the connections between the brain, intelligence, and verbal expression.

Coren, Stanley. *Sleep Thieves: An Eye-Opening Exploration into the Science and Mysteries of Sleep*. New York: Free Press, 1996. 304 pp.

> Sprinkling his text with numerous anecdotes taken from science and folklore, Coren provides a lively history of the human (and animal) propensity to sleep. In addition to describing the sleep patterns found among different species, he explores the history and prevalence of sleep disorders such as apnea and insomnia. Coren also chronicles the technological advances and corporate policies that have become responsible for depriving many people of adequate sleep.

Marsh, Margaret, and Wanda Ronner. *The Empty Cradle: Infertility in America from Colonial Times to the Present*. Baltimore: Johns Hopkins University Press, 1996. 326 pp.

> This collaborative effort between two sisters— Marsh, a historian, and Ronner, a physician—provides an extensive survey of infertility in America that demolishes many of the prevailing myths. Although the physical incidence of infertility has not changed much during the nation's history, advances in diagnosing the origins of infertility have helped alter public perception of the problem and have eliminated much of the stigma attached to it.

Regis, Ed. *Virus Ground Zero: Stalking the Killer Viruses with the Centers for Disease Control*. New York: Pocket Books, 1996. 244 pp.

> Author of the 1988 book *Who Got Einstein's Office?: Eccentricity and Genius at the*

Institute for Advanced Study, Regis follows the efforts of scientists working for the Atlanta-based Centers for Disease Control in combatting the threat posed by emerging viral diseases, including Ebola, hantavirus, Lassa fever, Legionnaire's disease, Marburg, and other pathogens. Like a good mystery writer, Regis employs a lively, anecdotal style that keeps readers engaged despite the book's grim subject matter.

Ross, Alan Duncan, and Harlan Gibbs, M.D. *The Medicine of* ER: *Or, How We Almost Die*. New York: Basic Books, 1996. 240 pp.

Drawing on their credentials as a television producer and an emergency room physician, respectively, Ross and Gibbs explain the medical procedures and vocabulary found in the popular NBC television series *ER*. While noting the limitations of the show's hour-long format, the authors give series creator Michael Crichton and the show's writers high marks for raising public awareness of the challenges faced by patients and staff members in modern trauma care centers.

Weinberg, Robert A. *Racing to the Beginning of the Road: The Search for the Origin of Cancer*. New York: Harmony Books, 1996. 288 pp.

Weinberg provides a detailed history of postwar research to discover the origin of cancer, noting the contributions of Nobel Prize winners such as David Baltimore and more obscure collaborators. Although his account stops with the 1986 discovery of the relationship between oncogenes and tumor-suppressing genes, Weinberg gives readers a much-needed human context for understanding the breakthroughs that have been made in cancer research.

Wills, Christopher. *Yellow Fever, Black Goddesses: The Coevolution of People and Plagues*. Reading, Mass.: Helix Books, 1996. 336 pp.

Known for books on evolutionary biology, Wills presents a survey of infectious diseases that reflects his firsthand experiences as a researcher and his eclectic interests. Chronicling the advent and spread of diseases ranging from the bubonic plague, syphilis, malaria, and yellow fever of the past up to the Ebola virus of the late twentieth century, Wills shows how many of these pathogens have negotiated a somewhat Faustian compromise, modifying their structures to fit the conditions found within their chosen hosts.

PAST, PRESENT, AND FUTURE

Gould, Stephen Jay. *Full House: The Spread of Excellence from Plato to Darwin*. New York: Harmony Books, 1996. 256 pp. Illustrated.

Noted science writer Gould employs his knowledge of fossil evidence and biodiversity to challenge the accepted notion that the human species represents the inevitable pinnacle of evolution. Instead, Gould argues that humanity represents an "utterly unpredictable, partly random, and entirely contingent" blip in a distribution pattern—the "full house" of the title. His challenging ideas are sure to prompt further discussion as scholars in various fields consider the ethical, philosophical, and theological ramifications involved.

Horgan, John. *The End of Science: Facing the Limits of Knowledge in the Twilight of the Scientific Age*. Reading, Mass.: Helix Books, 1996. 320 pp.

> In interviews with many prominent scientists and science writers, including Stephen Hawking, Daniel Dennett, Freeman Dyson, and Stephen Jay Gould, *Scientific American* columnist John Horgan asked them to consider whether there may be a limit to the discovery of additional theories about nature. In an era when most new scientific theories are abstract ideas that elude precise verification, Horgan challenges readers to consider whether the future of science may not be threatened by its own intrinsic limits.

Shapin, Steven. *The Scientific Revolution*. Chicago: University of Chicago Press, 1996. 225 pp. Illustrated.

> Opening with the provocative statement, "There was no such thing as the Scientific Revolution, and this is a book about it," sociologist Steven Shapin considers how the late sixteenth and seventeenth centuries fostered a new way of looking at science—one that viewed science as the product of rational, disinterested inquiry into natural phenomena. Examining the key figures of the period, the knowledge they gleaned from scientific experiments, and political, religious, and cultural contexts in which their investigations took place, Shapin helps general readers understand how this "new" view of science continues to shape modern theories of science.

Trefil, James. *The Edge of the Unknown: 101 Things You Don't Know About Science and No One Else Does Either*. Boston: Houghton Mifflin, 1996. 368 pp.

> In an effort to improve scientific literacy among the general public, Trefil has produced a handy summary of timely scientific topics and areas of ongoing research. From modern advances in gene therapy to the search for the perfect fat substitute, this book addresses a wide range of scientific quests which may have important, practical benefits for humankind.

Walsh, John Evangelist. *Unraveling Piltdown: The Science Fraud of the Century and Its Solution*. New York: Random House, 1996. 304 pp. Illustrated.

> Using documentary evidence and other research, Walsh reconstructs the events that led to the 1913 discovery of Piltdown Man and its exposure as a fraud in 1952—leading readers to discover the identity of the forger. Combining the excitement of a true crime story with first-rate science, Walsh makes a convincing case against discoverer Charles Dawson, who used prominent friends and acquaintances such as Sir Arthur Conan Doyle and Pierre Teilhard de Chardin to lend credence to his fossil find.

PHYSICAL SCIENCES AND TECHNOLOGY

Baldwin, J. *Bucky Works: Buckminster Fuller's Ideas for Today*. New York: John Wiley & Sons, 1996. 243 pp.

> Writing from his vantage point as a close friend and associate, Baldwin introduces general readers to the theories and inventions produced by Buckminster Fuller, who was perhaps

best known for his invention of the geodesic dome. Although somewhat uncritical of the shortcomings of some of Fuller's concepts, Baldwin does a fine job of conveying Fuller's enormous enthusiasm for science.

Billington, David P. *The Innovators: The Engineering Pioneers Who Made American Modern.* New York: John Wiley & Sons, 1996. 245 pp. Illustrated.
> Surveying the structures and engineering processes developed by nineteenth century innovators such as Thomas Edison, Samuel F. B. Morse, and Robert Fulton, Billington provides general readers with a thought-provoking and well-illustrated introduction to the origins of American engineering.

Brian, Denis. *Einstein: A Life.* New York: John Wiley & Sons, 1996. 512 pp.
> Incorporating a wealth of material from new sources, including the FBI file on Einstein, Brian focuses on the famous physicist's family life, interest in current affairs, and various aspects of his public persona while providing a rudimentary introduction to Einstein's scientific theories.

Campbell-Kelly, Martin, and William Aspray. *Computer: A History of the Information Machine.* New York: Basic Books, 1996. 336 pp. Illustrated.
> The authors have assembled a fascinating tale of the evolution of the computer, tracing its origins from the mathematical theories of Charles Babbage in the 1830's through the advent of the Mark I, ENIAC, and EDVAC up to the contributions of Silicon Valley engineers, corporate giant IBM, and the entrepreneurs who launched Apple Computers and Microsoft. Necessarily selective in its approach, this work provides a highly informative overview that is sure to appeal to computer novices and experts alike.

Holton, Gerald. *Einstein, History, and Other Passions: The Rebellion Against Science at the End of the Twentieth Century.* Reading, Mass.: Addison-Wesley, 1996. 240 pp. Illustrated.
> Taking the young Einstein as his chief example, Holton works to restore creativity to its rightful place within scientific endeavor. He sees Einstein as fostering a sense of playfulness and wonder in scientific thinking and argues that those who care passionately about it engage in scientific discovery for the challenge and sheer love of science.

Lindley, David. *Where Does the Weirdness Go?: Why Quantum Mechanics Is Strange, but Not as Strange as You Think.* New York: Basic Books, 1996. 251 pp.
> Lindley tackles the challenge of explaining the intricacies of quantum mechanics for the nonscientist. He guides readers through brief histories of important experiments and discoveries by Albert Einstein, Erwin Schrödinger, Niels Bohr, and others and relates these developments to advances in the theory of quantum mechanics in the 1980's and 1990's.

Perkowitz, Sidney. *Empire of Light: A History of Discovery in Science and Art.* New York: Henry Holt, 1996. 176 pp.
> Perkowitz surveys the development of human understanding of light from the vantage

points of science and art. Taking readers on a journey from the temples of ancient Egypt to the particle accelerators of the twentieth century, he discusses the role of light in the work of scientists from Galileo and Newton to Einstein and the work of artists from the French Impressionists to the Ashcan school of urban realists.

Sime, Ruth Lewin. *Lise Meitner: A Life in Physics*. Berkeley: University of California Press, 1996. 526 pp.

This biography of experimental physicist Lise Meitner places her life and work within the social and political context in which she lived. Based on archival study and contact with surviving family members and friends of Meitner, this work helps redress the slights experienced by Meitner as a woman during her lifetime by providing a detailed examination of her contributions to the discovery of the process of fission that ultimately led to the production of the atomic bomb.

Tenner, Edward. *Why Things Bite Back: Technology and the Revenge of Unintended Consequences*. New York: Alfred A. Knopf, 1996. 352 pp.

Edward Tenner provides an entertaining and enlightening account of how humanity's immense trust in technology has come to grief in modern times as the result of scientific systems that have increased the very frustrations or dangers they are designed to solve—a phenomenon Tenner deems the "revenge effect." Instead of indulging in pointless despair or foolish overconfidence, Tenner advises a middle way of vigilant caution, reigning in human technological ambitions in order to become better stewards of the earth and its resources.

Acknowledgements

The Animal and Plant Worlds
How a weed once scorned became the flower of the hour
©Katharine Whittemore. Originally published in *Smithsonian Magazine*, August, 1996.

Natural Allies
©Ted Williams. Originally published in *Sierra*, September/October, 1996.

New ideas in the air at the National Zoo
©Bil Gilbert. Originally published in *Smithsonian Magazine*, June, 1996.

Ranchers Ride to the Defense of Mountaintop "Sky Islands"
© 1996, The New York Times Company. Reprinted by permission.

Snatching scientific secrets from the hippos gaping jaw
©David M. Schwartz. Originally published in *Smithsonian Magazine*, June, 1996.

Applied Science and Technology
The Electronic Nose
Gary Taubes/©1996 The Walt Disney Co. Reprinted with permission of Discover Magazine.

Ground Tests Loom for Ultimate Hot Rods, Supersonic Cars
©,1996,The New York Times Company. Reprinted by permission.

Japan's Micromachine Project Draws Envy and Criticism
©,1996, The New York Times Company. Reprinted by permission.

Kinder, Gentler Push for Metric Inches Along
©, 1996, The New York Times Company. Reprinted by permission.

Next Wave of Electric Cars: Hybrids
Reprinted with permission from SCIENCE NEWS, the weekly newsmagazine of science, copyright © 1996 by Science Service, Inc.

Pulsing Magnets Offer New Method of Mapping Brain
Copyright © 1996 by The New York Times Company. Reprinted by permission.

Drilling for Oil Under Windsor Castle
Copyright © 1996 by Webster's Unified, Inc.

Tagged Out
Reprinted with permission from SCIENCE NEWS, the weekly newsmagazine of science, copyright © 1996 by Science Service, Inc.

Astronomy and Space Exploration
Galileo Arrives at Jupiter
Copyright © 1996 by Webster's Unified, Inc.

Life on Mars?
Copyright © 1996 by Webster's Unified, Inc.

Novel Rocket Chosen to Power Shuttle Successor
Copyright © 1996 by The New York Times Company. Reprinted by permission.

Planet Discoveries Around Nearby Stars
Copyright © 1996 by Webster's Unified, Inc.

Russian Mir Space Station
Copyright © 1996 by Webster's Unified, Inc.

Shuttle Flies High in 1996
Copyright © 1996 by Webster's Unified, Inc.

The View from Above
Copyright © 1996 by Webster's Unified, Inc.

Illustration Credits